Sheila Garvie: Mastermind or Victim

A M Nicol

Ringwood Publishing
Glasgow

First published in Great Britain in 2022 by
Ringwood Publishing
0/1 314 Meadowside Quay Walk, Glasgow G11 6AY
www.ringwoodpublishing.com
e-mail mail@ringwoodpublishing.com

ISBN 978-1-901514-69-8

British Library Cataloguing-in Publication Data
A catalogue record for this book is available from the British
Library

Typeset in Times New Roman 11
Printed and bound in the UK
by Lonsdale Direct Solutions

Dedication

To my sisters

'Those who like a simple clean story will not find it here. If life in a Mearns town is compounded of indecencies, sneers, ill-will, spying, gossiping, downright cruelty, then this Mearns town is consistent.'

Press and Journal critic on Lewis Grassic Gibbon's *Cloud Howe* in 1933.

Foreword

They say that if you can remember the sixties you were not really there. I was too young to fall foul of the reasons which may make that statement true for some people, but old enough not to be completely unaware of what they were. I remember, for example, the discussion about Lucy in the Sky with Diamonds. On the other hand, I thought swingers were musicians and lovers were people who happened to like each other.

Sex was not, as far as I know, invented in the sixties, but perhaps that decade contributed more to its commercialisation than any other and opened up discussions about matters which had previously been taboo.

Maybe it was that openness and the desire to cash in on the public's thirst for scandal that made the media publish so many details of the Garvie case and its *dramatis personae* – some of which my 14 year-old-mind managed to take in without fully realising the implications.

I say this because, while the name of Sheila Garvie is etched in my memory, it was not until I read this book that I appreciated exactly what was involved.

Allan Nicol has skilfully managed to bring the case to vibrant life in a manner which both informs and absorbs the reader. He does this not by a mere chronological narration of events, but by taking different time lines and weaving them together like an old-style telephone cable. He places these events in their legal context and finally he makes a few educated guesses about what really happened, with an Agatha Christie-esque denouement.

Yet the book provokes almost as many questions as it answers. While the fate of Brian Tevendale might seem obvious, would Sheila Garvie have been convicted of murder if the trial had taken place a few short years before and the death penalty had been available? Would she have hanged then even if convicted?

What would happen to her in this day and age? The trial would probably not attract as much attention given the surfeit of prurient material which is available, but, given our greater understanding of domestic abuse and gaslighting, it would probably have had a different emphasis.

Today any evidence which was at variance with prior statements would be poured over at length and it would not be possible for one co-accused to give evidence incriminating another without giving notice well in advance of the trial. There would be minute interrogation of mobile phones to determine who was in touch with whom and when.

Who can tell how all this would have affected matters? Perhaps all that can safely be said is that nowadays a three accused murder trial would take considerably longer, as would the jury's consideration of the verdicts. Oh, and the deceased's skull would never be produced in court now. Even upsetting photographs are discouraged.

The sentencing regime has also changed. A conviction for murder in a case of this kind is likely to result in accused persons spending at least 20 years in prison before being released on a life licence. A period of 10 years in prison is not unusual where there is a conviction for culpable homicide, which might not have been an unrealistic result nowadays for Sheila.

Maybe to modern eyes substantial justice was done, in her case at least.

As for Alan Peters, I adopt the approach of Thumper in Bambi: "If you can't say somethin' nice, don't say nothin' at all".

Lord Matthews

Lord Matthews is a judge in Scotland's Supreme Courts, having been appointed in 2007. Before that he defended and prosecuted in High Courts throughout Scotland and served as a Sheriff in Glasgow and Strathkelvin.

Author's Introduction

Having spent all of my working life immersed in Scottish criminal law, I naturally gravitate to reading about cases from the past, some more high profile than others. Two of the more infamous I have focused on in previous books involved serial killers Peter Manuel and Archibald Hall. Both were ruthless psychopaths who killed without compunction for their own personal gratification.

Sheila Garvie, on the other hand, was a gentle mother of three who had lived a blameless life up until her husband Max chose to join in what he imagined were the 'Swinging Sixties'. What happened after that has been the subject of ongoing debate, some condemning her as 'hard as nails' whilst others took a more forgiving view of events.

The passage of time can change perspective. For many, the trial of Alan Peters, Sheila Garvie and Brian Tevendale in Aberdeen High Court in 1968 was memorable only for its then sensational revelations. To this day, people of a certain vintage remember the name Sheila Garvie. Many recall that she was convicted of murdering her husband and that there was a sexual element to the story. Few remember that the evidence disclosed her physical, psychological and sexual abuse, possibly because 'that's just the way it was back then'. And didn't the jury find her guilty anyway?

In writing this book, I wanted to fully understand the basis of her conviction for murder and expected to emerge at the other end of the process convinced that justice had been served. Now, I'm not so sure.

She was charged with murdering her husband by police officers who initially believed her co-accused and lover's story that *she* had shot and killed Max Garvie and that Tevendale, her lover, had only helped dispose of the body. When it became clear that Tevendale was the killer, the prosecution case evolved into proving her guilt by her failure to somehow intervene in the assault on her husband, then doing nothing to bring Tevendale to justice before the three accused were arrested. And, of course, continuing to share his bed for a further three months after the murder neither helped her in court nor in the public domain.

Sheila Garvie undoubtedly told lies and covered up for Tevendale after he killed Max. She also told her mother, Edith, that Max would not be coming back and it was Edith who eventually went to the police.

It has to be wondered what sort of cold-blooded assassin tells her mother that her son-in-law has been murdered and makes a point of implicating herself in the crime in order to protect her lover.

I was interested in how the prosecution approached the case against her. Should she have done more to stop her husband's execution? Should she have phoned the police the second Tevendale and Peters left the house or, perhaps, waited a day or two before making the call?

In studying the case, it became clear, however, that the evidence given by Tevendale's sister, Trudy, and Sheila Garvie's co-accused, Alan Peters, unexpectedly bolstered the Crown case in suspiciously tabloid-sounding ways.

Perhaps now, after all these years, the truth is beginning to emerge and, at the very least, it has to be acknowledged that 'chequebook journalism' helped seal Sheila Garvie's fate.

Yet, ever since the verdicts in the trial, there have been some who have questioned her guilt in the crime, including her solicitor, Laurence Dowdall, and a journalist and publisher, Paul Harris, who wrote a book about the case. Sheila Garvie herself wrote a book in 1980 about her life with Max and the events leading up to his murder and, for what it's worth, she continued to maintain her innocence; Brian Tevendale, on the other hand, continued to insist she was complicit in the crime. Some might say 'well, he would, wouldn't he?', whilst others might say the same about her.

The reader must decide, but my hope is that in this book, I have given them a better basis for an informed judgement.

The book has to be seen as 'based on a true story.' That said, I have tried to stick to the main facts of the evidence heard at the trial as well as details known about the accused, the legal representatives and the eventual verdicts. I confess to embellishing certain facets of the legal personnel involved in the case, hopefully in accordance with their known characteristics. Only one or two of the characters are added or adapted, solely to progress the story.

Incredibly, the quotes from the *News of the World* are all verbatim, bizarre as they seem now to the modern eye.

For obvious reasons, there is little mention of the Garvie children, whom, it is hoped, have overcome whatever problems they must have encountered before and after the trial.

Chapter 1:

Laurencekirk Police Office, Kincardineshire,

Wednesday, 16 August 1968

As the haar slowly lifted that morning, rain edged in from the North Sea to moisten the red clay of the Mearns again. It was *wet* rain, the sort that floods the fields and beats out a loud, steady rhythm on the glistening roof slates before it relents and the clouds give way to clear blue summer skies. 'Like Mither's mood improving as the day goes on', some would say.

An early 50s split screen Morris Oxford splashed its way into the car park just as Geddes started two-finger typing a crime report on the station Olivetti and Sergeant Archie began pouring tea into an enamel mug through a cheap tin tea strainer. Known as 'SA' or 'Essie', because he had gone as far as he was going to go in the Scottish North-Eastern Counties Constabulary, Sergeant Archie slowed pouring to let the tea subside beneath the strainer, then stopped completely as he watched the car's urgent progress. He was fascinated by its wipers, which lazily ploughed their own half of the screen at different speeds and angles, like bickering twins taking turns at swiping out at each other. It made sense. Unlike the brakes, the bodywork and the points, the wipers were about the only part of the car that Dougie wouldn't have faithfully maintained, because he never had any need to.

Essie put the teapot down beside the half-filled mug. 'Jesus, Bob, there's Dougie Scrimgeour parking his pride and joy outside here *in the rain*!'

The news made Geddes come to the window. Everyone in the Mearns knew that the Farm Grieve at West Cairnbeg would never take his beloved car out in the wet. His wife Lizzie often said that even if it *looked* like raining, Dougie would take no chances, and the trip to Stonehaven or the visit to her sister in Bervie would be off, with him oft times adding that he'd prefer that *she,* rather than the Oxford, got soaked. If it rained when they were out in it, Lizzie's job was to open the garage door after they sped home so he could chamois the polished bodywork dry, in case rust set in the wheel arches or bubbled up beside the boot hinges.

Essie and Geddes watched as Dougie parked at an angle, pulled up the handbrake and got out, forgetting to switch the lights off as he did so. He was in a rush. He walked briskly round the bulbous bonnet at the front, opened the passenger door and reached in to help the other person out, the rain running down the *faux* red leather fascia of the interior and pooling underneath the open door. Eventually, a diminutive right foot dangled over the door sill, followed by a leg clad in thick, matronly stockings, and the figure of a small grey-haired old lady finally emerged, clinging tightly to Dougie's arm with both hands as she firstly steadied herself, then trod shakily towards the normally quiet rural police office. A plastic rain mate covering the back of her head gave up the uneven contest with the heavens and slid onto the collar of her shapeless brown tweed coat as the pair steadily made for the building through the downpour.

Geddes recognised her as Edith Watson, the mother of Sheila Garvie of West Cairnbeg. She was therefore the mother-in-law of Sheila's husband Maxwell Robert Garvie and grandmother to the couple's three children.

Maxwell Garvie – known to all except Sheila as 'Max' and to her alone as 'Maxie' – had been officially missing now for three months, and Geddes had taken *both* missing person reports, Max's sister Hilda beating his wife Sheila to the door of officialdom by several days. Well known in the area, Max farmed West Cairnbeg, only a few miles from the office, and Dougie was his 'right-hand man'.

Before going to open the front door, Essie looked at Geddes, his Detective Sergeant, and said, 'It's taken a while, but I suppose *something* had to give.'

Geddes thought so too, but – putting his official duty to one side – hoped deep down that Sheila had little or nothing to do with Max's sudden disappearance, although, with Dougie's desperate journey and Edith on her way into the office in the frail condition she seemed to be in, *little* now looked far more likely than *nothing*.

Geddes had spoken to Sheila twice since Max had gone and had come to realise that she and Edith had a connection few would understand, beyond that of mother and daughter, so Edith's attendance that morning *had* to be important. And Dougie taking the Oxford out the garage in the rain meant it had to be *very* important.

After Essie took the pair straight into the interview room, one look at Edith convinced Geddes she needed calming down before she could speak. Her rapid breathing, tears and shivers convinced him he should call out Dr Conway, the casualty surgeon, before taking her statement.

Meantime, Dougie was able to speak for her.

'Max will not be coming home and Mrs Watson thinks Sheila might have something to do with it.'

Chapter 2:

The Annual Bannockburn Rally, near Stirling,

Saturday, 24 June 1967

Brian Gordon Tevendale was definitely angry about
something. Unlike his older brother, Brian had failed to
live up to his father's expectations and had found life in the
Regular Army too much for him to handle. Instead of seeing
it through, Brian and another squaddie had begun stealing
cars and causing trouble near their barracks in Aldershot
and Reading, leading to a discharge from the forces and
disappointment for his mother, the widow of the boy's war-
decorated father, Major Tevendale, formerly of the Gordon
Highlanders. Being that kind of person, though, Brian was
able to justify all he did, especially to himself, and later tried
to convince people that the numerous thefts and punch-ups
were actually part of a plan to get kicked out of the army.
Once he had gone, most folk said that The Major would never
have understood why his second son – the one honoured with
the middle name reflecting his father's love of Regiment –
got three months for smashing up cars and windows *after* he
got his wish and had been discharged *dishonourably*.

Some said, 'It is just as well the Major never came back
out of Stracathro Hospital with breath in his lungs before
the boy blackened his father's good name,' but others said,
'Aye, but had he still been here, the boy would be fine.'

Then Brian saw a way. Blame others. Blame the system.
Blame your sergeant. Blame your school. *Blame the English,*

4

that's it, blame them for all Old Scotia's woes, for her lack of money, for the barefaced neglect of all who live north of Hadrian's Wall and, whilst we're at it, for the way I don't like my life.

Bannockburn Rally over, and victory sealed again, Brian was determined not to go back with the couple he had travelled with on the way down from the Mearns. He could take no more of the mind-numbing chatter about economics, the exciting prospect of North Sea Oil and the 'socio-economic factors that determine levels of inner-city poverty' that Reg and Marge had enjoyed debating on the journey south.

What did economics have to do with independence anyway?

Brian's lack of interest in their arguments – and his one-word answers to their anxious enquiries about what *The Average Scot* might think – had quickly confined the discussion to a whisper between the hosts in the bench seat in the front; him going on to explain that the only sure way to secure independence was to plant bombs in London 'if they don't listen' ensured complete silence from all three travellers all the way from Perth to Stirling.

Being friends of his mother, Brian had agreed to travel south with them from Stonehaven in their ancient, beat-up VW Caravanette, replete with miniature Saltires fluttering from both side windows, which occasionally blocked sight of pennants from Penzance and Somerset, from where the couple came. Unable to face another enforced bout of Reg and Marge's political views about the future of their adopted country, Brian decided to try to make other arrangements for travelling home.

Wearing his black and yellow SNP zipper and at just under six feet tall, with his dark slicked-back hair offsetting his carefully trimmed edge-of-face beard, Brian was confident of his attractiveness to women; once in conversation, hints of special forces involvement and life-risking missions usually did the trick and at least led to more chat about him and more drinks paid for by her. Once he told Reg and Marge to leave without him, they gladly jettisoned their volatile passenger and quickly drove off, leaving Brian to scour the car park field for 'RG' or 'RS' suffixes denoting Aberdeenshire vehicle registrations.

He noticed the car first. The high-powered mark X Jaguar with the walnut dashboard and steering wheel was badly parked, selfishly straddling two or maybe three indistinct parking spaces in the field set aside for rally attendees. It was spattered with mud to half-window level as if the driver had slalomed across the field, through puddles and into the spaces at speed. More interesting were its Aberdeen plates.

Then he saw them.

More truly, he saw her.

Picking her way across tufts of grass and between muddy pools in her light blue high heels, which now bore dark, uniform brown mired stripes, she seemed out of place in her matching blue twinset and skirt amongst a sea of wellie and Barbour wearers. As she criss-crossed her way towards the Jag, Brian realised that the distinguished-looking, cigar-smoking male gleefully splashing his way in the same direction might be with her. Unlike the woman, he was heedless of both his clothing and his surroundings: his substantial brogues and the bottom few inches of his buff-coloured moleskin trousers were wet with mud and grass.

That made sense, Brian thought. Mr Moleskin Trousers had parked the Jag badly after having too much from his hip flask, he'd carried on drinking, and now she was in a bad mood because she had to drive home.

Just as the woman unlocked the driver's door, Brian hurriedly squelched across the boggy surface until he caught up with the man and tried his luck.

'Any chance of a lift if you're going north?'

6

The man stopped walking, his left foot stationary in a muddy puddle, the dark brown liquid the height of the laces. His reaction to the question made Brian think they maybe knew each other, the man reaching out to shake his hand even before he spoke.

'Like us, you must be one of the chosen few, then! Grand turnout this year!'

'My first year,' Brian answered, wondering if that fact might jeopardise his chance of free transport.

It seemed not.

'Got to begin sometime, just good you've seen the light!' said the man, clapping Brian's shoulder and then flicking the lit cigar towards the Jag, the engine of which was now making rumbling, powerful noises, and the brake lights flashing on and off as the woman adjusted the seat. The cigar bounced off the paintwork and came to rest, sizzling as it self-extinguished in a puddle.

'I'm called Max, but get known as the Skipper. The wife's put her dainty little foot down, cos she says I'm too pissed to get the damned Jag out of here! What's your name, young fella, and where exactly are you headed?'

Before Brian could answer, Max beckoned him closer as if his next words were secret. 'She thinks we're going home, but don't worry, we're going for a bucket in the Bannockburn Inn like we always do, and she really knows it too. It's all about treating them in a way they understand you mean business. She'll do anything I want her to; you know – eventually ...'

Max thumped the roof of the car before opening the front passenger door. 'We've got company,' he bellowed. 'This young man wants a lift to the pub and, seeing as he looks like your type, I said yes!' he said, laughing heartily at his own imagined humour.

The woman tutted, shook her head and turned to acknowledge Brian, who had opened the rear nearside door.

'Hello, I'm Sheila,' she said politely. Brian announced his name and apologised for his presence. From the back seat, Brian could now take in her slender, pearl-clad neck and her model-like high cheekbones as well as her well coiffured, bobbed blonde hair as she looked over her left shoulder to negotiate reversing out of the space. The manoeuvre parted her legs slightly, and Max plunged his hand between them, roaring with laughter. She slammed on the brakes and then turned back to face him, her cheeks red with indignation. Her voice, though, was surprisingly calm, Brian thought, and her choice of words was odd, as if addressing a child.

'Maxie, I'm terribly keen for you to stop doing that sort of thing, please. You know what will happen, don't you? You'll have to drive everywhere yourself *all* the time and none of your police pals will be able to help you when that new breathalyser test comes in.'

Max was unrepentant. 'Just a bit of fun! Stop being so, so … Sunday school about things! Hurry up, our new friend and I are dying of thirst and they'll be closing in five hours!'

On the way to the pub, Max talked incessantly, his topics including teaching the ruddy English some manners and how important it was that youngsters like Brian took control back from Westminster. When he turned to speak to Brian in the back seat, the latter could see Max's eyes had a glassy sheen to them and could smell fresh alcohol on his breath. 'I *do* beg your pardon, young fella,' he suddenly announced, reaching into the inside of his Barbour jacket and producing a curved silver hip flask. 'Care for a snifter?' he asked as he unscrewed the top, passing it over without waiting for an answer. In truth, Brian rarely drank malt whisky, but a rapid, angular contact with his lips fulfilled and acknowledged the host's hospitality. As he did so, he fancied that the glamorous female in the driver's seat had fleetingly broken her intense concentration on the road ahead to glance at him in the rear-view mirror. Was she concerned that her overbearing husband was doing what he always did – forcing those around him to do exactly what he wanted?

The bar was packed.

Max, Sheila and Brian squeezed through the throng of drinkers and, once at the bar, Max attracted attention by opening a heavy leather wallet thick with notes and waving it towards the overworked barmen. After no sign of immediate service, Max winked at Brian, Sheila lowering her head and cupping her forehead in her hand in anticipation of what was about to happen.

'Gentlemen, can I have your attention!'

The noise level stayed the same.

Max took a gold fountain pen from inside his jacket, picked up a used empty pint glass from the bar and dinged the two together several times.

'Gentlemen, CAN I HAVE YOUR ATTENTION!'

The hubbub slowed, then stopped. Still clutching the open wallet, Max raised his arms in the air and announced, 'Barman, DRINKS ALL AROUND!'

A mighty cheer was soon followed by Max's order being taken and a queue of grateful recipients competing to lighten his wallet.

Max winked at Brian again. 'There you are, young fella, that's how you get served in a busy bar! Now, where was it you said you're going? *I'm* driving us back to Fordoun when we're finished drinking.' He said it with Sheila standing beside him looking powerlessly vulnerable.

'I'm in Stonehaven,' Brian replied imprecisely, trying to disguise the admiration in his voice for this awesome, intimidating man with the tolerant, understanding, attractive wife. Another sign of his obvious authority over her. Between stolen glances when the Skipper drew breath, Brian continued to monitor her gorgeous presence. She was just old enough to be the experienced, mature sort of woman he and the other squaddies he had previously been billeted

9

with dreamed of after they flopped into their barrack bunks directly from the kind of exhaustive roustings on the parade square he still had bad memories of.

To cackles from his drinking pals, one of the locals, clutching his free pint, said he reckoned it would take them a couple of hours to get home, possibly three if the lady was driving. The accompanying laughter was spontaneous, but had a faint, patronising ring to it. Brian noticed that Sheila ignored the comment. She appeared to be used to male company and to the sort of jibes they made, her husband's tacit consent being automatically assumed or perhaps even encouraged.

After several rounds of beer with whisky chasers, with Brian and Sheila standing either side of him, Max coiled his arms round both their waists and drunkenly pulled them towards him in an inappropriate show of faux sentiment, all three heads nearly meeting in the middle. Max grinned at his own laddish behaviour, but Brian noticed that Sheila looked annoyed, as if she would rather be anywhere else than standing in a public bar sipping her one and only gin and orange for the day, even though her husband had made it clear he deemed himself both capable and drunkenly focused enough to resume control of the Jag's powerful four litre plus capability.

'Great! Leave it to the Skipper and you'll both be home soon. Or we'll have a damned good try!' he bellowed, to the approval of the intoxicated rabble their presence had attracted. His hand outstretched, Max silently but publicly demanded the keys for the Jag. Rather than create a scene, Sheila unzipped her blue leather handbag, retrieved the car keys and meekly handed them over to a restrained murmur of public approval from the drinkers round about.

'Can't let the little lady drive all that way hame, it wouldnae be safe for her or the other two! Wummen can't really drive, like for real, like men!'

Drink in hand, a lift home and a shapely woman to ogle from a seat in the rear on the way up the road, Brian was well pleased with the enterprise he had employed so far; Father would have approved. All was well with the world and it looked like Brian's number plate gamble had paid off.

Or so he imagined.

Chapter 3:

West Cairnbeg Farmhouse, Kincardineshire,

Tuesday, 21 May 1968

Local gossip meant Geddes had already heard of Sheila Garvie and the goings-on at West Cairnbeg farmhouse before he went there on a warm summer's day in May. Now, his job was to untangle rumour and Chinese whispers from hard fact. For the past while, Max had been well known as an impulsive man who drank too much and popped too many pills, but that did not seem to affect the running of the farm. Most said that was down to Dougie Scrimgeour guiding him through his first few years, teaching him when to take chances and when not to.

To be fair to him, Max had worked hard when he had to and had built good relations with many of the local farmers. He also had the nous to heed Dougie's wise words and, together, they had not only made the venture work, but had turned it into a great success, so much so that Max could afford expensive holidays for him and his family and a two-seater plane for himself. At the time of his disappearance, he had three cars, including a white Cortina estate used mainly by Sheila.

Like others, Geddes then started hearing the stories as the local rumour mill geared up. It seemed Max had become bored and reckless with his possessions, often driving the fourteen or so miles home from Stonehaven when blind drunk and even flying his two-seater plane in the same condition, mock-strafing startled drivers on the coast road. And there were other tales doing the rounds about him being careless with what he seemed to regard as another of his possessions – his wife.

As for her, Geddes's colleagues were quick to point out, she stood to gain big time should Max, say, disappear forever. Sheila would become wealthy in her own right, for a start. She would also be rid of the man who gave her everything so she could set up in his house with her children and her young lover, Brian Gordon Tevendale. 'She kens fine what's happened to her man,' they all said, 'just wait and see. The truth will out.'

Locals had been abuzz about what had been going on in the Big Hoose at West Cairnbeg near Fordoun. Max had started a nudist club in Aberdeenshire everyone called 'Kinky Cottage' and, it was said, had persuaded his wife to flaunt her naked body there in front of other men, 'and her a Sunday school teacher in her time too'.

And there was more.

When Edith looked after her grandchildren in Stonehaven overnight, rumour had it that the Garvies and their shameless pals wore no clothes about the Big Hoose, Sheila's constant sexual demands being such that being stripped and ready for action 'saved time'. Even Geordie Forbes, the local milkman, swore blind he heard *an orgy* going on early one Saturday morning as he left the gold tops in the unlocked washhouse. Questioned by disbelieving friends in the Bervie Arms – who really wanted convincing it was true – about the sort of noises an eavesdropper to an orgy might hear, Geordie stood his ground and refused to concede the wailing sound from upstairs could actually have been Sheila – or one of the three children – crying and upset.

Even so, as Geddes drove up the driveway and parked outside the farmhouse, he had heard too much about Sheila

Garvie not to think he might be about to meet a scantily clad *femme fatale*.

He saw the house was a substantial detached two-storey property, with an outside porch over the front door and a large double garage attached to the main building at the end of the driveway. Several outhouses were dotted around it, including a large greenhouse, and there was a generous, well-kept lawn to the front. He also noticed that any car parked in the white pebbled driveway would be directly outside the sitting room, so that during daylight hours anyone inside the house could easily see when a visitor arrived by car. She would know Geddes had arrived on time.

Essie might have been serious when he warned Geddes not to go to West Cairnbeg alone in case *the wanton bitch* should try to seduce him to compromise him, or claimed he'd tried it on with her if he rebuffed her. Geddes paid no heed of the uniformed sergeant's advice.

When she eventually came to the door, she was nothing like his expectations. Wearing an old, oversized faded dark tartan dressing gown tied in the middle with an incongruous blue satin belt, she looked tired and drained of strength as she led him into the sitting room, then perched herself on a large, worn green leather chair. She had a sling on her left arm, her hair was unbrushed and, despite obvious mascara stains underneath her eyes, Geddes could see why she was said to be bonny. She had a rounded, feminine face with high cheekbones and wide-set eyes, which complemented her dainty ski-run nose above lips that naturally pouted.

She trembled slightly as she lit a cigarette, a *Passing Cloud* no less, using an expensive-looking silver table lighter curiously fashioned in the shape of a cow. She placed it back on the table beside two heavy crystal tumblers, which still had some flat clear liquid and stale-looking lemon slices in them, along with clear imprints of post-box red lipstick. Noticing Geddes looking at it, she picked the lighter up again and held it up for him to examine properly.

'Like the cow, then? Solid silver. A present from Maxie. His idea of a joke.'

Geddes smiled as if he understood what she meant, but decided not to ask. 'So, what you said on the phone was that your husband went missing last Tuesday into Wednesday morning, that's 14 into 15 May. Has he done that kind of thing before?'

She nodded, explaining that he liked to 'keep her on her toes' so they wouldn't 'get bored with each other'. 'He'd often say monogamy, monotony, what's the difference?' She recounted his words in a jaded, slightly bitter tone.

Geddes asked her where she thought he might have gone and she sat in silence for a while, making him wonder whether she was actually thinking or just trying to make it look like she was.

'Oh, I have no idea this time. Last time he went to London. By himself, or so he said …'

'And you didn't believe him?'

She took a lingering draw on her cigarette, then shook her head slightly before answering. 'No. Poor Maxie. He really was terribly clueless at times. I mean, things have to be done his way or he becomes huffy, like a child.'

Geddes noticed how she had corrected herself, almost seamlessly. The missing man really *was* clueless, but he *becomes* huffy like a child. *Which is it? Is Max Garvie past or present tense? There's more to this than she is telling and it's going to take time.*

Geddes explained his visit was only to take some basic details and that he would come back to get more information from her, 'should that be required'.

She confirmed she had wakened early, at about 5.30 a.m. in the morning of Wednesday 15 May to find herself alone in their double bed. Assuming her husband had gone to the bathroom at the end of the corridor, she lay for a few minutes

15

before putting her dressing gown on and checking the toilet, then the children's room next door and then the rest of the house. When she saw his new Cortina 1600E was gone from the driveway, she realised he was too.

'Maxie would still have been drunk when he left, as he was pretty well oiled when he came home from the SNP meeting in Stonehaven that night. He insisted that we both had an extra-large gin and orange nightcap as he always did, no matter when he made it home. Sometimes he'd even wake me up no matter what time it was and I'd have to go downstairs for a drink before he decided *he* had to go to bed. That night we came upstairs before midnight. I remember I let the girls watch the rest of *The Avengers* in their room. It finished about half eleven and Maxie was home by then.' A slight smile almost formed on her lips as she added an explanatory detail. 'My eldest daughter's in love with John Steed.'

Geddes scribbled her words on his notebook as she spoke. 'And so you had a nightcap downstairs. Did you go straight to bed after that?'

'Yes, we did.' She looked out across the lawn as she spoke and not directly at him.

'And straight to sleep?'

She turned away from him to stub her three-quarters smoked cigarette out, hoping he might not notice her discomfort. Fumbling with a mahogany cigarette box, she took another out, then lit it using the silver cow before turning back to look at him.

'No. Maxie has addiction issues that make him push at barriers – drink, pills and the like – and sex. He insisted we had sex that night even though the bedroom door was wide open and one of the children might have come through at any time. I knew there would be no point in arguing about it, as that would just prolong things, but I also knew how to make sure we got it over with quickly.'

Geddes wondered what she meant. What did she do to 'get it over quickly'? If this was going to be a long enquiry, discretion at this early stage might be better. He changed tack.

'Anyway, I understand his Cortina was found at the Flying Club. Was it you that noticed it?'

She confirmed that it was and that she had spotted it when she was driving by the previous Friday, the 17th. Since Max could have flown anywhere, she had done nothing except ask a friend if he could supply a key for the car so it could be driven home, which he, Alec Donald, did.

Geddes thought that odd, a possible false trail. Surely someone at the Flying Club must be able to say if their founding member had taken off for wherever in the early hours of Wednesday 15 May?

'You know someone else has already reported your husband missing?'

Sheila took in the information calmly. 'I didn't, but I am not surprised. That'll be his sister Hilda. We don't get on and haven't spoken in years. Maxie would tell her packs of lies about us to make him sound good and me sound bad and she was more than willing to believe him. She has no idea what he is really like. Anyway, the reason I waited till now is because he was due to attend a meeting at the Flying Club last night and, when he failed to show up, that did it for me and that's when I called you. Alec Donald agreed with me that waiting was the right thing to do, as Maxie never missed those meetings.'

'Can I have a look at his car? I noticed it in the driveway beside the white Cortina Estate. Is that yours?'

'Yes, and there's a Mark X Jag, which is at the garage right now. Maxie had one of his little spills with it when driving home. I'll give you the key for his Cortina and you can take a look at it. I don't know if there is anything wrong with it, but then I didn't drive it back here, Alec did.'

Geddes went outside to the driveway. Curiosity made him try the garage door. It opened and he went in. No vehicles were parked inside, but there were tins of Castrol and Redex, one of which was on its side, a thin blood-coloured trail snaking away from it etched in the bare concrete floor. He righted the can and then tried the door into the house, which opened into a boiler room and washhouse. He noticed a washing machine and a large white chest freezer in it, which he opened slowly. Inside were frozen joints of meat and poultry, including what looked like the carcases of several game birds, probably pheasants. *No sign of the missing man, but you never know* ...

Geddes retraced his steps outside and searched the Cortina thoroughly, found nothing of note, and then went back inside through the front door and handed the car key back to Sheila. She had lit a third cigarette, a turquoise cocktail type that lay on the edge of an onyx ashtray beside the two half-smoked oblong cigarettes from earlier.

'How did Mr Donald get a key for it? I will have to speak to him if Mr Garvie doesn't turn up in the next few days.'

'Alec owns a shop that supplies car parts. He told me the wipers came on when he got it started and that the choke was fully out as if the engine was cold when it was started, presumably from the driveway outside.'

'Ok, did he know if your husband had flown anywhere? I take it his plane's still there?'

'Yes, Maxie's Bolkow Junior's still there and so is the trainer the club owns, but nobody at the club knows about him flying anywhere.' As an afterthought, she added, 'Not that he couldn't have. Maxie could be impulsive, sometimes infuriatingly so.'

Geddes noted her choice of words, then asked about Max's guns. Sheila confirmed they were both still in the house. She took him to a room beside the washhouse he had just been in. Geddes saw the weapons were insecure, lying on top of a cabinet, and one of them, a .22, was lying at an angle, the barrel protruding over the edge of the cupboard by several inches, enough for anyone to see where it was kept. And anyone could get in through the double garage where they were.

'Have the rifles always been kept here? You really must get a lock on those doors.'

Sheila seemed oblivious and merely stared silently out towards the garage.

He tried again. 'Do you know when either of them was last fired?'

Sheila shook her head. 'By him?' she said unexpectedly. 'I've no idea when Maxie last went shooting, he pleased himself and certainly didn't tell me.'

Geddes nodded, then arranged to come back in a few days to check any progress. 'Just in case he turns up.'

Sheila agreed and said she'd prefer they spoke when the children were at school, but she would call him if she heard anything in the meantime.

As he drove away, Geddes puzzled over all he had heard, starting with what she had said about Max's car. The weather had been warm, it hadn't rained for over a week and surely neither the wipers nor the choke would have been needed, particularly if Max had driven the car again only a few hours after returning home the night before. Somebody was definitely covering up, pretending the car had been started from cold and in wet conditions that had just not happened. And what if the missing man flew back to Fordoun that night and his car was gone? Arranging for it to be driven to West Cairnbeg might mean she *knew* Max would not be flying back into Fordoun Flying Club any time soon. And it had been Sheila who had noticed the Cortina parked in the club's grounds. Was that by chance or was that just one of the places she would have instinctively checked hoping to find signs that her erratic husband had been there?

The rifles were a concern, though. Many local farmers seemed to forget how lethal even low calibre weapons could be in unauthorised hands, despite having seen first-hand what they could do to game and vermin.

And Sheila herself?

She was a puzzle. Her past tense slip-up spoke for itself, yet she had visibly reddened when she said that she and Max had had sex the night she had apparently last seen him. How could a brazen husband killer be so sensitive about natural, sexual behaviour between a married couple? That really was odd – as if she was admitting to doing something wrong, something with her own husband that had offended her.

Sure, the gossip about what the Garvies got up to was the major talking point in every pub, club and knitting circle in the Mearns, but Sheila Garvie was not your usual suspect in a murder enquiry.

If it came to being that, of course.

Chapter 4:

The Marine Hotel, Stonehaven,

Saturday, 19 August 1967

Max lurched towards the Gents toilet, double vodka and coke spilling over his fingers and soaking into his gold signet ring and the skin underneath. Finding the cubicle door closed, he called out to the supposed occupant that he, the Skipper, needed in, and to be quick about it. No reply. Applying a leather-soled shoe to the door, he pressed until it creaked open to reveal nothing except a grubby, upright toilet seat angled over a bowl half full of water, toilet roll, brown stains and fag ends. Max stepped inside, closed the door, pushed the lever over to lock it and placed the glass on top of the cistern. He removed his herringbone tweed jacket, cursing as the sleeve button caught briefly on the door lever, then hung it from a hook on the back of the door. Placing a sticky hand into the change pocket, he retrieved a handful of Pro-Plus tablets, which he scooped into his mouth, swilling them down by draining the glass.

'Ready to go again,' he said to himself, straightening up and blowing his nose on toilet paper unravelled from a roll somehow dampened by a previous occupant.

Glancing ahead into the bar on the way back, he noticed Sheila, Brian and his school friend George all chatting together and three young men standing behind them, obviously talking about his wife, the only woman in the bar. Making towards them with his arms wide open, Max feigned disbelief that they should be gawping at her. 'Right, you lot – eyes off the missus. She's old enough to be your mother!'

The boys looked surprised. 'Sorry, Skipper, didn't see you there,' one said. Max tapped her shoulder, causing her to turn round to face the four of them. 'Alright, lads, feast your eyes on her while I get the round in!'

Sheila smiled at the boys, then turned and headed for the Ladies, leaving the boys shuffling nervously in case their bar-room talk had sparked off a domestic incident. When Sheila returned, Max was drunkenly explaining the physics of aviation to George, extending both arms and corkscrewing from side to side. Brian saw a chance to take her aside.

Not sure of proprieties yet, he asked Sheila if he should say to Max that *he* rather than Max should drive them back to West Cairnbeg. Max was in such a state. 'His eyes are gone. Maybe it would be, well, safer if I did it. I've only had three large vodkas. He's had a dozen. And maybe some pills too. You know what he's like better than I do.'

Sheila shook her head. 'Some hope. It's a matter of honour. If you even as much as hint he might not be able to drive safely, it will only make him all the more determined to do it. It's the chance we take every time we go home. He takes those pills in the toilet.'

Brian understood. 'Ok, it was just an idea. It's been really good helping out in the farm and the Flying Club these past few days, and I thought Max might appreciate me trying to do him a favour.'

Sheila patted his hand. 'You've been a great help, Brian. Thank you.'

Spotting her gesture, Max broke off his story and butted in. 'Break it up, you two. Closing time. Into the car, some food, drop George off, then a nightcap when we get home.'

The Jag was parked on the pier just outside the bar and, as they approached it, Max made his way to the driver's door and told George to sit in the front. Sheila stopped at the rear of the car, realising there had been a change in the usual seating arrangements. Brian got in behind Max and Sheila behind George as Max started the engine, squinting out of one eye in an effort to focus properly. He somehow negotiated the short distance to the chip shop along the narrow, cobbled streets without hitting any pedestrians, then pulled up outside it and turned to Sheila and Brian in the back.

'Right, George and I will get the chips. You two stay here …'

After the other two had left, Brian and Sheila sat in silence before he pulled on the door catch, swung the door open and left the car too. As Brian entered the shop, Max stepped out of the closing-time queue, put his hand on his shoulders and physically turned him around.

'What did I say to you, young Brian? Go back to the car and keep her happy, that's an order from the Skipper! She's a woman! Give her a treat! Understand?'

Understanding what he had said but not sure what he meant, Brian went back to the car, where Sheila was now smoking at her open window. She looked around briefly as he entered, then resumed puffing smoke into the cool evening air without saying anything.

Brian broke the ice. 'Can I ask you something? Why does your husband do things like this? He's just told me to come back here to keep you happy and give you a treat. What do *you* think he means?'

Sheila continued to stare at the stars in the clear night sky. 'Who knows? Max has become terribly difficult. I think it's a combination of the drink and the pills. One of them on its own is bad enough, but the mixture's making him nuts! Best to just ignore him when he's like that. That's what I do, anyway.'

Brian leaned forward and planted an uncertain kiss on her right cheek, which she acknowledged by briefly reaching out and squeezing his hand. Without comment, she then removed her hand from his and went back to blowing smoke out of the window.

After George had been dropped off, Max made for home along the coast road, peering out of his right eye and occasionally swerving to avoid non-existent images on the roadway ahead. Approaching West Cairnbeg, he turned in his seat – the vehicle still travelling at speed – and asked if 'the lovebirds' in the back had enjoyed their little jaunt.

Safely back in the farmhouse, Sheila poured three large gin and oranges and served them in the sitting room, where Max was busy selecting LPs to put on the stereo. Jim Reeves and Tom Jones were lined up ready to play and, as Sinatra came on, Max turned the volume down, switched the main lights off and lit two candles in the centre of the table.

'Early start for me tomorrow, young Brian, but you can have a long lie. Don't need you till half ten, then we'll have to go to the club to spray weeds on the runway, then we'll do a bit of shooting. You can have the .22 for the rabbits.'

Downing his gin in two large gulps, Max bid the pair goodnight and went upstairs.

Sitting facing each other, they listened to a couple of tracks until *The Lady Is A Tramp* came on and Sheila finished her drink, stood up, put the overhead lights back on and blew the candles out.

'He's doing it again,' Brian said. Sheila lifted the needle arm from the vinyl and agreed with him. 'Yes, he's doing it again alright …'

She seemed blasé, unconcerned, even, about what was happening, but something told Brian it was wrong, a sixth sense that it might be a trap, that he would be tempted into taking it too far, that Sheila would scream 'Rape!' and Max would dash to her rescue, a .22 at shoulder level, the barrel pointing at his forehead, an enraged Max shouting, 'Brian you're a bastard, Brian you're a bastard, SAY IT!'

She switched the table light back on, said 'Goodnight' without looking back and went upstairs, leaving Brian alone with his thoughts. *She's worth the risk even if it is a trap. He doesn't care. Anyway, I know more about firearms than that drunken old sod does.*

Before falling asleep in the spare bedroom, he recognised a rhythmical creaking coming from along the corridor, a loud grunting noise bringing it to an end.

No female sounds, not even a cough, before bullish snoring rent the night silence.

Chapter 5:

The Ross Clinic, Cornhill Road, Aberdeen,

Wednesday, 10 April 1968

It had been a chance remark by the Garvie family doctor that sparked the argument a few nights before. In his referral to Dr Heaton, Dr Lyle had suggested that *both* Garvies attend the clinic so that the psychiatrist obtained 'a holistic view' of the couple's situation. Max was *damned* angry.

'It's not me who needs the shrink, it's you!' he bellowed at his wife when he heard the news, returning from the Marine unexpectedly early at 9 p.m. that night.

The strain of the unravelling marriage had affected Sheila badly, and her anxiety levels had reached new, almost suicidal proportions, causing her to make an emergency appointment with the GP, who had unhesitatingly prescribed 5 milligrams of Valium per day. Arguments about Bradford, about what she and Brian had done there every night and about whether she was still seeing him *on the side* dominated every conversation between her and Max. He needed adolescent-like reassurance that she still loved him and not that Bastard Brian, but Sheila, being Sheila, had a basic inability to pass off great monstrous untruths as convenient, unimportant, little white falsehoods, like the wedding dress fuss thirteen years before. She just couldn't pretend, and Max retreated further into his default world of imaginary wellbeing brought about by the usual melange of uppers, gin and whisky.

Then, one night, it occurred to him that her intake of the sedative might actually work in his favour, so he encouraged her to take the prescribed dose as instructed, although he still expected them to continue with their nightly ritual of a large gin and orange nightcap. To begin with, he found her stubbornness had been replaced with a new, compliant frame of mind, so that she would seemingly indulge his talkative post-closing time behaviour by awaiting his return, then duly pouring a final drink, washing her tablet down in large gulps of alcohol. The period of calm was to be short-lived, though, as the combined effect of gin and Valium led to instant oblivion on Sheila's part at bedtime, thwarting Max's plans for a new, sexually submissive partner between the sheets. Tensions that were never far from the surface rose again. This time, Max phoned Dr Lyle to report that his wife had taken an overdose – 'a handful of tablets' – and that she needed specialist help like the last time, a few years before. Knowing that the Garvies played childish games, the GP referred her to Dr Heaton, a psychiatrist based in Aberdeen, recommending that both the Garvies attend the appointment.

For what it was worth, when Dr Lyle and she spoke later, she denied there was any truth in the overdose claim, but by that time he had tired of the Garvies using a disproportionate amount of his time to air their differences confidentially in public.

Dr Heaton was a smallish man with a thick Yorkshire accent, a greying goatee beard and a multicoloured bow tie.

When the Garvies appeared that morning, Max instantly disliked him, imagining that he would automatically side with Sheila, even though it was clear that it was she alone who was being assessed. Sheila looked exhausted, was wearing no makeup and her hair was dishevelled, whereas Max looked every inch the country squire, his oxblood brogues complimenting his maroon cavalry twill trousers and light brown tweed jacket.

To begin with, both of them sat in with him whilst the doctor meticulously ticked off what he regarded as the building blocks necessary for successful relationships. When it came to family holidays, he sensed Max's antagonism growing until he asked the doctor outright if he knew Bradford well.

Dr Heaton reacted by splitting them up. 'Alright, I think I should see you separately now. Perhaps you might wish to remain here, Mrs Garvie, whilst your husband takes a seat outside?' It was less of a request than a professional demand and Max trudged out the room, storing up match-winning points in his head for later.

The doctor sighed, then sat back in his outsized chair. Time for the sympathetic sounding, homely chat. 'Tell me, Sheila, what do you think are the problems between you and Mr Garvie?' The use of her first name, then Max's surname was designed to make her think he was somehow sympathetic or predisposed towards her. Sheila, too, was having doubts about the reason for her being there. Still, she had to tell the truth.

'A few years ago, Maxie woke up one morning and realised, like all of us, that his time on Earth was limited. He simply wasn't satisfied that he had all he needed in terms of his work, his possessions and his family.'

'You have two girls and a boy now aged four?' the doctor observed, flicking back through the file.

'Yes, that's correct,' she confirmed. 'Maxie should have been happy with his lot in life. He worked so hard to turn the farm around and I did all I could to help.'

'Tell me what changed, if you can.'

Sheila had to think deeply. There was no glib way of explaining her husband's unexpected dissatisfaction with his life. 'He always thought differently from the other farmers round about. I mean, like some of them, he worked hard and had a drink on a Friday night, but Maxie was always going to go further. You mentioned the importance of family holidays. He took the girls and I to a nudist beach on our first break abroad. He didn't even tell me that he was going to do it. The girls were mortified, but Maxie just laughed it off. Then he blamed me for being prudish. He's done that ever since.'

Dr Heaton sat writing Sheila's words for a while, then continued reading sections of the file inwardly to himself.

'And do you consider yourself to be prudish?'

'Not at all. I have indulged him as far as I can.'

The psychiatrist weighed that idea up. 'And how was it you came to form a relationship with Mr Brian Tevendale? In your view, did that start off by you indulging your husband?'

Sheila knew that topic was bound to come up, but she remained defiant. 'If you call leaving us together night after night or pushing me into the room Brian was sleeping in, indulging my husband, then yes.'

He noted her answer. 'Was there no desire on your part to see someone else outwith the marriage?'

'None at all. I was, and am, in an impossible situation. I was forced into Brian's arms by my own husband, but I can't leave the children. He's got all the money.'

When it was Max's turn to speak to Dr Heaton, a different account emerged. Putting his initial antagonism towards the psychiatrist to one side, Max's easy charm came to the fore and he put an entirely different slant on things. Speaking calmly and with a smile ready to meet any awkward questions, Max was able to at least sound convincing about the sequence of the infidelity that had caused such a major rift in his marriage.

'I tried, Doctor, I really did. My heart sank sometimes when I went into the kitchen and saw how miserable my wife looked. All I've ever done is try to cheer her up!'

'By that you mean taking her and your daughters to naturist retreats, that sort of thing?' Dr Heaton was testing the water to gauge Max's reaction.

'Yes, of course. Sheila came from a very straight-laced family and I saw it as my job to make her a bit more experienced and sophisticated so she might be happier. Widen her interests, make her more worldly-wise, that kind of thing.'

The psychiatrist nodded. 'Your wife says you crave excitement. Do you agree?'

'Who doesn't, Doc? I don't believe in reincarnation and intend to live life to the full whilst I'm young enough to appreciate it. Did she tell you about my plane, the Bolkow?'

'She did, yes. She says there's a pattern to some of the things you do. She says you throw yourself into things you're interested in, then you just walk away from them when you tire of them.'

Max stopped smiling. 'Listen, who's the one being assessed here today, me or her?'

The doctor backed off. 'Alright, tell me – if you wish – about Brian Tevendale.'

Looking and sounding annoyed at the mention of his name, Max shook his head before speaking. 'Him? I wish we had never met him! He's become a real nuisance. Did she tell you she ran off to your part of the country with him? You *are* from Yorkshire, aren't you?' Max's observation sounded more like an accusation.

Heaton nodded in agreement without speaking.

Max continued. 'I thought I had already explained this to you. She needed to get out more and, through some young folk I know, we sometimes ended up at parties on the weekends and Tevendale would often be there as well. I stupidly gave him a lift from Stirling last year, and it must have been around then he saw his chance to bed Sheila.'

Heaton remained professionally inscrutable. 'Your wife

claims you slept with his sister first, *then* encouraged her and Tevendale to get together. You don't seem to accept that?'

Max was resolute. 'She's in denial! Listen, Doc, do I have to remind you again? She's the one that needs your help, not me! Yes, I admit to having an affair with Tevendale's sister, but that was only to make my wife jealous, and after she had begun to see Tevendale on the side. After all I've done for her! After all I've done for both of them!'

The doctor decided to gently explore the rich seam of angst that Max had just revealed. Was he assessing the wrong partner in this marriage? 'I'm sorry, remind me of that lady's name again, if you please.'

Max sat glaring at him for a few seconds before spitting Trudy's name out. 'She's called Gertrude! She's married to a wimp called Fred Birse. You really couldn't make that up, could you?'

Leafing through the file once again, the doctor realised that subtlety would be needed to explore this next point further. 'I take it that you did not form any lasting attachment to this woman Trudy?' The question played nicely to Max's macho ego.

Max looked astonished at the idea. 'Me and her? Definitely not! She was just a means for me to remind my wife that two could play at that game and it was dangerous for her and Tevendale to carry on humiliating me in public.'

Dr Heaton considered the implications of what had just been said. Foremost was the reaction of the other woman. Might she feel just a little bit exploited? 'And did Trudy display any feelings for you?' Another chance for him to reveal his vanity.

Max smiled an all-lads-together smirk. 'I suppose she must have. She thought I could rescue her from a stale marriage and a dull husband who had lost interest in her. Yes, the answer has to be that she probably fell head over heels for me.'

31

Heaton had to consciously hold back from pursuing the matter further. As Max had said, it was Sheila who was today's subject. 'Thank you, Mr Garvie, I have enough information now. I'll speak to your wife again, if you wouldn't mind taking a seat again in the waiting room.'

Max reached out to shake Heaton's hand, convinced he had persuaded him that, of the two in the marriage, the real victim was him, Maxwell Garvie.

Dr Heaton reported to Dr Lyle a few days later. He noted a previous episode of depression Sheila had suffered accompanied by a general feeling of insecurity. That had been several years before and the use of anti-depressants – along with the birth of her third child – had led to a complete and rapid recovery. Whatever had been at the root cause of her anxiety – maybe her interaction with her husband? – it had surfaced again. Did she feel she wasn't good enough for her husband and did he employ his knowledge of that to manipulate her? Had that been the case from the start of the relationship?

In his view, she was a highly intelligent woman who had a marked tendency to become disproportionately upset at times of stress. Her husband's attempts to 'broaden her interests' had included the use of pornography to try to persuade her to go along with his desire for some *unorthodox* sexual practices between man and wife. This had also led to him attempting to make her orgasm, something she had never achieved in the course of their marriage. She reported, however, that, with the aid of one of the books her husband had borrowed from an American friend, she had succeeded in climaxing after self-stimulation. Whilst that was reported by her husband to the psychiatrist, the subject, Sheila Garvie, was unable to confirm or verify it. Might that have been a facet of her desire to please her husband – by falsely recounting something he wanted to hear?

The husband's insistence on seeking younger, unattached company at weekends was justified by him as part of an effort to combat her shyness in social settings. She reported that she had never liked these occasions, but withstood them for the sake of trying to make her husband's 'scheme' for repairing the marriage work. On those occasions, one of the persons they met was Brian Tevendale, whom they already knew. The husband described him as psychopathic and the sort of individual that others shunned because of his criminal background and alleged drug-taking. According to Garvie, Tevendale had boasted he had a tattoo on his forearm of a scorpion along with the word 'Sheila' above it.

If true, what did that tell an outsider about her younger lover's opinion of her? And what did it say about him?

The subject, Sheila Garvie, had heard from Tevendale that her husband and he had arranged for Tevendale's sister, Trudy, to be at home in the flat she shared with her policeman husband and children in Aberdeen on the night when the Garvies called to visit for the first time. The idea was for Mrs Garvie to experience a jealous reaction to her husband's seemingly instant attraction to her. Trudy was happy to play along with the scheme and was confident that her own husband would not have a similar response to her and Garvie flirting with each other. When asked about that, Mrs Garvie claimed to have no knowledge of what had been planned, although she did express sympathy with Trudy as another one who had been 'used' by her husband in the apparently Machiavellian plots he took pleasure in dreaming up. Garvie himself denied there had been any prior arrangement of that nature, but expressed the view that Trudy was clearly still bitter towards him.

In the psychiatrist's considered opinion, there was fault on both sides and neither the subject nor her husband presently

33

had the wherewithal to resolve their marital problems should they continue to embark upon '*a succession of adolescent sexual and emotional escapades designed to explore the other's capacity to endure jealousy*'.

He noted that Mrs Garvie had declined his suggestion that she consider a short admission to the clinic. It seemed that whatever crises Max underwent, whether personal or marital, he offset at least some of the blame onto Sheila, who then dutifully undertook whatever the suggested remedy was.

Whilst appreciating the Garvies' circumstances were difficult, Dr Heaton was only slightly surprised to learn that the man he had interviewed that day in April had been reported as missing just over a month later. The most likely explanation had to be that the couple had failed to work out their differences and the man had used his obvious wealth to start afresh and set up home with someone else more skilled and willing in arcane bedroom practices. That Brian Gordon Tevendale's arrest in connection with murdering the missing man made the local news headlines four months later came as more stunning news, which, once digested, became more logical, given the potential for trouble that had been brewing.

However, the information that followed the next day – that Sheila Garvie had been arrested on the same charge – genuinely made him question his initial opinion. Was she secretly behind the whole escapade from the start and had successfully hoodwinked him – together with the rest of the local population – into hiding her real, evil, malicious character? Even at that juncture, that still seemed unlikely to him.

Chapter 6:

West Cairnbeg Farmhouse, Kincardineshire,

Tuesday, 11 June 1968, 2 p.m.

Geddes called Sheila on the Monday to make sure she would be in and, when she answered, she sounded in better shape than the last time they had met. 'Hello, Mr Geddes, yes, still no contact or any sign of him. Yes, that will be fine. Two o'clock tomorrow will suit. See you then, bye.'

He and Essie had agreed to differ, the sergeant insisting it was 'bloody obvious' *Lady Muck* had done her man in and Geddes countering there was definitely more to it than that. That led to Essie saying the Detective Sergeant's head had been turned by the beguiling temptress, which Geddes refuted. 'Come on, now, you don't really think that? Alright, she's become involved with young Tevendale, but that's because Max was on a mission to spice up his life, and don't forget it was him that wanted it to happen.'

'Aye, but she didn't have to enjoy it so much!' said Essie, triumphantly ending the conversation.

Assisted by Constable Fred Birse of Aberdeen City Police, a notice was prepared for the *Police Gazette* based on information the constable was given by his brother-in-law, the same Brian Gordon Tevendale. It turned out the police officer was married to Brian's sister, Trudy.

Geddes felt uneasy about what it said, but what would Sheila make of it?

It certainly pulled no punches; if being a drink-and-drug-crazed suicide risk wasn't enough to blacken the absent farmer's character, then chucking in porn dealing and sexual debauchery with a hint of homosexuality – a criminal offence – wasn't likely to nominate him for a civic award. Still, Geddes reasoned, Tevendale knew the man, and there was the added reassurance that Birse was a serving police officer with a reputation for steadiness rather than enthusiasm in his chosen career. The notice described the missing man as follows:

Spends freely, is a heavy spirits drinker and often consumes tranquilisers and Pro-Plus tablets when drinking. Is fond of female company but has strong homosexual tendencies and is often in the company of young men. Is a man of considerable wealth and until four years ago was completely rational. Of late became very impulsive, probably brought about by his addiction to drink. Has threatened suicide on at least one occasion. Deals in pornographic material and is an active member of nudist camps and an enthusiastic flyer. May have gone abroad.

The sound of the tyres crunching on the driveway, then the sight of Geddes's unmarked and underpowered police Morris Minor pulling up outside caused Sheila to put down the copy of *Tatler* she was reading and come to the sitting room window. As Geddes turned the ignition key to kill the engine, he noticed the curtains moving, then the porch door opening. Fully made up and wearing a mauve cashmere jumper and white slacks with matching white sling-back high heeled shoes, Sheila met him at the front door. She looked radiant, the arm sling was gone, and it occurred to Geddes her whole demeanour was that of a woman unconcerned that others might say she was apparently celebrating rather than mourning her husband's mysterious departure. At least she wasn't being devious about it.

Closing the front door behind him, Geddes recognised the scent of Chanel No. 5 as he followed her through. It was his wife Irene's favourite and he had saved up to buy her some for her last birthday. Once he was seated, Sheila offered him tea from a bone china tea set and a biscuit from a porcelain and silver barrel. He accepted both, immediately thinking she was much more in control this time, no smudged makeup and no stale drinks or half-smoked cigarettes lying about.

She definitely did *not* come across as a loving wife fretting over a beloved husband who had gone AWOL.

'So, still no word from Max?'

She shook her head. 'None. I really have no idea where he is,' she said, adding, 'I mean that.'

Geddes pondered her words. Why add that last bit? Was she trying to tell him something, even discreetly?

'And there's been no bank activity. We know that because they are keeping us informed after we organised the disclaimer. If your husband's still alive, he's not needing any money to live on unless somebody else is paying for him or he's opened a new account somewhere.'

'That's just not Maxie. He needs to be the one who pays for everything. It's just the way he is.'

'And how are you coping?' Geddes wanted to let her know she was sending out all the wrong vibes and that her transformation from his last visit hadn't gone unnoticed, as she had probably wanted.

Sheila remained calm. 'I'm fine and my mother is helping with the children. You must know I'm still seeing Brian and that fact alone puts me at a disadvantage. I can just imagine the sort of things the rest of the wives and the Young Farmers are saying about me round about here.'

Her candour surprised him into answering.

'You're right, I do know that – as do my colleagues – some of whom think you might have something to do with

37

Max's vanishing act.'

'Do *you* think that?' she asked directly, placing her cup and saucer on a side table and looking him squarely in the eye.

'Certainly not at this stage – he's a missing person until we find out otherwise. How long have you been seeing Brian for? Officially, I mean.'

For the first time, she looked uncertain. 'On and off since September last year, when Maxie thought it would be fun to fling me into Brian's bedroom one night. For the record, it was after he started an affair with Trudy Birse. You might as well know, Max has no concept of love. He does whatever he wants and always has, so much so that all the wallpaper, paintwork, chairs and couches you can see in here, and even the cup you are drinking from, were all ordered by him without even asking me if I liked any of them.'

She noticed Geddes glancing at the silver cow lighter again.

'That? That was a present Maxie bought me when he flew to London to pick me up after Brian and I ran off to Bradford. I know, Bradford.'

Now she was talking freely, Geddes saw no reason to discourage her from carrying on. 'Why go there, Mrs Garvie? It's maybe not everyone's idea of a place to build a love nest ...'

'Please call me Sheila. Brian's sister Trudy organised a room there through a friend from Aberdeen. She even drove us down, as we didn't have the train fare.'

'That's very decent of her. Trudy's married to Fred, isn't she? Fred the policeman.'

'That's right. PC Fred. Poor Fred, he never had a chance from the start with Trudy. Anyway, Maxie presented me with that silver cow after seeing it in a second-hand shop in Aberdeen.'

Geddes reached over and picked it up. 'It's heavy enough.

Silver-plated, looks like. Maybe a farming connection – you don't have any cattle here, do you, just arable?'

Sheila smiled. 'Right, just crops, but no real livestock connection, apart from a few pigs. You see, after Maxie came to London to pick me up, we were at Heathrow to catch a flight home and he was terribly angry. After a taxi went by, he laughed and said he should have paid the driver to take us all the way back to West Cairnbeg. He said its registration number had the letters C. O. and W. in it and Maxie kept repeating it, over and over, "cow", "cow", then looking at me and saying "cow" again. Then he came home one night and threw that in my lap.' Geddes noticed that she stared at the object for a few seconds after she spoke, her lips curling slightly downwards exaggerating their natural pout.

'So, was he jealous of the time you and Brian spent together?'

She was beginning to lose her composure and gulped before she answered. 'Not so much jealous, well, not to begin with, anyway. It was all his idea because it turned him on so much that a younger man was, eh, intimate with me. Maxie's only interest after that was to make me tell him all the details of what had happened between Brian and me during the terrible time we were away.'

Geddes was having trouble seeing it from her point of view.

'But you left the children to go away with Brian – that must have been difficult for you?'

'Heart-breaking. By that time, Maxie made me do things – sexually, I mean – that I had never realised could happen between a married couple, and he had become forceful towards me if I didn't do them. Before that he had me convinced there was something wrong with *me*, that I was frigid and needed to unbutton a bit. "C'mon, old thing", he'd say. "Loosen up, it's the swinging sixties, for Christ's sake!" After meeting Luke, an American air force officer based at

Edzell, Maxie really thought the answer to all his dreams was pornography and pills, nudism and Polaroids, drink and drugs … at least Brian was tender and cared about me. Maxie wasn't capable of understanding that.'

Past tense again, Geddes noted. *He* wasn't *capable*. Was it the context she was saying it in or was it something more sinister?

Now she was talking freely, she seemed to need to carry on. As the missing man's wife and not an actual suspect – yet – Geddes did not foresee any future difficulties with asking her questions and carefully noting what she said. She was speaking freely and not as someone under suspicion.

'The last time I was here, you mentioned that you and Max had sex when you went to bed on the night of the 14th, just around midnight. Were you sexually involved with your husband and Brian at the same time? By that I mean, sometimes be with one of them, then, say the next night, the other?' It sounded prurient, but the answer might shed light on what Max's problem was.

To Geddes's surprise, she looked genuinely embarrassed. After all she'd said and done, something of the Sunday school teacher still seemed to survive in her.

'After the first night I spent with Brian in the spare bedroom, Maxie couldn't wait to "get his shot at me", as he put it. So I had to get into our double bed in the morning where he was waiting and, let's say, he was excited, very excited. The night he came home, the 14th, I knew he needed to prove something to himself and he would want to make love – there was no way he would let me be. When I say make love, I mean have cold, unfeeling sex. By that time, it felt to me as if I was being raped by my own husband every time he did it. You see, I now thought of Brian as my real partner. Remember I told you I had a way of making sure "it" would be over quickly?'

Geddes noticed a tear making its way down her cheek,

leaving a tiny light path in her carefully applied makeup.

'Well, by that time, all I had to do was be crude, really crude when he was on top of me. One mention of Brian doing the same to me made Maxie lose control, and that quickly let me get back to pretending life was bearable.'

This new, assured version of the supposedly bewildered Mrs Garvie was a puzzling improvement on the first one Geddes had witnessed three weeks before. Something about her answers and explanations struck him as measured and possibly unchallengeable. She had told him things that only confirmed what he already knew from local intelligence, but they were qualified in a way that somehow enhanced her credibility. Why tell him details about what turned Max on unless it was true? Why mention her feelings for Brian at all, when she could have pretended she felt too fragile to answer questions from the CID? That's what some wives would have done if they had anything to do with their husband's disappearance. It was as if she was *trying* to tell him the truth by giving him half the jigsaw pieces together with the picture on the lid of the box so he could make use of what little she had allowed him to have.

A direct question might be in order. For effect, he took his notebook out, removed the pencil from the loop at the back and poised ready to record what she might say. Depending on her answer, he might have to caution her.

'From what you've told me, I think it's fair to comment that life with your husband was far from ideal for you. Some in my profession might say you had the perfect motive for getting rid of him. I have to ask you this. Did you have anything to do with Mr Garvie's disappearance?'

Sheila seemed calm, with no outward signs of a reaction, guilty or otherwise. She placed her cup back into its saucer with a steady hand, then focused on him. 'Mr Geddes, I can assure you I had nothing to do with Maxie leaving West Cairnbeg and I have absolutely no idea of his present

41

whereabouts.'

Geddes carefully jotted her words down; months later, he was to compare them to what had been discovered and find no fault with the second part of that statement, the first bit being a matter for the jury.

Once finished writing, he reached into his inside pocket and pulled out a piece of paper carefully folded in half. 'There's something else I need to ask you about.'

After Geddes read out the notice that was going into the *Police Gazette*, she said nothing, stood up, excused herself, and left the room. When she came back, her makeup was perfect again. 'Must it say all that? What about the children? What will they think if they read it?' She clearly had no issue with the defamatory nature of the piece.

Geddes tried again. 'Well, is any of it *not* true?'

'No. Well, the homosexual bit's new to me. Did Brian *really* say that about Maxie?'

Chapter 7:

Dunnottar Parish Church, Stonehaven,

Saturday, 11 June 1955

With the Romans recently departed from the land, the Picts built the first church at Dunnottar fifteen hundred years ago. It was said that God grew weary of them and their backsliding, though, so he wiped them out, destroying all traces of them, allowing only their mysterious, carved cross-slabs and a few quaint place names to linger on. In the Rev James Cameron's view, the ancient peoples and the owners of the bones beneath the mossed and broken stones in the kirkyard's uneven turf had all been duly judged and had paid their dues.

It was the living, in the here and now, who were the problem.

Take today's wedding.

The marriage of one of his Sunday school teachers to her handsome young fiancé should have been a plain-sailing, joyous occasion, but had instead been beset with problems no-one could have foreseen.

Sheila Watson was a valued member of the congregation. She came from a family of reasonably stout believers, although her mother Edith's leanings towards Spiritualism were distinctly odd and definitely out of step with the church's teachings. Sheila's family's links with the church predated their time in the Royal Estate at Balmoral, where her father William had been a stonemason for a few years and where Sheila herself had matured so much, playing Queen Victoria in a pageant, which, it was said, had even gained tacit Royal approval. Behind the scenes, of course, Edith had darned and sewed and begged and borrowed to make sure that her daughter's outfit was perfect on the day, which it had been.

In the build-up to the big day, though, the first difficulty Rev Cameron became aware of was the thorny subject of Sheila's virginity.

She had confided in her mother that walking down the aisle in white might not be quite appropriate and, fearing the wrath of either God or the Spirits, Edith had brought that difficulty to the minister's attention. Being a practical woman, and without waiting for the minister's final adjudication, she also quickly helped organise Sheila's choice of a dark tailored suit, peach-coloured floral spray, hat and matching cotton gloves as an alternative to a traditional trousseau. Edith hoped that her deeds might stifle the inevitable gossip that her daughter's choice of wedding outfit would attract, and that swift, pre-emptive action also might prevent further discussion on the subject. 'They can be affa coarse aboot these pairts wi their chattering,' she explained to the bemused cleric.

Rev Cameron reflected that few brides and their mothers took the matter so seriously, preferring what he described as 'white-clad hypocrisy' to the obvious but honest want of chastity Sheila's outfit suggested. It seemed that Sheila being presented with a crayon drawing of a stick figure wedding party – a smiling, red-lipped bride in white at its centre – by one of the girls in her Sunday school class had unwittingly forced the issue between the bride-to-be and her increasingly anxious mother. Trusting her mother implicitly, Sheila was inclined to tell her everything; Edith instinctively knew what to do and so *did the right thing* straight away.

Sheila's trusting naivete surfaced a second time when she also asked Edith if it was usual for the groom to present his bride-to-be with an American published illustrated guide to sexual positions and techniques a few days before the big day, but – unaware that such manuals even existed – Edith could offer no opinion. For those who knew them, there could be no doubt that mother and daughter were bound together in an umbilical, lifelong bond that no-one might fully understand and very few could breach. But that was for the future.

As the day loomed, nobody could help Edith, though. What started as minor worries about the important step her daughter was on the verge of taking soon became a constant, nagging foreboding about the Garvie family generally and Max in particular. There can be no earthly explanation – nor any cure – for a deep, irrational sense of dread. Nor can there be any satisfaction when it later turns out to be agonisingly justified.

The wedding party was small, ten in number, the bride's choice of her best friend as best maid being overruled in favour of the groom's sister, Hilda. The respective families were ill at ease together, the Watsons walking to the church from their cottage in Fetteresso and the Garvies arriving in modern limousines from West Cairnbeg. In the knowledge that the bride's father, William Watson, could only afford a small, alcohol-free celebration dinner, the groom and the best man had taken the precaution of several rounds of doubles beforehand, so much so that Rev Cameron now had two immediate concerns – whether the groom and his best man would be capable of carrying out their ceremonial duties and whether Edith would be able to control the outward effects of her dramatic premonition.

He need not have worried for the groom and his friend, who merely swayed slightly and occasionally smirked at each other in a silent, shared secret.

The bride, though, was becoming preoccupied with her mother, who was experiencing one of the visions she called her 'spookies', just as the marriage was being blessed by the minister. Conscious of Edith's wailing getting louder, Rev Cameron raised his voice to overcome the eerie moaning, and, to her later regret, the bride glanced over to try to calm her mother.

Sheila saw Edith's face was a ghastly white colour, her eyes full of fear and her hands desperately gripping the pew. As if used to it, her husband William was resignedly staring straight ahead and making no effort to calm her. 'In truth, someone stirring the porridge withershins could have started her off that day,' he later told Sheila.

During the ceremony, Sheila vowed to 'obey' her new husband, as was the custom, and in return he promised to 'love and cherish' his new bride. There can be little doubt that she at least tried to carry out her side of the bargain and that the groom largely failed in his, particularly in the later years of the marriage.

Afterwards, at the reception in Stonehaven's Bay Hotel, relations between the families remained awkward as the soup and steak were served along with a choice of water or orange juice, short, forgettable speeches by William and an unsteady Max rounding the day off. Once there, though, Edith's 'spookie' had thankfully abated up until Max spoke to her and encouraged her to cheer up, the addition of the words 'sons-in-law like me don't come along every day' causing the troubled woman to relapse into a distant, ominous dwam.

The reception, for what it was, was all over by 2 p.m. that afternoon, and the wedding party broke up with the Watson family walking home again, but not before the groom's mother, Mrs Garvie, made a point of giving a present of silk pyjamas – to her son.

Edith's apprehensions about her daughter's marriage stayed with her and lasted till her death, or, more exactly, Max's death. They were also the subject of an explanatory letter to Sheila from beyond the grave fourteen years later. Perhaps because mother and daughter shared everything throughout their time together on Earth, Edith was well aware that Sheila was not *passionately* in love with her new husband, having previously experienced that sensation with another before she met him, and so held her emotions in check so as 'not to be hurt again'. What Edith knew, but Max didn't, was that her daughter was as equally capable of deep, contented love as she was of profound, unforgiving hatred, and Max was to earn both.

It turns out Edith's spookies *were* well founded, this time at least.

Chapter 8:

Laurencekirk Police Office, Kincardineshire,

Tuesday, 11 June 1968, 4 p.m.

Geddes intended to return to the office after speaking to Mrs Garvie at West Cairnbeg that afternoon. It was another warm, sunlit summer's day, and, as he carefully drove along the farmhouse's stony driveway, he braked briefly to take in a Red Admiral, which fluttered towards the car's windscreen from a small compost heap hidden nearby behind upright corrugated iron sheets. As it perched on one of the car's wipers, he stopped the vehicle completely to take in its full vibrant glory, its dappled wings crowned with white, flashes of red daubed nearer the centre and tipped with an iridescent auburn at the base. It was as if a child in nursery had been given a tiny, raven-coloured butterfly body and had been let loose with a brush and tin of acrylic paint and had daubed at it randomly until satisfied. Just after the little creature alighted for more fruitful pastures and Geddes restarted his slow journey along the crunching pebbles, he noticed Mrs Garvie anxiously surveying the scene from the sitting room window. He had been alerted to her presence when he caught movement of the curtains in his rear-view mirror. She was definitely uneasy about something and he doubted it had anything to do with the safe return of her domineering husband.

Reaching the main road from the farm complex, he seriously considered using up some of the overtime he

48

had built up, which he knew he would never get paid for. He might surprise his wife, Irene, by going home early. She frequently said that he spent too much time at work. Perhaps they could go for a drive or 'dine out' in Stonehaven – Irene's term for buying chips – and go for a stroll along the seafront. He drove through Laurencekirk and made for the coast along a minor road, past Lauriston, but something made him take a right towards St Cyrus, where he stopped at the first phone box he saw near the local pub to give her a call, deciding that if he returned to the office it would be more difficult to extricate himself from the daily, humdrum problems that continually came his way. Pennies inserted, he was about to dial home when he had a sudden change of heart and pressed button 'B' to get his money back. It had occurred to him that although Irene was right and he had been working too hard recently, it would hardly be fair for him to take her somewhere like Stonehaven with all its Max Garvie connections. No matter where they went, he knew he would undoubtedly be unable to stop himself thinking – or even talking – about the circumstances of the case. He decided he *would* go back to the office and make it up to his wife as soon as he could, once the current major enquiry was finished.

Several months later, that journey was to etch itself in his mind as unnervingly similar to where the Garvie enquiry was to lead; even the phone box was to come back to intrigue him.

On the way back to the office, he mused that perhaps one day in the distant future technology might come to the aid of police investigations of serious crime. Imagine being able to trace a vehicle's movements by tracking its progress using something like its number plate? He could hear Essie's voice saying that he was 'havering' and that 'he isnae really cut oot for the polis but should hae written trashy stories like thon loon fae Arbuthnott'. Essie was right. Geddes knew he was being fanciful.

Nothing for it in the meantime but to head back along the route he had taken and go back to Laurencekirk.

Letting himself in by the rear door, he heard Essie cautiously tip-tapping on the station typewriter in the public office at the front. Hearing the familiar sound, he shook his head, wondering if his colleague would ever become proficient in preparing reports. Of course, it might help if he was able to use more than his left and right index fingers, and if those fingers were normal-sized rather than having thick, sausage-type dimensions.

Geddes made straight for the kettle, which he filled, and then put two heaped spoonfuls of tea in the station teapot. Essie sat back in his chair, then extended his arms in front of him before intertwining his fingers and cracking them. 'It's been a bloody long day. I wish to God Mrs Slaven still worked part-time here; she could type a week's work in a couple of hours!'

'Stop moaning, Essie man, you're sure to get a secretarial job somewhere after you've got your pension.'

Geddes placed a mug of tea on Essie's desk, then sat down at a desk on the other side of the room, out of sight of the public. He put his feet on it and took a mouthful of hot, milky tea. 'You know, it's so nice out there today, I nearly never came back here. I thought about taking Irene out instead.'

'Why didn't you? You're owed a lot of time off.'

'I'll make it up to her when I get a chance.'

'You've been saying that ower too long. The way it's going, the poor woman's not going to see much of you this side of Heaven. Here, how did you get on seeing the Merry Widow this afternoon? Was I right about her? Did she offer to take you upstairs?'

Geddes shrugged and ignored the last question. 'I really don't know what to make of her. Remember the last time I went to see her, I told you she looked really rough, smudged makeup, old dressing gown, chain-smoking and hair all over the place?'

'Aye.' Essie had leaned forward in his chair, eager to hear the latest instalment.

'This time was different. She was waiting for me, all made up and smartly dressed. She poured me tea in a china cup and we spoke for a while.'

Essie became professional and listened carefully. 'So, what did she say? Any word from the missing man?'

'No, nothing so far, but, as I said, she was really different today, even in her manner.'

'And did she say anything different this time?'

Geddes took his notebook out of his inside pocket and looked at the pencilled notes he had made. He closed the book and placed it face down on the desk. 'At one point, I reckoned I might have to caution her, but there was no need. After I asked her if she had anything to do with her man's disappearance, she said something that might tell us everything or nothing. What do you make of this? She told me she had nothing to do with him leaving West Cairnbeg and had no idea of his present whereabouts.'

Essie mulled her words over. 'Sounds like a proper denial to me, except she added that she had no idea of his present whereabouts. Why say "present"?'

'It's all very odd, like she's wanting to tell me something but just can't do it. For instance, you'll remember she told me about the silver lighter – the one shaped like a cow?'

'Aye, what was the story behind that?'

'She was quite open about it. She ran away with young Tevendale, just as we all heard in all the local shops and pubs, but to be fair to her, she didn't shy away from that.'

Essie interrupted. 'Bob, we both know she's got no option but to admit that. My wee niece is in the same class as one of the Garvie girls and all the bairns there knew about it!'

'Of course, that's right, it's common knowledge, but it's interesting hearing it from her point of view. The missing man went down to pick her up from Bradford and it wasn't what you could call a happy reunion. He started off telling her she was a cow, then he bought her the lighter as a gift. Some present!'

Essie took up the cudgels on behalf of the confused men of the western world and the Mearns in particular. 'Jesus, Bob, it's the so-called swinging sixties! Women all over the world are burning their simmets in protest at us men ruining their lives by getting killed fighting to save them in wars and by working every hour God gives to pay the heating in the house they sit in all day, drinking tea and gossiping with the wifie next door! How would you feel if Irene ran off with her young lover?'

Geddes tried but failed to picture his ever reliable and steady wife suddenly announcing she was off to California with a young ex USAAF engineer, both with flowers in their hair. 'I'm not sure she's a good example of what you're talking about, Essie ...'

Essie grinned. 'Aye, you're right, but you know what I mean.'

'This Women's Lib thing cuts both ways, you know,' Geddes continued. 'People like Max Garvie can't have his cake and eat it. I mean, he can't force her to do whatever he wants, then complain about it when she does it.'

'What's she saying he forced her to do?'

'She told me he flung her into Tevendale's bedroom one night when he was staying over, then demanded she had sex with him the next morning. She described him as very excited.'

'Well, you two seemed to have got into some detail, alright. The lassie's mibbe not what you'd call the shy type, then? What made her tell you that, if you don't mind me asking?' Essie was enjoying playing the role of cynical commentator, having learned it from his wife down the years.

Geddes withdrew his feet from the desk and sat up straight. 'All that came from the first time I saw her, the cow lighter and something she told me Max Garvie had said to her about marriage. "Monogamy is monotony" is what she said was his point and that they needed to jazz their sex life up a bit. I don't think she was that keen to go along with it. To begin with, anyway.'

'Bloody Yanks! That airbase at Edzell has brought free love to our doorstep. It's like the south of England in the last conflict, with all the women's heads turned and all the men trying to compete.'

Geddes wasn't convinced. 'Not sure about that. Whatever was going on was down to one man's fantasies. You know what I thought was strange? She must have been telling me at least some of the truth because after she told me about her first night with young Tevendale, she reddened up when she said she had sex with Garvie in the morning. Like he was raping her. Come on, Essie, no woman could act as convincingly as that. I don't doubt much of what she said, but it's really frustrating, like she wants me to know what really happened to her man, but she can't say. Oh, did you see the notice that's going into the Gazette?' He handed the folded paper to Essie, who read it over in silence.

'They certainly didn't miss and hit the wall, as they say, with that! Who gave the info for that one? Must have been somebody that didn't like him, if you ask me.'

'That's what I wondered about, too. It was Tevendale. Detective Inspector Wilkie at Bucksburn called Constable Fred Birse in and he came back with all that stuff. It reads like the missing man was no loss to anybody and we shouldn't be wasting time looking for him. Two things, though. His wife had nothing to do with compiling it and her reaction after she read it was peculiar. She didn't get angry, she didn't protest, she didn't cry. All she said was that she was worried what their children might think, and there was another thing. The bit about his homosexual tendencies – she said that bit was new to her and did Brian really say that about Maxie?'

Essie stood up and took his mug through to the sink next door. When he came back, he said, 'Aye, that is strange. It's like Fred Birse was being used by young Tevendale to tarnish Garvie's reputation and the Merry Widow wasn't in on it.'

Geddes noted that Essie still called Mrs Garvie 'The Merry Widow'. Having now met her twice, he wouldn't have described her as 'merry', 'troubled' being a better word for her guarded behaviour. 'And that wife of constable Birse, Trudy, I think she's called. Her role in all of this needs looked at. You know she organised accommodation down south for her brother and Sheila Garvie *and* she drove them there? What was in it for her?'

Essie glowered at Geddes. 'Surely you heard that she was sleeping with Garvie when her younger brother was seeing Mrs Garvie?'

'Aye, Mrs Garvie would have you believe her husband's affair with Trudy Birse happened *before* she began sleeping with Tevendale, but how does that explain why Trudy was so concerned about Sheila Garvie that she drove her to Bradford? We'll never know how this all pieces together until Maxwell Robert Garvie turns up. Dead or alive.'

Chapter 9:

The George Hotel, Edinburgh,

Sunday, 22 October 1967

Trudy Birse awoke early when the prim Edinburgh sun first pushed its way past half-hearted rain clouds and into the penthouse suite through a disapproving gap in the heavily brocaded curtains. Lit up in the sliver of sunlight were her dress, girdle with stockings still attached and last night's high heels, all discarded on the carpet at Max's sudden whim for what he called 'fun sex'.

So far, she thought, her plan was going well. As Max snored loudly, she ran the events of the last few weeks over in her head.

After her young brother Brian told her and her forbearing husband Fred about the Garvies, Trudy had come up with an idea that she had only half-explained to poor, easy-going Fred, to replace the current Mrs Garvie with her good self at West Cairnbeg. She pulled the Egyptian cotton sheets up to her chin as she recalled the night only a few months before when Brian explained things in his own faltering, get-there-in-the-end way that so enchanted her mother but so annoyed her.

'So this rich man Max just came out with it and told me he wanted me to make sure his wife had a night to remember ... and her standing there ... looking a bit frightened ... wearing a short white nightie ... the Skipper made her take it off before he went back to his bed ... and she then came into my bed …'

Fred, in his own plodding fashion, had asked one of his stupid, policeman-type questions. 'So, did you, you know, see to the lassie, then?'

Brian had smiled like the short-arsed loon he really still was and said, 'Aye, twice!' Like he got bonus points for it or something. *Men are so shallow!*

Sensing an opportunity to at least see where this might go, Trudy had wangled that Brian – so macho, so dense – get the Garvies to call at their flat in Aberdeen's Birkhall Parade the night the Birses came back from that dreadful caravan fortnight in Lendalfoot. Lendalfoot! It had never occurred to her it could rain *anywhere* for a whole fortnight, not even in Aberdeen, and she needed – no, *deserved* – cheering up after endless games of *Snap!,* rain-sodden walks to the edge of the sea and coping with three youngsters with cabin fever. Fred, on the other hand, had apparently enjoyed himself boiling kettlesful of water on a primus stove and frying bacon and eggs, the acrid smell of which lingered in the stuffy confines of the little caravan and made her retch.

Things had moved on, though, and she had been proved right. If a husband wants – no, *makes* – his wife sleep with other men, then *he's* the one who needs a real woman. And, so far, it had worked.

Fred hardly noticing, Trudy had put on her shortest skirt and highest heels the Friday night the Garvies had visited and Max had made straight for her, perching himself on the arm of the settee she was sitting on and speaking only to her, inviting her flying in his two-seater plane on the Sunday. Compared to Fred, Max was class, down to his chunky gold pinkie ring with diamond inset and his heavy Barker brogues. Only her oldest girl – and Sheila – had picked up on what was going on, but Trudy knew she could justify it, even if just to herself. At the very least, there was money and good times in it for her and her young brother; at the very best, she might just turn out to be the next mistress of West Cairnbeg.

She imagined Max as a kind of debauched Red Baron figure as he drunkenly coaxed the little plane into the ether that morning as Fred and the kids sat idly grounded in his old Standard Vanguard estate. Although Fred annoyingly pointed out her oft professed fear of flying, as the Rolls Royce engine wound itself up to full volume and the plane left the ground, a beaming Trudy allayed her fears by convincing herself it would all work out well in the end.

It got off to a promising start as Max evened the wings, dropped the engine revs and propositioned her.

Pretending she knew little of what had possibly been going on between Brian and Sheila, she continued, smiling fixedly as Max wondered if she might have some free time next week for them to get to know each other a little better. 'You see, the problem is that my wife of twelve years craves more excitement in her life – I mean her sex life – and so it's only fair I do the same. Do you agree? Do you need to live a bit more as well?'

No wonder women spies are so effective, she thought. *Men think us women have turkey stuffing for brains, so I'll play along with it.*

After she let it slip that Fred was on day shift on the Monday and the kids were not back till three, Max was at the door with a bottle of vodka for a quick screw on the same creaking sofa it had all started some four days before. Since then, he seemed to think he had already crossed the finishing line although the race hadn't even begun. *He imagines he completely owns Sheila, that he owns Brian because he uses him and pays him to 'entertain' her, and he thinks he owns me because I give him all the kinky sex he craves. Oral and anal, sometimes deliberately in the wrong, foul-tasting order.*

Hotel after hotel, every glass of champagne and every oyster – all booked and paid for by him – and every time he finishes having his painful way behind me leaves him needing me more than anyone. What is marriage if not a way of keeping unhappy people together for the sake of children and relatives? Yet, I've noticed him sometimes looking at Sheila in a needy, boyish way as if to ask her, 'Is it not time you just gave in and admitted you're a prude so we can get on with what I need?' And all the times he makes me knock on their door in the morning so she can go into his bed straight after me, and my brother and I lie awake in separate rooms sometimes wondering, sometimes hearing, as they argue, then Max makes that grunting sound to signal satisfaction of some kind, if not exactly what he wants.

Then there was that time he booked us all in at the Central Hotel in Glasgow. We had all been drinking bubbly before we checked in, so by the time we ended up at reception, he had his arm round my waist and was already whispering what he was going to do to me in our room. Brian and Sheila were behind us, quietly holding hands as usual, as Max blustered on about loafers and hippies, also as usual. He insisted all of us check in together. The young male receptionist had longish hair and Max stage-whispered something about a hippy working in a top-class hotel to which I sniggered without really getting the joke. Max then put on a Home Counties accent – he called it his Noel Coward – and demanded the youngster check through bookings that night for 'The Bolkow Set'. When the receptionist apologised and said there were none, Max guffawed, waved his hand and told him to try Mr and Mrs Garvie and Mr and Mrs Tevendale instead. Maybe Sheila failed to notice, but by that time, <u>she</u> was Mrs Tevendale and <u>I</u> was Mrs Garvie, which felt good.

People talk alright. Fred has not been a problem so far, but he tells me that some of the men on his shift in the City Police have been asking what's going on.

I had to explain to him that Max and I sometimes shared a bed – I decided not to let him know what turned Max on as

58

it might still be a criminal offence, which Fred might want to do something about! – and when I mentioned it to Max, he came up with the perfect solution. 'Next weekend,' he said, 'we'll have an orgy and get Fred involved.' I doubted he would, Fred being a bit, well, docile in things like that, so I shared my thoughts with Max as he untwisted the cage on another champagne cork. Max took the half-smoked cheroot from his mouth and spoke as he poured another glass for himself and then another for me. 'Don't think I've not noticed what your man's like. Strikes me he's into kids or young girls anyway. I know the very girl he's been looking for, but he doesn't know it yet. Leave it to me.'

The following weekend, we went to a hotel in quiet, douce little Edzell and Max persuaded a girl of about eighteen, but looked younger, to come with us to West Cairnbeg. I heard Max tell her he would pay her if she poured the drinks and give her extra if she did more. I have to admit, it did not sound like Tracey had any idea what he meant. Anyway, lights dimmed, soft background music on, Sheila and Brian were the first to dance cheek to cheek and the first to go upstairs. Fred just sat there, making small talk with Tracey and, after Max and I went upstairs to the master bedroom, I heard the Standard engine starting as Fred drove off with Tracey. I found out the next day that he had taken her home to Edzell without so much as a peck on her chubby rosy cheek, then he had gone back to Aberdeen. Fred can be so dull sometimes and what an argument we had when I got back around 2 p.m. the next afternoon! Fred had picked the kids up and made a roast beef dinner without making any for me! Did the idiot think I'd stopped eating? Does he not realise I have other needs too, ones that he can't fulfil because of the kind of man he is?

Men?

Really!

Trudy's reverie suddenly ended when Max stopped

59

snoring, rubbed his eyes and sat up. 'Trude, old girl, get me a black coffee, would you?' Trudy peeled the covers from her side of the bed, then made her way towards the kettle. Completely naked, she went into the bathroom to fill it with enough water for two cups. On the way out, she heard Max on the internal phone to Brian. 'Yes, Trudy's coming through to your room to shower and change after she's made me a coffee. Yes, send Sheila through in fifteen minutes ...'

Trudy clattered a cup onto a saucer before placing the second cup and saucer back onto the tray and plugging the kettle into a socket.

Men!
Really!

Chapter 10:

The Watson House, New Street, Stonehaven,

Saturday, 12 November 1967

Edith rinsed out the thin film of dust from the Windsor bone china tea set she got from William's parents when she married him in Aberdeen in April 1930. The set had been kept for an important social event involving discerning and genteel guests that had never happened and it had languished in a bow fronted glass and walnut display cabinet ever since. Noticing spaces in the cabinet, William put down *The Press and Journal* and walked into the kitchen. 'So, what's the occasion?' he asked, fearing Edith's answer might involve aged, hatted female relatives, tea and empire biscuits.

Edith had hoped he would not notice the missing crockery until 'The Conference' was in full swing, by which time his mind would be on other, more weighty matters. Being married for nearly forty years gives a wife handy tramlines of certainty in her dealings with her man, and she knew how to get him involved in what was about to happen. He would bluster at first, then come round to her way of thinking.

'I thought we should try our best to save their marriage …'

'For goodness' sake, woman, as if wee china cups are going to make any difference,' William blurted, 'to what those two have been up to!'

Edith's resolve emerged in her steely tone of voice. 'All that matters now is that the marriage goes on, mostly for the bairns' sake …'

William backed off at the first signs of his wife's seemingly supernatural understanding of issues he could never comprehend. 'Aye, you're right, I suppose. There comes a time in every marriage when somebody's got to back down. After all, it is for life …'

Ignoring her husband's scarcely hidden barb, Edith remained on course. 'As we both know, Sheila's put up with a lot and it's Max that wants this meeting now, so we have to make sure Sheila stops seeing that young Tevendale.'

'What a pity she didn't meet and marry him. The Major's son would have been a good man to have in the family. I knew the Tevendales from Stonehaven, you know …'

Edith quickly closed the door on her husband's oft-repeated recollections and admiration for the Major. 'Wheesht and stop that right now! She's ten years older than him and the bairns need their parents to be together. *You* have to speak to Sheila, then Max, then her again, if need be.'

Accepting it as part of his duties, William managed a meek 'Aye' as Edith unpacked vanilla slices from a box and placed them on a cake stand that had never been used before.

Pressing home her advantage, she continued, 'We have to ignore what he's done to her and what she's done to him and, anyway, how many cups should I set for? Do you think Max is going to bring that Trudy and Sheila's going to bring young Tevendale? I mean, they are also involved. Mind and be tactful!'

She had her answer an hour later when the letterbox rattled. Edith recognised her daughter's presence. 'That's her now, go and let her in.'

William went to the door and opened it, unsure of the etiquette when your married daughter brings her young lover to your house so he can be dumped. Sheila looked heartbroken as she shuffled in first without even speaking to her perplexed father. The two men stood awkwardly looking at each other until William extended his hand and announced both his Christian and last name. Brian reached out and delivered a weak, sweaty grip in response, causing William to drop his plans for a doorstep resume of how well he knew the Major.

Against expectations, he instinctively disliked this young man. That there was something *sleekit* about him made William's forthcoming task much easier.

Once in the cramped confines of the living room, Sheila introduced Brian to Edith, instantly regretting it as Edith looked pained and Brian looked shifty. *If one of Edith's spookies is on the way*, thought Sheila, *there can be no way back for Brian and me.* From the start, Edith had been right about Max, after all, even though it took time before he eventually showed his true colours.

An excruciating twenty minutes went by before the letterbox clattered again, Brian sullenly refusing repeated offers of tea, cakes and biscuits, and Sheila worried about the outcome of this Max-inspired get together. It looked like it was going to be three versus one, with her parents siding with Max, and Brian and Trudy not even having a vote. Yet again, all Max had to do was stamp his feet to get his own way, the greetin' bairn ayeways gettin' fed first.

Max and Trudy had driven to 'The Conference' together, him hoping she might not sense the outcome before they got there and her determined to have her say, not just for herself, but for her younger brother as well. She still had a notion she might replace Sheila at West Cairnbeg, so she might have to take a stand, perhaps along the lines of: 'It's too late, I've already fallen head over heels for this handsome man who insisted on stealing me away from my faithful husband and anxious children.' Throughout her relationship with Max, Trudy had not been surprised by her lack of feeling for what she was doing to Fred. After all, her husband had made it clear he had given up on any notion of loving her, either physically or emotionally. He was the ultimate 'safe pair of hands' that other women seemed to crave, a good provider and loving father to the children. *Well, they're welcome to him. Fred likes going to places like dreich old Lendalfoot to live like tinkers in a caravan, but I'd be much more at home on a nudist beach in Corsica or Sardinia. This is my big chance to live a richer, happier life, and, like Sheila, Fred is just another casualty of what happens when grown-up people become dissatisfied with their lives. I'm not going to give this up easily ...*

When Max had pulled into a lay-by, killed the engine and turned to face her, she wondered what he was going to say. Whatever it was, he was obviously going to be all male and clumsy about it, so she was confident she could preserve her bargaining position at the family summit conference.

This was not the brash, assertive man who enjoyed shouting '*Garçon!*' at fresh-faced barmen just to see them squirm, or who commanded breakfast tables at five-star hotels with invented tales of flying to St Helier or Paris. Instead, he made Trudy think of her young son about to confess to eating the last chocolate in the box, the one she had kept for herself.

Max got off to an unconvincing start.

'Trude, old thing, we've had some great times, and I've got to say you have given me more pleasure in the last two weeks than Sheila has in twelve years ...'

She sensed the coming 'but'.

'Could you do me a massive favour, though?'

Trudy nodded rather than spoke, keeping her powder dry.

'Just to keep things sweet with the old in-laws, could you maybe tell them that, despite everything, you have no doubt I still love the mother of my children?'

The coward can't even say his wife's name!

For several moments, Trudy pretended she was

considering his words, then shook her head angrily. 'Why should I do that? You don't love her, do you?' she said stubbornly.

Max flushed with anger, then quickly regained control of himself. 'You're right, I don't, but just to keep them happy. I mean, they're such simple people. When their daughter married me all those years ago they felt as if they'd won the football pools.'

Already knowing the answer, Trudy knew she had him on the run. 'So, whose idea was this meeting? Was it yours or theirs?'

Max realised he had been rumbled and that Trudy knew it was all down to him. 'Well, mostly theirs, but I've had to go along with it of course ... for the kids' sake really ...'

Time to be strong, she thought. 'No, I'm *not* going to say something that isn't true, no matter how many times you ask me! For everyone's sake!'

Max angrily sprang out of the car, strode to the passenger's side and opened the door. 'In that case, get out! There's no point in you coming to this conference!' he shouted.

Trudy switched on her sugar-sweet smile and remained firmly seated. Putting on her best Sheila voice, she said, 'You know, Maxie darling, I'll just turn up anyway, so better get back in and drive. We don't want to be late now, do we?'

Max stood holding the door open for some time. It occurred to him that turning up late for 'The Conference' would not impress the Watsons, who were always punctual, though in a toadying, proletarian way.

He got back in, swore, and started the engine.

From then on, Max drove furiously, crunching the gearbox and cutting up the sedate motorists of the Mearns in his haste to get to Stonehaven and get it over with. After he parked the car, Trudy nimbly followed him along the street and up the stairs like a predatory fox stalking a territorial rival. Max's mood magically changed at the Watsons' door, clapping

William's back and warmly shaking his hand. Trudy could playact too. Extending a limp hand at the door, she reminded William of one of the princesses he had seen at Balmoral, feigning pleasure at meeting a petty local dignitary.

Once assembled, the plan was for William to become the stern *pater familias* he had never really been. Sure, he had set strict standards at home; no alcohol was ever allowed in his house, the girls were expected to obey his word on pain of a severe, disapproving look across the dinner table, and whatever transpired in the marital bed was strictly between a man and his wife, but this was beyond his remit.

Perhaps it was just as well that Edith had already made the big decision beforehand.

William talked privately and separately to the estranged Garvies in the bedroom, away from the others, who sat silently sipping tea or staring out the window. When Sheila returned tearfully to the room, Max stood up and went through, like a schoolboy about to see the business end of the headmaster's Lochgelly.

As Brian sat vacantly awaiting his fate, Sheila glanced over in his direction, loving him for being so helplessly ineffective and so different from her forceful, bullying husband, who was now so obviously faking sincerity for the sake of her parents. Trudy was livid. All her scheming might be for nothing if this went the way she thought it now would. To make matters worse, Max's laughter carried through from the bedroom, laughter that sounded false and hollow, laughter that she imagined was put on solely for her to hear. *If he thinks he's going to use his kids to emotionally blackmail me into letting go, he's going to have to think again!*

When William announced the final decision – surprise, surprise, that the Garvies were getting back together and the Tevendales were dumped – Trudy wondered if Max had any real idea what he had just done, what the wrath of an angry woman was. *And not just any woman, a Tevendale, the daughter of a Major, a man who fought on till the end, no matter what he had to do to win. Maxwell Robert Garvie did not even have the balls to end it himself! He is an empty shell of a man only interested in his own pleasure. He is a coward. He is a coward who will regret ever crossing the path of Gertrude Margaret Tevendale!*

Conference over, Trudy was no longer welcome in Max's Mark X Jag, so she took her feckless, taciturn brother aside and warned him that Max – no, *the Garvies* – would be sorry for treating them that way, not even allowing them a right of reply. As the Major's son, it was up to him to do something about it, even if just to uphold the family honour. No need to mention thwarted dreams of living in West Cairnbeg, dining out in expensive restaurants or jetting off to sunny climes.

The weak link, of course, was Sheila, so that would be a good starting point for Trudy to work on. Because she still loved Brian, she was bound to do something impulsive. On cue, she walked falteringly from the side of the Jag towards Trudy and Brian, tears wetting her hair and cheeks before Max barked an order for her to get back into the car so they could drive back to West Cairnbeg together, physically at least.

Boy, are they going to regret this! Trudy resolved as Max over-accelerated away in a swirl of twin exhaust fumes with his erstwhile wife silently weeping by his side.

Chapter 11:

West Cairnbeg Farmhouse, Kincardineshire,

Boxing Day 1967

Over time, Rev Arthur Thom got to know all about the Garvies and their problems, as did most of the Mearns. *All* of their problems. Both Garvies had spoken to him individually, Sheila complaining of Max's drinking, pill-taking and his demands for *unnatural* sex with her, and Max protesting his wife had fallen in love with another man. Neither of them regularly attended church, but being the local minister – and by rights a natural confidante – he was happy to help in any way he could in his own, limited way.

Sheila was candid about things. She *had* vowed to try her best to make the marriage work, but she said that, when they returned home after 'The Conference', Max had announced that, from then on, she had to understand that she *belonged* to him and, as such, he was free to do as he pleased with her, including *all* his bedroom demands; she had explained that she needed time to repair her injured feelings before they could move on and he flew off the handle at her, although he stopped short of hitting her.

Max, however, told an entirely different story. From him, the minister heard that she had laughed at his lack of performance in bed, her young lover easily outpacing him and, most hurtful of all, giving her all the sexual satisfaction she craved. Something about Max's account sounded manufactured, something a desperate man would invent, thinking others might sympathise with him. It lacked insight. It lacked credibility. It sounded tailored to fit in with one party's dangerously slanted view of a delicate situation.

Rev Thom instinctively knew who was telling the truth, but thought it better to cajole and encourage both of them from an apparently neutral position, so he listened patiently to them individually without passing judgement, urging them both to be patient.

The minister had become involved as unofficial referee when Max had impulsively convened another meeting between him and Sheila in the Bay Hotel in Stonehaven shortly after 'The Conference' in the Watsons' house. Neither the Watsons nor Trudy or Brian were invited, but Max had specifically requested that the minister attend. The minister reasoned that, now that he had wrested his wife back, Max's ego couldn't work out that she might have returned to him reluctantly, and he really needed a clerical stamp of approval to make her stay.

Max denied he had done anything wrong, but Sheila's latest instalment again sounded more credible when she said that Max had made her choose between him – the father of her children with all his property, money and possessions – and Brian, who had nothing. Sounding like an uncomprehending child, she said Max had been 'terribly annoyed' when she chose Brian and reacted by threatening to 'put a bullet between her eyes' before he stormed out, taking the key of the Cortina estate she had driven to Stonehaven in and leaving her stranded there. 'Luckily,' she continued, 'Trudy was on hand to help me by taking me to her house. It was raining heavily and I was not dressed for the weather, so it was really decent of her to help me, in the circumstances.'

Trudy being 'helpful' and Sheila being ingenuous yet again, the minister suspected.

Knowing the Garvies socially, the Thoms discussed the situation between them to see how they could be of help.

They collected the Garvie children from school when they could and dropped in to West Cairnbeg if they were going into town, in case they needed anything from the shops, trying to bring normality to a particularly awkward situation.

It all seemed to be in vain.

Sheila went on to tell of Max bashing her head off the Jag's passenger side window when she was crying on the way home from a joyless party they had recently been at; Max had asked him to mediate when he discovered that Sheila and the children had gone to yet another hotel in Stonehaven where they had booked in for the night. All very well, except that Brian had also booked in the same place that night, albeit in a single room for himself.

Rev Thom felt some progress had been made when both Sheila and Max had separately agreed to his suggestion they go home from the hotel and perhaps go away together on a holiday to patch things up. Max visibly cheered up when he told him that she had agreed to his idea of a holiday together, but the man of the cloth later puzzled over what Sheila had added when she agreed to the idea. She said she would go with Max and the children, but was afraid of what Brian would do. A year later, in Aberdeen High Court, he made sure the jury heard that candid but revealing remark with all its possible implications for future events. What *would* Brian do? Up until then, it was Max who had been the problem, Brian doing very little wrong, very little that was different from what any normal young man would have done. Had things *drastically* changed so much after the unsurprising decision arrived at 'The Conference'?

Rev Thom and his wife Jenny had visited the Garvies at West Cairnbeg at Christmas that year, bringing mince pies and raspberry cordial and a pious hope that tensions had settled.

They were to be disappointed.

Max was drunk and Sheila sullen and silent, the children

subdued. The diplomatic Thoms did not stay for long. Leaving Max in the sitting room nursing an oversized gin and orange, Sheila at least tried to smile as she thanked them for their kindness and escorted them to the front door. On the way out, Rev Thom said he hoped 1968 would be a better year for them, words he came to regret when Max went missing a few months later.

As they drove home, the Thoms discussed the Garvie situation.

'How could Max do that to Sheila?' Rev Thom said as the car bumped and scraped its way along the short track that led to the manse.

'You mean him actually wanting her to be with someone else?' Jenny spent much of her time untangling her well-meaning husband's thoughts, sometimes even tying back her long, slightly greying hair, pushing her small gold-rimmed glasses onto the bridge of her nose and making him sit at the ample kitchen table to straighten out the *actual* meaning of his forthcoming sermon.

'Yes. I find it hard to believe that some folk can be . . . well, intimate with people they have no feelings for.' Her husband sounded genuinely troubled.

Jenny shook her head in bewilderment. 'There you go again, Arthur, dear. Some folk would find it hard to believe how naive you can be. The world has changed and is changing as we speak. People these days want gratification and, if it makes money, someone, somewhere, will supply it.'

He was puzzled. 'What do you mean? There seems to be no money angle with the Garvies. It strikes me that that's about the only trouble they don't have at present.'

'No, I'm talking about pornography. That's how Max got started, isn't it? That sort of thing encourages some men to treat women as objects, as if they have no feelings.'

Rev Thom considered his wife's words. 'Yes, I suppose you're right. Max must have honestly thought Sheila could have a purely physical relationship with Brian Tevendale and that would be that. No emotions. Nothing. No repercussions. Max had no idea that she would fall in love with him.'

Jenny agreed as they parked at the front door. 'Well, as they say around here, he kens noo!'

Chapter 12:

West Cairnbeg Farm, Kincardineshire,

Wednesday, 12 June 1968

After Geddes and he had discussed Maxwell Robert Garvie's puzzling disappearance, Essie suggested that he visit the farm in his sergeant's uniform and make it obvious he was searching the grounds. From his standpoint, his actions might 'flush out' or panic anyone with something to hide. Such as Mrs Sheila Garvie. Or her boyfriend. Or anyone else who bore a grudge towards the missing farmer. Who knew? Maybe the grieve, or the cleaning lady, or a disgruntled agricultural supplier had developed a deep, vengeful desire to rid the Mearns of that flamboyant riddle of a man.

The sergeant borrowed the Scottish North-Eastern Counties Constabulary's only police dog – a large rust and black German Shepherd controversially but unimaginatively called Himmler – and drove the short distance from Laurencekirk to the farm complex at West Cairnbeg. Essie had agreed with Geddes and Detective Inspector Wilkie, from the neighbouring force at Aberdeen City, that the cover story for the operation was to conduct a search of the estate in case Garvie had somehow innocently gone missing somewhere on the grounds. In the absence of any leads, who knew what might have happened to him? Perhaps he had exited the front door of the farmhouse in the early hours of 15 May only to meet his end at the hands of a hidden, unlikely attacker or attackers who had not only despatched him from this life, but then had hidden his body somewhere on the grounds of the estate he leased from the owner, his father. After that, they had covered their tracks by moving his recently purchased, high powered Ford Cortina 1600E to the airfield nearby. The thinking was that, unless Garvie had met and run off with some floozie – of either sex, according to Messrs Tevendale and Birse – and was currently enjoying some sort of continual sexual fulfillment in a dingy hotel room in Edinburgh, or Glasgow, or maybe even Bradford, then he had met his end inside his house or just outside his front door that beautiful summer's morning. Had that happened, it could only mean one thing – the deed had been committed by someone close to him, someone who knew enough about him to move the Cortina to the Flying Club, as evidenced by the vehicle's discovery there.

Rather than use the unmarked CID car, Essie had also borrowed the dog handler's Ford Anglia van for the excursion on the basis that it advertised itself as belonging to the local force. This was to be an exercise in publicity designed to agitate any guilty conscience out there.

West Cairnbeg was far more than a farm. The Big Hoose itself was at the centre of a complex of cottages tied to the farm, occupied by the grieve and his wife, by the pigman and his wife – who cleaned the Big Hoose – and who would have a story to tell about that too in due course – and other farmhands whose occupancy of the cottages dotted around the estate necessarily meant their income was low. There were several large storage barns and nearly two hundred hectares of land to explore all sitting in the shadow of the granite glare of the Grampians.

Arriving uninvited at a deliberately later hour to attract maximum publicity, Essie pulled up outside the Big Hoose at 11 a.m. He stepped out of the van, flicked imaginary oose from his sergeant's stripes, then went to the rear doors of the van to retrieve the good-natured but intimidating-looking

Himmler. He knew their presence was already drawing much attention. He was aware that, even only by driving into the farm past the ornate wrought iron curlicued sign at the road entrance to the complex in a police van, he had caused curtain-twitching activity in the little cottage at the front that faced the main road.

Taking a bold approach, Essie led the gentle giant towards a storage shed where two men in overalls stood chatting. Seeing the figure of a uniformed representative of the forces of law-and-order approach, one of the men quickly departed towards an ancient tractor and started the vehicle's engine before reversing away towards a grassy track and some outlying fields. To Essie's satisfaction, the man who remained stood rooted to the spot. He needed word of his presence to spread.

As Himmler strained on the short leather leash, the man looked apprehensive about the dog's intentions until Essie tugged at it and grunted, as instructed by its usual handler, bringing the dog to heel.

Essie made an instant decision to go native. 'Aye aye, min. Fine mornin!' he bellowed towards the anxious employee. The man mumbled something indistinct about the weather in return as the sergeant and his canine assistant approached.

'We're going to search around the place, but I decided not to bother the lady of the house. Maybe you could tell her we're here?'

Essie himself had come up with the notion that making the search an unexpected surprise would have more impact. Both he and Geddes had decided that seeking a search warrant from the local Sheriff lacked subtlety and implied the kind of focused suspicion that didn't exist yet anyway. This way, anyone who objected or acted oddly would be drawing attention to him or herself.

The plan got off to a good start when the man quickly scurried off in the direction of the Big Hoose. It seemed to be working and all Essie and Himmler had to do now was to actually carry out some leg work and a few cursory, public searches. Essie followed the dog's trail through tall, wavy grass until he arrived at a track with distinct tyre marks on it that ran behind a cluster of whitewashed buildings that shielded the main farmhouse itself. Letting the obedient animal off the leash, he continued on the path until it led to the rear of the farmhouse itself. He retraced his steps and discovered that the track that ran along the rear of the house joined up with a side road that ran towards a patch of woodland.

Both man and dog enjoyed their trek in the country, the Alsatian forgetting his training and scampering towards a group of startled rabbits that sprinted off as he ran towards them. Essie enjoyed the warmth of the sun and the smell of the summer breeze that wafted long-forgotten childhood scents of lilac and pine.

At one point at the very boundary of Garvie land, where it meets East Cairnbeg, a neighbouring farmer called him over to offer his take on the mystery.

'Don't listen to what they're saying about Maxwell Garvie', he insisted. 'He's not coming back now, that's for sure, but all that stuff about him being drunk all the time is bunkum. How could he run a place like Muckle Cairnbeg and do half the things people say he did? To me, he was a reliable, hard-working man you could count on. Worked hard and played hard. Fair enough. Anyway, you're wasting your time looking for him around here, whoever did him in wouldn't have left his body in these pairts.' With that, the man about turned and left Essie wondering how he knew so much. Or was it that everyone now had their own, homespun view on the Garvie case?

Over the coming weeks, the sergeant returned regularly to the farm, sometimes without the dog, until he got to know the layout of the place as well as anyone who worked there. His visits were never discussed in advance with anyone at West Cairnbeg and he never as much as spoke to Sheila Garvie, although on one occasion he met her mother Edith as he rounded the corner of a barn. She was a short, bespectacled woman who looked troubled and world-weary, but who still faced him with a confident dignity, something that made him doubt whether she could be able to keep a dark secret for long. The lady explained that her daughter spent much of her time in Aberdeen with her boyfriend, leaving her, Edith, to look after the children. The way she said 'Tevendale' spoke volumes about her obvious dislike of the man and the situation her daughter had got herself into.

Essie reasoned that somebody was going to crack eventually, somebody who knew what had happened to Max Garvie. Somebody like Edith? It would be mid-August before he saw her again and that would be in the police office at Laurencekirk.

Chapter 13:

The Church of Scotland had no time for fripperies such as a minister's household comforts and, in keeping with manses countrywide, that at Fordoun was old, cold and draughty. As the minister's wife, Jenny understood her husband had a 'calling' rather than a mere job, so she willingly accepted the privations of their situation and the meagre stipend they lived on.

The couple had met in the idealistic days of the Iona Community, where one man's vision of a world based on respect for others and peaceful co-existence was shown to be tragically short-lived, with war breaking out again within a year of its foundation. Even so, the ideal lived on, and after Arthur and Jenny met on a windy Sunday afternoon in the magical island's Martyr's Bay, they realised they both wanted to change the world for the better. Nothing new there, you might think, but Arthur's elastic capacity for forgiveness for his fellow man's sins soon came to surprise his new wife, who began to suspect he was probably more gullible than compassionate. She made do, though.

Should any reminder be required that *making do* was the first requirement of their chosen path, when the Fordoun Stone – with its original Roman script and a hunting scene added by a Pictish craftsman centuries later – was rediscovered in the church in Victorian times, it was being

78

used as a paving stone. Make do and make do again.

An honours graduate in Medieval English Literature from St Andrews, Jenny spent much of her time reading poetry, history and – although her university chums would have regarded it as inappropriate and a little *infra dig* – Agatha Christie. Unlike her husband, Jenny believed in the here and now, rather than the hereafter promise of rewards to come, so she made the best of everything down to repairing frayed curtains and growing vegetables. She often marvelled at the age of the manse telephone – perhaps 1920s vintage – and how the Church was too mean to replace it with something more modern. Quite ironic, really, that it was probably now gaining in value through time, but, as they say, 'good things come to those that have the patience to wait'. It had a sturdy Bakelite box at its base with a chromed dial topped with a plated silver rest for the elaborate mouth and earpiece receiver, both hallmarked silver, and attached to the base with a three-stranded light brown barley twist wire that had darkened down the years to a deep mahogany colour. During long calls from needy parishioners, she had noticed her husband's time-passing habit of ravelling and unravelling the wire to reveal the original, lighter, tawny shade on the inside.

Whilst admiring the apparatus, though, she had come to dislike its urgent, high-pitched ring.

That Thursday morning, Arthur was in his study when it chirped into life and, as she was polishing the sturdy oak table in the hall, she felt obliged to answer it.

'Hello, Auchenblae 213, Fordoun Manse, Mrs Thom speaking.'

The snorting sound at first made her think it was a misconnection or youngsters playing a joke, so she repeated her usual answering spiel. The snorting turned into a male voice clearing its throat, then to speech. It was Max Garvie sounding very drunk.

'Is the, the minister there … nee, need to s s speak to him … she's r r run off with him … Tevendale …'

'I'll get him, hold on, please.' Her manner was curt, showing she had no time for drunk men looking for solace they would probably not remember later. Anyway, as Max was rarely sober, her patience was wearing thin with him and, despite all their help, the Garvies seemed as far apart as ever. She placed the receiver on the telephone table and slowly went to her husband's study. In his inebriated state, perhaps Max might hang up if she took her time and he had to wait. She pushed the large brass study handle, opened the door and looked round it. Arthur was sitting at his writing bureau going through correspondence by the light of an ancient angle-poise lamp left by the previous minister.

'It's that Max Garvie person and he's dreadfully drunk. He's muttering something about her running off. You really should make it a rule that no-one telephones here when they've been drinking, Arthur.'

Standing up from his desk, he said the news did not surprise him, then made his way to the hall. Squeezing himself into the threadbare red velvet seat attached to the telephone table, he settled down to a long wire twisting session, his wife listening into the one-sided conversation as she conveniently polished surfaces round about him. Eventually tiring of her husband's usual, repeated platitudes – 'No, don't despair, this will work itself out' and 'Have faith in your love for her' – she went to the kitchen to begin preparing dinner.

Half an hour later, they sat down to eat after Grace had been duly observed.

'I'm surprised you could understand him, dear. What was he saying about his wife?' Jenny said. 'I could hardly make out a word.'

Rev Thom answered in instalments, in between mouthfuls of cabbage and potato. 'It's not lovers heading to Paris in the

80

Spring … she's in Bradford, of all places … run off with young Tevendale … making a new start, apparently … no warning, it seems … just upped and away, leaving West Cairnbeg, the children and her car … oh, and Maxwell too.'

Jenny was hardly shocked by the news.

'How did she get to Bradford if she left her car at West Cairnbeg?'

'Tevendale's sister – Trudy, is it? – drove them there and got them lodgings with a lass from Stonehaven she knows who's down there now. I'm amazed Sheila would leave her children, but her mother's stepped in to help. I told him she likely wouldn't last long there.'

'Is Trudy not the one Maxwell was having the affair with?' Jenny's analytical mind was whirring towards a – possibly illusory – *sensible* explanation for such bizarre behaviour.

'Yes, that's what he told me, the wife seeing the brother and the husband seeing the sister. Maxwell thought he could play games with people's lives, then stop them when they got out of control. There has to be something in the Scriptures about this that can come to their aid at this difficult time, you know …'

They sat in silence, him racking his brains for a passage he vaguely remembered and her wondering why Trudy should be so keen to help split the Garvies up.

'Here's one for you,' she eventually said as she cleared the dinner plates away. '"*Heaven has no rage like love to hatred turned, nor Hell a fury like a woman scorned.*" William Congreve, if I'm not mistaken.'

Later, much later, the minister realised he might be wrong thinking his wife was talking about Sheila when she said that.

Chapter 14:

The Watson House, New Street, Stonehaven,

Sunday, 28 April 1968

Edith knew Sheila was at the door by the familiar rattle of the letterbox. She stopped what she was doing and left the carpet sweeper propped against the dining room table to go to the door. Sheila looked ghastly. Her hair was matted as if she had used glue instead of hair spray and her eyes were puffy from crying. Edith thought it best to get her inside as quickly as she could. She beckoned her in and closed the door.

Once in the living room, Sheila stood helplessly like a child in the middle of the room, as if awaiting instruction or comfort from her mother. Edith removed her pinny, stepped forward and put her arms round her daughter, who immediately began sobbing. 'There, there, ma lass, let it all out …'

Sheila cried bitterly as Edith reached up and cupped her daughter's head in both hands. 'What's he done now – you know you can tell me anything?'

Sheila slowly regained control and sat down, wiping her tears on her mother's discarded pinafore.

'It's been terrible, Mam, he's got worse since I came back.'

Edith had hoped otherwise. Ever resourceful, she immediately took stock of the state of affairs. 'When you were in Bradford, Max phoned me a lot, sometimes drunk, but always crying. Your father and I both still think you should keep working to save the marriage for the bairns' sake. But you do know, whatever happens I will always be there for you, even if you get a divorce …'

Sheila shook her head. 'If only it was as easy as that, Mam.' She explained she had gone to Aberdeen to see Mr Cuthbertson, the divorce lawyer, but after she told him the whole story, he shook his head and said there were no grounds for a divorce.

Edith was puzzled. Her daughter had been assaulted, had been sexually abused and had been publicly humiliated by her husband, mostly in pubs in Stonehaven. 'So why did Mr Cuthbertson say that?' she asked hesitantly.

'You know I always tell the truth, Mam, that's how you brought me up, so when I told him about Bradford, he put his hand up and stopped me saying any more …'

Eager to explore the outcome of the meeting, Edith butted in. 'Did you tell him how it was you started seeing that young man, that it was Max who forced you together?'

'I told him *everything,* but it made no difference, because whilst Maxie was committing adultery with Trudy, I was doing the same with Brian. You see, the law says we're both at fault. It would have been fine if he was the only one who strayed, then I could have raised a divorce action.'

Edith pondered what she had just heard. 'Seems daft to me if your husband gets away with doing all that to you. Alright, we just have to get on with it. You're still not seeing him, are you? Tevendale, I mean.'

Sheila's face reddened. 'I did as you said, Mam, and tried my best not to, but when I was in Aberdeen last week, I walked straight into him. It was fate …'

Edith tutted and shook her head, but Sheila continued. 'I said I was sorry for leaving Bradford without telling him, but that Maxie had let me hear the children crying when I phoned West Cairnbeg and that I knew, then, I had to come home.'

Edith anxiously wrung her hands together. 'So, you're still seeing Tevendale?'

'No, we went for a coffee in Union Street, that's all, but by the time I got back to the farm, Maxie already knew we had met. I think my young brother must have told him …'

'William? Now, why would he do that?' Edith had no idea her son might be involved in this.

'I've never told you, Mam, but Maxie's managed to use him as well as everyone else and, of course, William thinks he's great.'

'So how did Max react about you meeting Tevendale? When you were away, he told me he would stop drinking and would make sure the marriage would work …' Edith stopped talking after Sheila emphatically shook her head again.

'Words, just Maxie's empty words. He's called me "cow" ever since and all he asked about Bradford was how many times we had sex and what kind of sex we had.'

'He's not still asking for …?' Edith stopped short of describing her son-in-law's unusual sexual demands, those that had been at the centre of the couple's well-publicised bedroom troubles.

Sheila laughed bitterly. 'That? He still says I'm frigid because I won't do what Trudy used to do for him. There are other things, too. The other night, he started going on about how much I was meant to have enjoyed him and Brian tossing a coin for me when Trudy wasn't about and it was just me, him and Brian. You know how that made me feel? It's disgusting! He thinks I'm a whore!'

Edith patted her hand. 'He needs help, maybe if he stopped taking the pep pills and cut down on the drink …'

Sheila interrupted. 'That's another thing. He made *me* see a psychiatrist last week …'

'You? Not him?'

'Yes, me. It was someone Dr Lyle recommended after Maxie told him I tried to commit suicide ...'

Edith was horrified. 'Surely you never tried to ...'

'No, of course not, but it's all part of Maxie's plan to make the world believe that I'm the problem, not him. He's twisting my insides, though, when we're on our own, lighting candles and playing all the records Brian and I used to dance to. Did I tell you he insisted we went to the Marine as soon as we got back from Bradford, just in case Brian was there? It was as if he wanted to show all his drinking pals who had won the prize. Of course, Brian was not there – he was still trying to get back from Bradford. So what does Maxie do next? He gets us invited to a party in Aberdeen *because* he knows Brian will be there, then he insists Brian and I dance together and he pretends he and Brian are friends again. Then, he gets two men to attack him a few days later. Maxie's playing his little games with all of us!'

The news of violence erupting between the two men stunned Edith. It hadn't been at that level before. 'What happened? How did Tevendale know it was Max that was behind it?'

'Because Brian was walking along Main Street when they ran up to him. He heard them coming and, when he turned round, one of them tried to slash him, but Brian blocked him, although he still got cut on the cheek. One of them said it was a message from the Skipper.'

Edith was sceptical. She had an equally healthy disregard for anything either Max or the Tevendales said. 'Did you see him with an injury?'

Sheila answered with that familiar look of naive simplicity that Edith had always seen in her face. 'No, I just heard about it. Trudy phoned to tell me. She's been such a good friend despite all that's happened ...'

Chapter 15:

The light of the near-full moon gave the lush, high, swaying grass a silver sheen as Alan Peters drove his weary old Zephyr Zodiac into the rutted track behind the Big Hoose. Leakage of exhaust gases from the tired engine's manifold into the rusted and pitted front footwells led to Brian's habit of winding the vehicle's rear windows halfway down to avoid falling victim to the vapour's soporific effects. For that reason, Alan thought Brian was just being quirky when he began calling the fatigued old Ford, 'the Death Car' weeks before.

'Right, here'll do fine,' Brian ordered, causing Alan to grind the car to a noisy, reluctant stop.

After the engine coughed and stuttered to a halt, Alan looked across at Brian, who seemed deep in thought. A summer scented evening breeze drafted into the body of the car through the open rear windows, slowly replacing the combination of exhaust vapour, oil and sweat with the perfume of apple blossom and the sweet smell of summer grass.

They had been killing time until now for some hours and Brian had yet to explain to Alan what the point of the evening's excursion was, although he could guess. They had driven from Aberdeen and travelled through Stonehaven before going to two separate pubs for drinks, his associate sometimes mysteriously changing instructions whilst Alan drove as directed. Suddenly, approaching a farmhouse Alan had never been to before, Brian had seemed to change and had become insistent in his commands, directing him to the farm, then to the little-used track behind the house. The engine killed, he became silent and sat stroking his manicured beard and drumming his fingers on the worn PVC dashboard. What now?

Alan had been unsuspecting and a bit overawed when his passenger had befriended him a couple of months before, Brian Tevendale being the second son of the famous Major Tevendale of the Gordon Highlanders. The story – in the Mearns – was that the Major was transferred to the Leicesters when they needed toughening up, to bring them steel in their struggle with the Japanese. Brian was the son of a local celebrity, and the sort of man who usually shunned the likes of Alan's company on account of his public shyness and diffident character.

Alan and Brian had worked in Aberdeen Motors together, Alan a proper, time-served mechanic and his passenger a mere greaser, but Brian had lost his job after running off with an older woman called Sheila Garvie. Even so, Alan saw it as something of an honour that Brian had firstly sought him out at work, then befriended him above all others. Alan had tried to explain to his pregnant girlfriend, Helen, how pleased he was that Brian and he had become friends, but she seemed unimpressed. He told her Brian was like a film star with his good looks and his way with women, but Helen remained unmoved, her concern being that the other man might easily take advantage of her fiancé's simple and trusting nature.

Brian had even promised to be Alan's best man at his wedding to Helen, despite advising him to dump her as soon as he could after news of her pregnancy emerged; he even reckoned he could set Alan up with some 'nice chicks', as the in-crowd at the Marine would say, but after running it by his Mum and Dad, Alan naturally took the proper course and 'stood by the lassie in the family way'. Even so, Brian persisted in seeking him out at work and, although Alan earned more than him, Brian proved to be generous – in a restricted kind of way – buying tea and coffee for him and the occasional buttery with strawberry jam to go along with it. His new friend had even got them 'homers' to do at night, so – he explained – Alan could save up some cash for the forthcoming wedding at Aberdeen Registrar's office. Sure, they went out a few times to fix punctures, calibrate carburettors and give car owners some bad news about suspension springs, but, until that night, they had always worn their work overalls with the *Aberdeen Motors* logo on the left breast pocket to give them some professional credence. Tonight, though, Brian had decided they should both wear suits and ties despite them probably having to crawl beneath chassis and get their hands oily. Yet, thinking about it, it was really only Alan who had done all the crawling, wheel nut tightening and oil sump changing in all the homers so far, but that didn't really matter. Helen would definitely be impressed soon, especially as his best friend had confidentially let it slip that he had been seeing that rich, older lady from the Mearns whose husband once gave him £100 to take her out. £100! What Alan would do for that sort of money! What would Helen think if he turned up one night in the caravan they rented and said he had £100 to spend on her? Mind you, being Helen, she would make him put it down as a deposit on the sort of Aberdeen flat she lied to her parents she was living in.

A few weeks back, Brian had mentioned he had to 'sort a bloke out' who had been giving him some bother, and because his good pal Alan owned a car – even if it was a clapped out fifteen-year-old Ford – he might need to call on him to help him out for a lift. Alan was pleased he came to him rather than go to the many contacts someone like Brian must have had, so he immediately agreed to do what he could to help without even asking what 'sorting a bloke out' might mean. Who cared if it meant merely paying the bloke a visit or whether there was more to it, Brian was not a man to be messed about and Alan, for once in his life, was now likely to be on the winning side.

In Brian's mind, though, it had become kill or be killed after the Skipper had apparently paid to have him attacked by two different pairs of would-be thugs on two separate nights, Brian defending himself enough to fight them off both times.

Or so he claimed.

Then Sheila had told Brian that Max had threatened to slash her face with a shard of broken glass and nearly broken her arm, all because she refused to call her boyfriend 'a bastard' as Max had demanded. Brian now felt his plan for revenge was fully justified.

He was in full Major mode that day; apart from the suits, shirts and ties, he made it clear Alan had to be at his sister Trudy's house in Birkhall Parade in Aberdeen at 7 p.m. on the dot, so, being the obedient type, Alan was there on time. It was only on the way south, when Brian stopped talking and giving directions, that Alan wondered why Trudy never asked why they were curiously suited and booted rather than overalled, but who cared, he was happy to spend time with his new pal, with his trendy beard and wondrous attraction to women of all ages – according to the stories he told.

Brian had made him drive through Stonehaven and slow down outside certain pubs, then they had gone for a beer or two themselves on the way down to Laurencekirk. Brian kept looking at his watch as if he wanted to pass time – for some reason unknown to him, Alan later said – but before that, they went to buy petrol at a pump operated by an old creature in Bervie who had been in the Gordons with the

Major. Brian had chucked pebbles up at the window above the garage and, when the old soldier opened it to give the culprit a piece of his mind, his attitude changed as soon as he saw who it was and came downstairs and served them fuel. *Alan* paid the man 10 shillings – well, he figured, whilst the trip was a mystery tour, it *was* his car after all – as the man chatted to Brian about his wartime escapades with Brian's illustrious father.

After they left Bervie, Brian suddenly announced where it was they were heading for – West Cairnbeg, Fordoun, a place not known to Alan, who had never really had any notion to travel much beyond the safe confines of *The Geerie,* where he came from in Aberdeen. Brian directed him beyond the small Second World War airfield and on to the turning for Meikle or West Cairnbeg a couple of miles later.

'Right, go round behind on the farm track that runs behind the Big Hoose and we'll leave the car there,' Alan later claimed Brian said; Alan also made out he thought they were doing a homer that night and was surprised when Brian asked him to come into the Big Hoose as well, expecting Brian would take care of all the preliminaries and a car in need of repair would materialise for him to work on.

He negotiated the rattling, creaking old Ford along the bumpy track behind the farmhouse, using the moonlight to supplement the dismal beam the old car was able to generate, despite depressing the clutch and revving the engine to boost the power of the headlights. The order to stop was given by Brian with all the authority of his famous father, before he turned to Alan and told him to leave the car.

The jury at Aberdeen High Court heard at least three differing accounts of what had happened after that. All *they* had to do was work out which version was true.

What was beyond question, though, was that Brian smashed the butt of one of Max's rifles into the back of

Max's head as he slept face down and naked in bed in the master bedroom. Having made him insensible, Brian then shot him using a pillow to muffle the sound, the low calibre .22 bullet going through the base of his skull from behind in an upwards direction from left to right. Then, he produced a tarpaulin from the rucksack he previously put in the Zephyr's boot in Birkhall Parade, and he and Alan wrapped Max's body in it and bumped it down the stairs, the children in the room next door sleeping through it all, as they had the adults bed swapping a few months before.

That Sheila Garvie did nothing about what was going on was to go against her at the trial.

In line with Brian, Alan was to say she did more than nothing.

Trudy was not even there.

But she said the same.

Chapter 16:

Quarryfield Farm, by St Cyrus, Kincardineshire,

Wednesday, 15 May 1968

Unlike Rev Arthur Thom's central part in the drama, his namesake farmer Arthur Thom's testimony was to be almost comical by comparison. He had been the tenant at Quarryfield, near Lauriston Castle, since before the war and knew everyone in the area. Even so, it was unusual for members of the public to stray onto his land, but, that morning, his wife wakened him early, at 5 a.m., as there was a cattle lorry with its engine running right outside their cottage. The farmer got out of bed, went downstairs and gave the driver the directions he was seeking to nearby Lauriston Castle, the pigs in the large rear compartment becoming restless after their tiring journey from Carlisle and the wagon's springs being tested to the full as they nervously buffeted each other. The driver apologised and explained he had got lost after leaving the nearby coastal town of St Cyrus due to the fog reducing visibility to twenty yards in places.

Having guided the confused driver on his way, farmer Thom went back to his bed and was trying to snatch another hour of sleep when, incredibly, the doorbell rang again half an hour later. 'It'll be that bloody mannie with the cattle float again,' he said to his wife as he ill-temperedly got up out of bed a second time. However, on looking out the bedroom window, he saw two young men standing outside. He opened the window. 'And whit would you two be wanting at this time of the morn?' he bellowed irritably.

The taller of the two answered politely. 'Sorry to bother you, but could you help us out, please? You see, our car's stuck in the mud at the entrance to one of your fields. Any chance of you towing us out with your tractor?'

Resigned to an earlier start than normal, the farmer reluctantly flung on his overalls and wellies again and opened the front door, recognising the one he had been speaking to as one of the Major's sons. 'You're a Tevendale, if I'm not mistaken. You used to live in the Bush Hotel in St Cyrus.'

Brian must have been cursing inside at being recognised, but had no option but to brazen it out. 'Aye, that's true. My friend and I decided to turn off the coast road due to the haar, but when we reversed into the field, the wheels got stuck in the mud. You see, we need to be in Aberdeen by seven.'

The explanation was nonsense. For Alan, the events of the night were to haunt him, from seeing a man killed as he slept, to following Brian as he moved the man's car to Fordoun Flying Club, to taking an end of the dead body and carrying it over fields and helping Brian to move some large stones, which revealed an antiquated culvert that doubled nicely as a ready-made tomb. How long had his new friend nursed the idea of killing someone and hiding their corpse in there? The thought scared him. It hadn't escaped his notice that there was room for several more bodies as they were manhandling the man's corpse in the cramped underground space and was relieved to get back above ground without joining him there.

After the farmer listened impatiently to Brian's bogus tale, he went into an open barn, then emerged driving an ancient Massey Ferguson with a rusted, upright exhaust pipe that protruded directly skywards from the enclosed engine compartment and belched out a noxious blue-tinged cloud. After the other two were beckoned on board, they jumped onto the footplates on either side of the farmer and, under

Brian's direction, made their way to the field entrance where the Zephyr lay at an angle at the gate, its rear wheels sunk deeply in a viscous mire like a stricken russet-and-white-coloured bullock with its hind legs secured and tethered, helplessly awaiting castration. As farmer Thom unravelled a long blue nylon tow rope to the tractor's robust-looking structure, Brian and Alan readily collaborated in opening the car's bonnet and wrapping their end of the rope a few times round the front chassis before hooking it back onto itself, Alan resigned to his role as the one who prostrated himself in the mud at the front of the vehicle as Brian stood above him casually giving orders to them both.

With the farmer noisily engaging forward gear, the car lurched forward as its rear wheels emerged with a resounding squelch from their muddy prison and the two men were relieved to have the car back on the firm tarmac of the road. Brian thanked the farmer and gave him a 10-shilling note; once mobile and heading northwards, Alan promised to give Brian his share of it on payday.

Was it fear that made Alan so amenable, or was he just not used to having friends and was unsure of what to do in certain situations? Either way, Brian wasn't complaining as he acknowledged the promised debt.

Before Max's body had been buried in the tunnel that had been used as a water conduit for the castle in times gone by, Brian had produced a change of clothes for them both; once the corpse was safely underground, they had changed back into their suits, Brian explaining he used to play commandos there as a child and had discovered the underground chamber by accident many years before. He was confident that no-one would ever find Max's remains, as only the two of them knew where they were and, presumably, that confidence extended to Alan being too meek to tell anyone. Just to make sure, though, Brian made him swear to silence about the whole nightmarish escapade, which he did, clearly fearing he might be next for interment on the castle grounds.

They were back in Aberdeen before 7 a.m. that morning, Alan eventually going to work at Aberdeen Motors and Brian staying indoors at Birkhall Parade, where Trudy made him coffee.

Back on the road that morning, however, Brian stopped at the only public phone box in St Cyrus and called Sheila to tell her 'they' had mistakenly left a parcel with Max's clothes in it in the garage at West Cairnbeg. After a long, sleepless night downstairs, the call startled her and brought her back to the here and now. Trembling with worry, she lifted the receiver to firstly hear the distinctive beeps of a call from a phone box, then the strained tones of Brian's voice, urgently passing on the message before the cleaning woman discovered the package and became curious about its contents. Or maybe the milkman would notice it as he made his way from the open garage door to the washhouse, to leave the usual order for a household now depleted in number.

After she had put the phone down, Sheila scuffed her trancelike way through to the washhouse in her slippers and dressing gown, then opened the door into the inbuilt double garage that Maxie had been so insistent be constructed. A misshapen bundle wrapped in brown waxed paper and rough green twine was lying on the unpainted concrete near the inside of the cantilevered garage door. She quickly seized it, carried it upstairs and stuffed it into the wardrobe in the master bedroom. In the phone call, Brian had told her that Trudy would deal with it later. Slowly coming to terms with the enormity of the night's events, it occurred to Sheila she would have to make sure that the cleaning woman, Mrs Smart, was kept away from the master bedroom.

Several months later, when William Watson read about farmer Thom's strange, disrupted morning, he imagined what Edith would say about it – if he had been foolhardy enough to have asked for her views on the astonishing coincidence of not one, but two unwanted early visitors that morning. He could just hear her: 'You see, these two young men had broken Nature's rules and The Gods punished them by making sure they needed farmer Thom's help. After all, why would Fate make him get out of bed twice that morning unless to make it a morning he wouldn't forget, especially when he recognised the Major's boy with the car they took Max's body away in?'

Except, by that time, Edith had given evidence that could help sentence their daughter to life in prison.

Chapter 17:

There were actually two secrets.

To begin with, it was the eighteen-year-old bride who thought she was the only one who had a surprise to pass on. Helen eventually got round to telling Alan, her boyfriend of only a few months, then her parents, then her friends, that she was pregnant and an emergency date was set in July for her to become Mrs Peters. 'A genuine shotgun special,' some folk joked once the whole story came out, if it ever truly did.

Living in a cramped caravan and suffering a recurring kidney infection had made the build-up to her big day anything but memorable. Another concern was why the groom-to-be was so distant. Alan Peters had never been the life and soul of any party and could sometimes be painfully shy, but recently he had had a faraway look about him that went way beyond pre-wedding nerves.

The others had a secret of their own too. Of the four of them, it was only the bride who did not share the knowledge that her new husband and the two witnesses carried with them – that Maxwell Robert Garvie had been murdered by the best man, Brian Tevendale, and only he and the groom knew that Max's body was wrapped in a tarpaulin and rotting in an underground chamber at Lauriston Castle. Not that the wedding day photograph betrayed anything; all four smiled spontaneously at the photographer's request.

The two men stood side-on to each other grinning naturally and half-facing the two women to their right. They were both dark-suited and wearing thin, fashionable dark ties like members of a sixties rock band. Sheila had fussed over and affixed carnation *boutonniere* wrapped in silver paper to the men's suit jacket lapels and tended to larger, double white rose spray corsages for her and the bride, as well as bedecking Helen's hair with camellia. The new Mrs Peters stood proudly beside her husband, spreading the fingers of her left hand to show off her wedding ring whilst a joyful-looking Sheila's left hand was conspicuously lacking both engagement and wedding rings.

What could be worse? Sheila thought. *May we all live happily and die before what happened to Maxie catches up with us.*

The bride pregnant and ill, the groom traumatised and afraid, the best man a callous killer. Nothing for it but to be hopelessly optimistic and try to make it memorable for all the *right* reasons. Who was to know what could be round the corner for all of them?

High society it wasn't, but at least the staff at the registrar's office would have a brilliant story to tell later in the year – 'They were as bold as brass, the murder wedding party!'

As Trudy and Fred had agreed to host the wedding dinner in their flat – Why were they so obliging? Was it really only to help Brian in his time of need? – Sheila cooked a chicken she had stored in a freezer in the kitchen at West Cairnbeg, brought along a bottle of white wine and gave the newly-weds £5, but her efforts hadn't really helped. The bride put a brave face on things, but couldn't stop herself from sometimes grimacing in pain. The groom smiled when forced to out of politeness, but otherwise remained distant. The strain of now five out of six of the wedding party knowing about Max's murder seemed to weigh heavily on him.

Both at the Birses' flat and later in a lounge bar in Union Street, Sheila noticed how Alan reacted to Brian, who only had to suggest something for him to carry it out. Should the ladies be seated? Alan appeared with two seats. Should we have another drink before we go? Alan was at the bar ordering them, using, Sheila noticed, the £5 note she had given them as a wedding present.

Of course, when the story broke, the prosecution single-mindedly insisted that it was *Sheila's* way of controlling Alan, giving him presents and attending his wedding, all the time apparently keeping a wary eye on him lest he crack and run to the police. If that was true, how would she be able to influence him in any way after 8 July, the day he moved to Fort Augustus with his new wife? Was Alan Peters's silence really bought for £5, a bottle of wine and a cooked chicken? As for him, all he got out of assisting with Max's brutal end were regular nightmares about bullets, blood and worms, and for his name to be the first on an indictment for murder. That and having to pay Brian 5 shillings as he had promised.

And anyway, using Alan's services that night was Brian's idea, not Sheila's.

She had never even met him before.

Chapter 18:

Laurencekirk Police Office, West Cairnbeg, the
East Neuk Bar, King Street, Aberdeen, and Police
Headquarters, Bucksburn Aberdeen,

Wednesday, 16 August 1968

Geddes waited until she had been given a sedative by the
casualty surgeon before he took a statement from Edith.
During the hour or so it had taken for her to calm down,
Dougie Scrimgeour had told Essie that she had turned up
at his cottage not far from the main farmhouse in a state
of near collapse muttering something about Sheila and
Tevendale. Like everyone else on the farm, Dougie and
his wife Maggie had their own private suspicions about his
employer's sudden disappearance. Maggie had watched the
comings and goings to and from the Big Hoose from behind
lace curtains, sometimes getting up in the early hours when
she heard Max's car over-revving as he came home from
a night's drinking. 'He's had a proper skinful tonight,' she
would say when she got back to bed, 'and how he made
it home is a miracle! He hit the kerb on the way in.' She
sometimes woke Dougie up to report a full car load arriving
and she would lie awake listening to car doors slamming,
high-pitched female laughter and Max's strident voice
drifting her way in the night air as Dougie struggled to get
back to sleep.

Being fond of the Garvies, Maggie had, at first, refused
to believe the rumours about what was going on, but was

100

eventually convinced something was amiss after she spoke to the housekeeper, who, accurately or not, reported tales of Mrs Garvie coming out of a different bedroom from her husband. Dougie was loyal to his employer, though, and until the day Edith came knocking on his door, refused to join in with the tittle-tattle that had become rife in the area. To him, Sheila having anything to do with Max's disappearance was ridiculous and was a classic case of poison gossip; she just wasn't the sort of person who would get involved in doing harm to somebody, let alone murder. The Tevendale boy was, though, and Max had occasionally let it slip that there was bad blood between the pair of them.

All that changed on 16 August, after a hysterical Edith arrived at their door and blurted something about 'murder' and a body being in the sea. Maggie had heard the front door opening, had gone into the lobby and seen Edith there, barely able to talk. She sat her down, ran out and fetched Dougie from the farm office and brought him home. Despite the wet weather, he had run to the garage, started the Oxford and taken her straight to the police at Laurencekirk.

After taking Edith's statement, Geddes contacted the CID in Aberdeen before driving to West Cairnbeg along with DC Johnson, arriving just after midday. As Sheila was making lunch, the Garvies' twelve-year-old daughter answered the door. Geddes felt a pang of conscience when she invited them inside without question. Now it seemed certain that her father was never coming back, the strangers she had just admitted might also be taking her mother from her, was the disconcerting notion that flitted through Geddes's mind as he and his colleague walked through the open door. He thought back to his previous visit, when Sheila seemed to have regained control of herself, and he wondered if that had just been an act. There was no way round that now after what Edith had told them – it had to have been a total charade, complete with barefaced lies and false information. How would she be now? Would the act continue? And was his hunch that she wanted to tell him more that she knew about correct?

The child led them to the kitchen, where Sheila was boiling potatoes. 'There are two men here to see you, Mum,' she said. Wearing individual oven gloves, Sheila briefly glanced at the two of them as she lifted the pot lid and pushed a fork into the slowly bubbling contents.

She seemed unconcerned. 'How are you, Mr Geddes?'

Geddes waited until the daughter was out of earshot before he answered. 'I'm fine, Mrs Garvie. We need to speak to you about something.'

'Give me five minutes and I'll join you next door. I need to make the children's lunch. Won't be long.'

Geddes's tone changed. 'I'm sorry, Mrs Garvie, you'll have to switch the cooker off. We have to speak to you now, about your husband's disappearance.' She still seemed unperturbed. She removed the gloves and called on her daughter to take over making the lunch. Comparing notes later, Geddes and Johnson were both puzzled by her actions. It was as if they had come about a parking fine, about a trivial matter that needn't affect lunch being made. She either had a clear conscience or was now living in an artificial bubble after three months of deceit. The three of them made their way to the sitting room as the girl went into the kitchen. 'I'm afraid you will have to come with us. Is there anyone who can look after your daughter?'

For the first time, Sheila looked shocked. She reached behind herself with both hands and untied her apron as she spoke. 'You mean I have to leave now? I suppose Mrs Thom might be able to come over, you know the minister's wife, if I call her now. How long should I say I will be away for?'

Despite mixed feelings, Geddes saw no point in being subtle. 'It could be a long time, Mrs Garvie. A long, long time.'

He then said he had reason to believe her husband had been murdered and that she had been involved in it. Her mother Edith had told them so. Sheila looked genuinely stunned, but Geddes was now confident her shock was down to Edith spilling the beans rather than Sheila herself having no part in her missing husband's sudden departure from West Cairnbeg.

The two officers stood by as Sheila called the minister's wife, who came over within a few minutes. On arrival, Jenny Thom asked no questions and resumed preparing lunch in a practical, no-nonsense way, as if a friend and neighbour being arrested for homicide was a common occurrence in these parts.

Geddes then took Sheila aside and cautioned her that she was not obliged to say anything about her role in Max's disappearance and explained that he had reason to believe that she was implicated in it. Sheila replied, 'That's not true,' and was transported out of her home at West Cairnbeg and out of her children's lives. She was driven to City Police Headquarters at Bucksburn, where she remained silent. To the CID, her composure spoke volumes: 'That proves she kent what had happened to her man. Did ye see thon smug look on her face when we booked her in? There's nobody going to tell me she had nothing to do with it. Let's see how trig she feels when we get hold of her bit on the side and see what he has to say about it!'

Brian was then traced to the East Neuk Bar in Aberdeen's King Street, where he now worked as a barman after losing his job at Aberdeen Motors. It was early evening when the two officers in plain clothes came in through the side door on the vennel, silencing the few teatime customers standing around the bar who immediately recognised them as CID due to their unimaginative dark grey matching suits and their business-like manner. Brian was serving a customer who insisted on telling him all about Aberdeen's recent narrow victory over Dunfermline, Brian finding it difficult to appear interested. Hearing the door opening and then glancing back expecting to see regular faces, Brian's pulse quickened when he realised that two detectives had arrived, clearly on a mission to see somebody. They made for the bar's side-flap and beckoned him over, some of the customers noticeably sidling closer to pick up any available morsels convertible to juicy talking points over the next drink.

One of the officers turned side-on, away from the group of interested patrons in order to retain a degree of privacy. 'Are you Brian Gordon Tevendale, born 12 January 1945?' he asked in a quiet voice.

Brian mimicked curiosity. 'Aye, that's me. Why do you want to speak to me?'

'It's about an enquiry into a man that's been missing for a few months, a Maxwell Robert Garvie of West Cairnbeg, Laurencekirk.'

This did not look good, he thought. Somebody had blabbed. Aware he had coloured up, Brian struggled to appear calm. 'And what do you need to speak to me about again? Do you know I've already spoken to the police about Max? My brother-in-law's with the City force and he's told his bosses all we know.'

Realising how much interest their discussion was drawing, the second officer butted in. 'We know all that. You'll have to come with us. Now.'

Brian was followed by the first detective as he went to the storeroom and picked his jacket up after alerting the relief barman that he had to start his shift a few minutes earlier than he had planned. As the three left via the front door onto King Street, some of the customers, drinks in hand, emerged from the side door in time to see their latest barman being led into an unmarked police car that drove off into the thinning evening traffic.

Within minutes, the assembled drinkers had convened and unanimously convicted their former barman of both murder and cuckolding the dead man's wife. 'He was ayeways too sure o himsel' thon loon' being the basis of the decision, that and the fact he seemed just too familiar with the missing man's wife when she recently worked a couple of shifts in the bar at the owner's request, some of the staff having walked out during the Glasgow Fair holiday in July. 'Anyway,' the regulars decided, 'she didnae exactly fight him aff either!'

When he was told about the allegation that he had been involved in Max's murder, Brian said 'Jesus!' before he was also taken to Bucksburn. Once there, he denied any involvement.

By that time, Brian was in self-preservation mode. The officer in charge, Detective Inspector Wilkie, weighed up the options with his colleagues, Geddes amongst them.

'So far, the wife's in denial and lover boy's making out we've got no grounds for holding him. How sure are you, Geddes, that the old lady's not just havering?'

Geddes did not appreciate Wilkie's tone. 'I can say this; if she's not telling the truth, she's either a bloody good actress or off her head.'

Wilkie chewed the end of a biro, considering the options. 'Maybe they're all mad, unless we've discovered a whole new acting school at West Cairnbeg. Let them stew a while and we'll see whether the Ice Queen melts a wee bit.' Geddes stopped himself from pointing out that, no matter what, she could not possibly have done it all by herself.

Brian was getting nervous, sitting alone in a small detention cell. His hands trembled as he drank the cold black tea he had been given an hour before. Memories of painful previous scrapes with the police started to return and he decided he had to do something. The peephole in the door slid open and he gestured to the sergeant to open up. Within minutes he was again sitting in the interview room, this time with a suggestion the CID might be interested in.

Wilkie began. 'Right, Sergeant MacLeod tells me you wanted to see me. Now, what would that be for, Brian?'

From his short army career, Brian knew how much figures in authority liked meekness. 'If you let me speak to Mrs Garvie, I think we might be able to help you,' he said, head bowed and eyes on the floor.

Wilkie sensed a breakthrough. 'I'm not sure about that. What if she says no?'

'Trust me, she won't.'

Ten minutes later, Sheila and Brian were sitting across from each other at the desk of the station Superintendent. The two officers who escorted them in had orders to leave them *completely* alone, so they quickly left, making a show of closing the door noisily behind them. One of them managed to make a joke about not stealing the Super's pencils as he left.

Brian was first to speak. 'What happened to Edith, then? You said she would never let us down.'

There were times when Sheila felt the ten years between them were unbridgeable. He really was childlike at times and here he was sitting in police headquarters like a naughty wee boy caught stealing apples from the laird's orchard. Except he had done something far worse. He had killed for her. Or that's how she saw it in May.

Sheila reasoned she owed him an explanation. 'I told Mam about our plans to be nearer to each other and we argued. I had no idea she would go to the police, but I suppose I can't blame her.'

'Well, I can! What are we going to tell them? Should we say he was killed trying to rape you?' By playing to her protective streak, Brian was hopeful his central role in

Max's slaying might not be revealed. It had worked so far, and she hadn't come close to snitching on him, or, as he put it, 'squealing'.

Sheila was resolute. 'No. I'm not going to tell them lies.'

Brian felt a sudden anger, but reeled it in as much as he could. Should the truth come out, he alone might go down for life. 'We'll have to tell them something. That mother of yours has a big mouth. You should never have told her ...'

Wilkie sipped coffee as he listened to the recording of their conversation half an hour later. 'It worked! They've got no clue the room's bugged! She's hard as nails. At least the Major's boy's trying to help, but she's not for budging.'

Geddes watched as the tape was rewound again. 'There's no way this can be used as evidence, Inspector. The lawyers don't like secret recordings. They'll say it's underhand and unfair!'

Wilkie laughed. 'Yes, but nobody needs to know and prosecutors *do* like evidence that solves murders!'

Chapter 19:

Lauriston Castle grounds, by St Cyrus and Police Headquarters, Aberdeen,

Thursday, 17 August 1968

On the way south in a black police MG Magnette, Wilkie spoke freely to Brian. As always, he 'kent his faither' and the talk was of the time he worked with the Major in the police. As Geddes cringed, Brian took advantage of this unexpected bonus and tried to charm his police escort.

It had been close to 4 a.m. when he had offered to take the police to where Max's body had been entombed. He also said he hadn't shot Max, but explained he would tell them about that later. At first, Wilkie tried to avoid taking Brian with them, sensing some devilish plan to escape in the darkness, but after Brian's verbal directions became impossible to follow in the confines of police headquarters, he decided to take up the offer and arranged for several officers with pairs of wellies and overalls to be convoyed south in two cars. By the time they arrived at St Cyrus, dawn had broken and Wilkie and Brian had become too familiar on the journey down for Geddes's liking.

Geddes also disapproved of the way Brian was controlling things, using friendly terms like 'stop here, chaps' and 'this way, boys' as he retraced the route he had taken three months before. As he strode through dew-covered grass and a field of startled sheep, he also saw a chance to explain that he had once played in the castle grounds as a child, re-enacting what he could glean from his father's exploits in the war. Apart from anything else, Brian was carefully cementing his credibility with Wilkie, which might prove decisive when Sheila inevitably would have to relent and tell her side of the story. Brian stopped walking and pointed to two large slabs on the ground. 'Alright, boys, the body's down there,' he said as he walked a further twenty yards on. 'In fact, it's right under my feet now.' Geddes thought the suspect was enjoying it too much and took the initiative. 'Ok, we can have that checked,' he said as he took Brian by the arm. Wilkie nodded, but said nothing as Geddes explained his reasoning to him. 'We can't have the prisoner standing here if we find the body down there.' Wilkie agreed, but settled on a compromise, sending a uniformed officer with a torch down into a manhole-sized space created by moving the slabs.

A young constable was given a torch and sent on an underground search to confirm that Max's remains were nearby, although, from the stench that was now drifting upwards from the opening, there could be no doubt that some previously living entity had met its end and was languishing beneath them awaiting discovery.

The officer looked grim when he poked his head out five minutes later. 'Yes, there's what appears to be a body wrapped in a tarpaulin at the far end of the tunnel,' he announced gravely.

Brian was less chatty as they drove north to the Stonehaven police office, although, ironically, his bravado made an unexpected return when he was cautioned and charged with murder. At that stage, he said, 'Can I tell you what really happened?' He was reminded that he need not say anything and, due to the serious nature of the charge, was told that he really should have a solicitor present, but Brian insisted he did not need one. After he was given breakfast, he gave a lengthy voluntary statement, which he signed. It read as follows:

I met Max Garvie in the SNP outing to Bannockburn. I had a few drinks with him and his wife and was invited flying the next day. On the following weekend I went down to the Marine Hotel in Stonehaven with him and his wife, and when we left the Marine I sat in the back of his car with his wife at his request. When we arrived at the chip shop, he and the front passenger, George Hadden, went into the chip shop. I followed and was promptly told to get back into the car and keep his wife happy. The weekend following, I was invited up to the farm. We went out on the Saturday night drinking. We had a few drinks when we returned to the farm and I went to bed. A short time later, Sheila was pushed into the room and the door was shut. She said she had been told to spend the night in there or else. Later on that week, Sheila came down to the garage and picked me up from my work. She said Max wanted us to go out for a drink that night. When we arrived there, he handed me the keys of one car and told me to take Sheila out, as he was going out with someone himself. This happened a few weeks running. On three successive Saturdays we went to Edinburgh and Glasgow and Edinburgh again, spending the weekend in various hotels. On one particular night when I was out with Max himself, he started making strange advances. At the time, I was driving the car, and I pulled up at the side of the road and told him that, if he did not stop, I would belt him. He laughed this off as if it were a joke. When we reached Cairnbeg we had a few drinks again in the house and I went upstairs to bed. Shortly after I was in bed, he came in and sat on the edge of the bed. He was wearing a red-coloured dressing gown, which was open, and he was naked underneath. I told him if he did not leave the room I would get up, dress and walk home. He again laughed and left the room. One Saturday night, Sheila, Max and myself had been drinking in Laurencekirk. When we returned home, he suggested it would be a good idea to toss up to see who slept with Sheila that night. Sheila objected and was told to shut up. He tossed the coin and I won. He went through to sleep in the room I usually had. About 6 a.m. I woke up and found that he was also lying in the bed with Sheila and I. Sheila later told me he had tried to have kinky sex with her when he first came in. She refused and he was scared the noise would wake me up. He once told me that he loved me more than he loved Sheila. He often offered me pills of various shapes and sizes, which he usually took himself when drinking in the house. I once flew with him from Fordoun Flying Field to Bervie shooting up vehicles on the way. We were both severely intoxicated. When we landed, he told me he was going to try out a new variation in homo-type sex with Sheila. If she did not like it, he would break her neck. Matters finally came to a head and Sheila walked out on him. He came down to the Mill Inn, Stonehaven, and threatened he would shoot her, the kids and me if she did not go back. She did not go back, but went to stay in the Bay Hotel. She was forcibly removed at 3 a.m. approximately the following morning. She went to the family doctor to complain about Max's strange sexual ideas and the doctor immediately phoned Max. When she got home, he twisted her arm so far up her back that she had to get the doctor, who was told by Max that she fell. Shortly after this incident I was walking down to the Marine Hotel from my house. I was set on in an alley and received a slight slash on the face accompanied by the words, 'That's a present from the Skipper'. As I had only called Max 'Skipper' when we were flying, I assumed it was from him. I approached him the next time I saw him and he said, 'You won't get the chance to run next time.' A few months after this, I received a call from Sheila at about 6.30 in the evening. She came into the house and said Max had sent her down to borrow a record of mine. She had been told not to come back to Cairnbeg until the back of nine. The following day I again received a call at about 3.45 in the afternoon and Max had sent her

*down to spend the rest of the afternoon with me and not to go
back to Cairnbeg until 8 p.m. The last time I saw Max was
in the Crown Hotel one Sunday night. About six weeks later
I received a call from Sheila to go down to Cairnbeg. When
I arrived there, I found her in a terrible state. She said he
had come in and was pouring himself a drink so she went up
to bed. She said that a while later he had come up the stairs
carrying a rifle and told her that if she did not agree to let
him put it up her arse, he would shoot her. He had stripped
and got on to the bed. There had been a grab for the gun
and a struggle and he got shot. This is where I come in now.
I rolled him up in a sheet and a bit of canvas groundsheet,
trailed him downstairs and put him in his car, then drove it. I
have missed out the bit about cleaning up. I got a cloth with
water and with Sheila cleaned up the mess. I then drove the
car to a point near Lauriston Castle, removed the body from
the back seat and pulled it through the grass. I used to stay
in this area and remembered an old tunnel I used to play
in. I left the body in this tunnel and covered it with rocks. I
drove the car to the airfield, locked it and hitch-hiked back
to Aberdeen. I threw the keys of the car into the mouth of the
Dee. That's it.*

Statement over, Wilkie arranged for Brian to return to his
cell, patting his shoulder as he left the interview room.

'I knew he could explain it if he had the chance,' he said
to Geddes.

However, Geddes wasn't convinced. 'We've both been
out at Lauriston and seen the distance between the road and
the deposition site. Do you honestly think one person could
have moved the body that distance? Personally, I think he's
sold us a pup!'

Wilkie felt as if he was being undermined. Not just by a
lesser rank, but by someone from a lesser force. 'You don't
like him, do you? Essie says you've got a thing going for

112

that woman and I'm beginning to see why.'

Geddes had become used to hearing that said about him. 'Listen, that's just nonsense. Anyway, how could she shoot him accidentally in that story when it looks like the bullet went through the back of his head? He would have to be struggling with her facing away from her.'

'That's what it looks like, but we'll have to wait until the autopsy to be sure about that. Anyway, young Tevendale only acted on what she said. *She* might not be telling *him* the truth. Maybe she just shot him as he slept. Ever thought of that, Mr Perry Mason?'

Chapter 20:

Sheila spent another sleepless night in police custody. At 9 a.m., Wilkie arranged for her to come back to the interview room, where he broke the news that Max's remains had been found. He noted that she did not react, apart from cupping her hand over her mouth, a sign, he felt, that she was being deceitful. He cautioned her, then charged her with Max's murder. 'Sheila Watson or Garvie, you did on 14 or 15 May 1968 at West Cairnbeg, Laurencekirk, shoot your husband Maxwell Robert Garvie and did cause him injury from which he died and did thus murder him.'

She replied, 'I did not shoot, kill or cause any injury to my husband.'

The Stonehaven public had never seen so many press and cameramen outside the Sheriff Court before, the last murder accused going through the court seventy years before, when Queen Victoria was still on the throne. Sheila and Brian were taken inside the building with coats over their heads. Wilkie had provided them from the lost property store in Aberdeen just after he had called a journalist friend to tell him the pair had been charged with murder and were being committed for further examination, bail applications being incompetent.

The hearings took about two minutes each and the police

114

made sure the two accused did not see each other, Sheila going through first. She was led into the Sheriff's Chambers by the woman police constable she was handcuffed to. A young solicitor she had never seen before stepped forward to tell the Sheriff that he 'represented the pannel and she made no plea or declaration.'

It might as well have been in Cantonese, Sheila thought as she was wheeled out. The young lawyer came running out after her as she was led towards the cells and asked the escort if he could have a quick word with his client. The lady police officer said she was due to be taken to Craiginches Prison and the van was waiting, but then relented, removed the handcuffs and ushered her into a side room.

The anxious young man came in and perched himself on the edge of a table, which had ancient, musty-smelling law books piled on the other side of it; Sheila stood beside a metal bucket as she massaged some feeling back into her wrists. 'I'm sorry it's worked out this way. My name is Jeremy Brown and I only found out about this hearing an hour ago. You will be taken back to court in about a week for another hearing and my firm has arranged for Mr Dowdall from Glasgow to appear for you then.'

Sheila felt like crying. 'Have I got to stay in prison? I really need to get back to my children …'

'Yes, I'm afraid bail is not allowed when someone is charged with murder …'

'But it wasn't me who killed Maxie, it was Brian. I just protected him by keeping my mouth shut.'

The lawyer looked flustered. 'Listen, I really don't do much in the way of court work and I'm really only doing Mr Dowdall a favour. I did speak to Mr Tevendale's lawyer, though, just before the case was called. Haven't you heard? He said it was *you* that shot your husband and all he did was bury the body.'

Sheila was staggered. 'He said it was me? The other man

who was there, Alan Peters, he can confirm I had nothing to do with it ...'

Unsure of how to respond and now regretting any involvement in the case, Mr Brown had no wish to become trapped in the factual politics that dogged criminal cases. 'You are going to have to tell Mr Dowdall all that when you see him. I'm sure he will visit you soon.' That his temporary client had openly stated that someone called Peters was present at the time of the murder was deemed to be an inconvenient detail best left to others who acted in distasteful matters like this.

The door knocked and the escort's voice sounded urgent from outside. 'Time's up! The van's waiting!'

Sheila knew she had to do something, even if to set the record straight. Once out in the corridor again, she explained what she had heard to the escort and said she now had to give her side of the story. The escort then spoke to the driver and, after a whispered conversation, she told her they were going back to police headquarters so Sheila could make a voluntary statement. On her arrival, she told Wilkie it was time the true facts were known, and he then arranged for her statement to be noted by other officers. As he phoned to organise it, he cast a cynical eye towards her, then warned those tasked with taking the statement that she was 'about to try to worm her way out of killing her man, no doubt by blaming young Tevendale'. Both officers involved obviously knew all about the sensational discovery of Max's body, but, crucially, they were not directly involved in the enquiry. Sheila was taken into a small interview room, where a formal written caution was written out before she began to explain what her version of events was.

On Tuesday 14 May my husband arrived home just after eleven and we had a drink and watched television and went to bed about 11.30 p.m. Max had two Soneryls. I fell asleep

116

and I expect he must have been sleeping too. I awakened with someone standing and whispering to me to get up. The bedroom light was off, but the room was lit from the light on the landing. I recognised the figure and the voice as being that of Brian Tevendale. He took me by the arm out to the landing and standing there was a fair-haired man. I didn't know who he was at all. I was hustled through to the bathroom and told to get in and stay there. I noticed Brian was carrying a gun. I didn't know at that time that it belonged to Max. I heard our bedroom door closing and terrible thumping noises. About five minutes later, Brian came through and tried the handle, but I had it locked. I opened the door. He said something like, 'You won't have any more of him to put up with,' and asked me to stay beside the girls' door in case they came out. The two of them were a while in the bedroom and they were pulling Max out in a groundsheet type of thing. I can't remember whether they took sheets with them or not because I was terribly upset, in a hell of a state, but I do remember they weren't long in going away. The following – oh now, wait a minute – I was going to explain I heard one car leaving, but they had already told me that this Alan had a car parked on the side road. Brian phoned on the Wednesday morning about 6 o'clock to say that they had left Max's clothes in the garage and I got distressed on the phone and Brian told me to take the clothes into Trudy, his sister, and she would get rid of them. From that, I took it that she knew of what had happened. He told me that night on the Tuesday that, if I squealed, he would get me involved and get about 25 years in prison. When I asked him how he was going to get away with it, he said he was going to hide the body and I asked him where and he said he wouldn't tell me. I phoned Trudy on the Wednesday night as I was in a state about the mattress, which was saturated with blood. She said that she and Brian would come down and take away the mattress. I can't remember whether it was

117

the Wednesday or the Thursday that they came down and she brought her mattress from her bed, and she bought a new mattress and she said I could pay her £18. I can't remember, but I think it was the Sunday night I was in there and I was well aware that Fred Birse knew what had happened and the gun was mentioned and he advised me to wipe the gun with an oily cloth for fingerprints. Oh yes, I was told by Brian that the car had got stuck and a man had pulled them out, but I was never told where or by whom. I think the car has been sold now. This lad, Alan, I don't know his last name, stayed with his wife in a caravan and they now stay in Fort Augustus, apparently he has got a job there. They used to visit the Birses quite often after that.

After the statement was taken, Sheila was moved to Craiginches Prison in Aberdeen. Wilkie asked Geddes to come into his room so they could discuss what she had said. 'Read that,' he said as he slid the statement across the desk in Geddes's direction. 'I was right about one thing – she's getting even with Tevendale and blaming him now! Don't you just love it when they blame each other?' Before Geddes made the point, Wilkie added, 'She mentions a third person, right enough. I'm not sure what to make of it.'

Geddes picked up the loose, numbered pages, neatly handwritten by a woman police constable. As he read through it, Wilkie lit a pipe and the room filled with the heavy scent of Condor Thick Black Twist. After he had read through both pages, Geddes picked the first one up again. 'What are Soneryls?'

Wilkie removed the pipe from the side of his mouth. 'I wondered about that too. WPC Cunningham tells me they are sleeping pills. What about the next bit?'

'You mean the figure standing in the bedroom turning out to be Tevendale? Yes, I'm not sure about that. I mean, he definitely knew his way about the place, but what she's saying is that a couple of men turned up in the middle of the night and murdered her husband, and not only was this something she didn't know about beforehand, she hadn't even met the second one before. Just doesn't sound right to me.'

Wilkie agreed. 'I know you interviewed her a couple of times. Did you ever think of getting a warrant to search West Cairnbeg? Whatever happened, Maxwell Garvie didn't just disappear. We know that now and always suspected it, but about the only thing she and Tevendale agree on is that he was murdered in the master bedroom.'

Geddes felt that Wilkie had fairly acknowledged his point about it being unlikely that Tevendale would be able to move Garvie's corpse by himself, particularly given the location where it had been buried. 'We'll have to get the forensic team in now. So, who's the fair-haired man called Alan?'

'Essie says she's being cute here and she knows fine who it is. It's a lad from Aberdeen who got married a couple of months ago and moved to Fort Augustus, you know, on the Caledonian Canal at Loch Ness.'

Geddes read on. 'I checked the garage when I went to West Cairnbeg and you could get into the house through it. I'm sure Tevendale would know that. I'm pretty certain that she would not have had to go to the trouble of leaving a door unlocked to let him and the other man in.'

Wilkie was obviously sceptical about the content of Sheila's statement. 'So, let's say they could have got in and killed Max without her having anything to do with it. Fine. Surely the point here is that she didn't scream or react when someone carrying a gun turned up in her bedroom in the middle of the night, even if she did know him. She locked herself in the bathroom when they went about clubbing and shooting the father of her children, who were in the next bedroom!'

Geddes pondered the point. 'Yes, again, it doesn't sound

right. You might think she would react in some way. On the other hand, you know what women can be like. She had lost all respect for her husband and was in love with Tevendale. There was no way back for Max, despite appearances of them working to save the marriage.'

Wilkie smiled. 'Hark at you, talking about how a woman feels! What about how a mother feels? The three kids are asleep next door and what does she do when their father is getting murdered – she locks herself in the toilet, then, once she gets out, holds the bedroom door handle so they won't come out when their father's body is being dragged down the stairs?'

'Point taken. So, if she planned the whole thing, why would she take the chance of her own kids hearing or even seeing something to do with their father's murder? I mean, he *was* shot. Why not get him when the kids were out or on his way home or even in the garage one night? It's one of those cases. For every point in her favour, there's another against her. Let's just wait and see what happens when the fair-haired man is captured … if he exists at all.'

Chapter 21:

Stonehaven Sheriff Court, Stonehaven, and HM Prison, Craiginches, Aberdeen,

Thursday, 17 August 1968

Brian was taken to prison from the court hearing in the back of a dark blue, carbolic-smelling BMC van with sliding driver and passenger doors. As he was escorted from the cells at Stonehaven Sheriff Court towards the rear of the vehicle, the elderly officer let him light up a cigarette and stand at the open doors for a few minutes. His handcuffs had temporarily been removed and Brian savoured the roll-up whilst listening to the sound of gulls wheeling and mewing high above the building, competing for scraps and squabbling like children in a playground.

He thought about the many times he had been nearby, drinking at the Marine or meeting Sheila for a coffee at the Royal. The night it all started came back to him. Brian had always thought that Max's suggestion that he show his wife Sheila 'a good time' meant that he, Brian, had done nothing wrong. He had simply obliged a strange man to fulfil a fantasy about his wife being with another man and, because he had grown to resent him for being young and virile, Max had obviously brought the consequences on himself. Putting it about that Max had recruited two different lots of hired help to try to beat him up successfully took their differences to a new level and Brian had to demonstrate to Max that he was now out of his depth. The Major had become a hero by being decisive when it mattered, and Max had to learn that the younger son was no different from his father when it came to showing his true mettle when put under pressure.

As the van made its way north, Brian's only concern was how to get out of the mess he was in, whatever it took. He had been cute enough not to mention Peters's involvement to the CID as – compared to Sheila – he, Peters, was a likely weak link. God knew, it hadn't been hard to bring him into the plot, and, once in, he was in it up to his neck. Peters had got used to picking him up in his car so they could do odd jobs at night. Befriending him had been easy as he was a loner, his family being his only real friends, apart from his pregnant girlfriend, but he was not quite the daft young man some at work thought he was. Brian knew Peters would be grateful to have a friend like him. Stage two, confide in him about a bloke who was stupid enough to take him on, 'I know, Alan, he must have a death wish'. Stage three, plan ahead and dress up like you're two good pals out drinking rather than two murderers biding their time to strike. Until Edith had spoiled everything, Brian had felt smug about how well it had gone, Peters even paying his share of drinks and petrol before he helped move the body! No, Peters would not let him down – he was too scared to do that – and Sheila was too much in love with him to speak up against him.

After his brief court appearance, the court lawyer said he would call his mother, Mrs Gertrude Tevendale, and his sister, Mrs Gertrude Birse, to let them know where Brian would be remanded. Once processed and lodged in a cell at Craiginches, a prison officer unlocked and opened the heavy steel door to let him know he had an out-of-hours visitor, and the prison were prepared to bend the rules this time only as it was his first proper night in custody.

It looked like Trudy had been crying. With no makeup on and wearing an old pair of ill-fitting slacks, she looked gaunt. The officer stood at the door of the visitors' area, twenty feet from them, Brian at one side of a shaky plastic laminated table with unequal legs and Trudy sitting at the other. She was facing the seemingly impassive prison guard and Brian was facing away from him and able to make facial gestures to his sister as he spoke without being seen by the official. They began in a barely audible whisper. As there was to be no physical contact, they both sat back in their dirty orange moulded seats, hands above the table.

'How are you bearing up?' Trudy began.

Brian tried not to smile. 'Fine. You know me …'

'Yes, I do. I'll come up to see you every day if I can.'

'Do that,' he smirked, increasing the volume of his response.

Trudy wiped her cheeks with the backs of her hands. 'Our brother Lenny is taking leave to come home from Germany and Mother's very upset. She can't understand how you got involved in this mess. I mean, Max was Sheila Garvie's problem, not yours.'

The guard's ears began to pick up what they were saying. He angled his body slightly forward to hear better, hoping the prisoner and his visitor would not notice.

'I know that.' Brian was talking more loudly now.

'Why did you get involved, then?' Trudy was playing her part in the pre-arranged charade well.

'I really don't know. I suppose I must have wanted to help her after what happened.'

Cue for his sister to enquire. 'What happened? What do you mean?'

'She phoned me to say he had tried to stick his dick up her arse again, except this time he had a rifle with him and was going to kill her if she didn't let him do it.' Brian's voice had just the right level of indignation in it to sound innocent but cynical; innocent of murder but cynical about his chances of justice being done. 'All I did was help her hide the body after she'd killed him. So much for her having feelings for me.'

Trudy looked as astonished as she could muster, letting her jaw drop and staring fixedly at her brother as if stupefied by the news.

While Brian and Trudy did not know if the prison officer had actually been listening to their conversation before, they were confident they definitely had his attention now.

'So, tell me again what happened?' she persisted.

'Sheila told me that they struggled for the rifle and it went off and Max was killed.' Brian widened his eyes and moved his head slightly in the warder's direction, wondering if he was taking their words in. Trudy nodded. He was.

'Oh my God! What did you do then?' she continued.

'Sheila was worried because she was in trouble and she asked me to move the body, which I did. She made me swear I wouldn't tell anybody, and I didn't. Well, not until that old crone went to the police!'

It was Trudy's turn to try to sound convincing. 'You mean her mother? Edith? Is she an old crone? I don't know her. What made her do that?'

Dispensing with the hushed-tones-routine, Brian allowed himself to *absent-mindedly* speak at just less than full volume. 'After she found out her daughter had shot her son-in-law, she must have got our phone number, and, when you were out last week, she called and asked to speak to me. It was the day she went to the police. She said she was in West Cairnbeg. I told her it was me who was speaking and she went all Ma Baker on me and said she wanted fifty quid from me or she would squeal to the cops ...'

Hearing that, Trudy leaned forward resting her forehead on her right hand, blinking rapidly. 'So, what did you do? Where would you get money like that? After all, you gave up your job because that Sheila wanted to run away with you. You should have told Fred and I, we could have given her *something* ...'

Again, Brian sounded sceptical about him getting justice in the future. 'I know. I should have told you all of this before, but I really didn't want to burden you with it and, anyway ...'

'It was her that killed him, not you,' Trudy said, neatly finishing her brother's sentence for him.

Brian nodded dejectedly. 'I can't understand why the old witch did it. It's her own flesh and blood she's grassed up.'

The rehearsed routine had worked and, as usual with any conversation in which a remand prisoner was involved in and which might have a bearing on the case, was reported further up the tree. However, once investigated, there were two reasons why the conversation was unlikely to be used in court.

For a start, no call was recorded from Auchenblae 205 – the number for the main phone at West Cairnbeg – to an Aberdeen number on 16 August and, secondly, there was the point that Geddes had made after Max's body had been found. He had been shot in the neck from behind. How could a strong man with a rifle end up shot from behind?

It sounded more like revenge than an accident.

So, what was the purpose of the question-and-answer pretence between the Tevendale brother and sister and why did Trudy play such a key role in it? It was almost as if she had an interest in the case that went far beyond her own hurt feelings and the sympathy that anyone might have if their brother faced a sentence of life imprisonment for murder.

Her behaviour at the trial, together with some of the evidence that was to emerge, might hold the answer.

Chapter 22:

Fort Augustus, Inverness-shire, and Police Headquarters, Bucksburn, Aberdeen,

Sunday, 18 August 1968

Wilkie and Geddes had arranged for the local policeman in Fort Augustus to trace the recently arrived Alan Peters and for him to be in the local police station when they travelled through from Aberdeen that Sunday. After all, the City boys joked, 'it gives the local plod something to do other than chase stolen sheep in a jealous rage.'

Moira Wilkie, like Geddes's own wife, Irene, was particularly unhappy about her husband having to work more overtime, and Wilkie needed some reassurance from Geddes that the journey was necessary.

Wilkie had called Geddes at home on the Saturday night, seeking reasons to justify the trip. 'After what Sheila Garvie has told us, we have to speak to Peters right away. Do you agree? I told Moira that, but she's annoyed I'm having to work when her mother and sister are coming for Sunday lunch. You know what it's like ...'

'Listen to you now,' Geddes retorted, 'just yesterday you were accusing me of pretending to understand how women worked and now you're the one coming away with the clichés!'

Wilkie's laugh seemed to acknowledge that Geddes had made a good point.

How women work. That is what this case is really about,

Geddes thought. *Are they necessarily always in control? Or was Sheila Garvie just one of life's unfortunates with no say in anything, both inside and outside the house?*

It was a mild late summer's day and some of the trees were already showing yellow autumnal tints. At any other time, it would have been a comfortable, relaxing jaunt, but Geddes had reservations about its timing.

'You know, I have my doubts about charging this Peters character at the start. Do we have enough against him to do that? Maybe we should just caution him and hope he says something.'

Wilkie thought about stopping the car to go back over the evidence so far, but decided against it given the time. 'What makes you say that? You're the one that reckoned Tevendale had needed a hand to move the body, so here he is, the second man.'

Geddes thought they had to be realistic about the state of the evidence that was building daily, but still didn't complete the picture. 'That's as may be, but so far we've only got Sheila Garvie saying he was there. What if he says nothing?'

Wilkie was more bullish. 'From what I've heard about this man, he'll want to tell us all about it, so we have to give him that chance.'

The local policeman had traced Alan to his in-laws' house and reported that the young man had been as respectful as his new wife and that her parents were stunned by the allegation that the new, mild-mannered addition to their household was possibly involved in a murder. He said the prisoner was uncomfortably reticent – 'a man of few words' – and not given to long conversations. His wife had collapsed as her husband of just over three weeks was taken away 'to assist with the enquiry' and he wasn't even able to reassure her he had nothing to do with it, though he did say he would be home in a few hours. He just said nothing, traipsing out in handcuffs looking sorry for himself, not even glancing back at his prostrate and tearful new wife. That said, the local bobby related, Peters did go back inside on his recommendation, to retrieve his toothbrush.

The police station at Fort Augustus was small even by rural standards. Being on the route that ran alongside Loch Ness, road traffic incidents caused by drivers looking for the Monster were the main source of business, followed by drunken behaviour in local pubs and the occasional theft of farm equipment.

Within living memory, a detainee for murder was unheard of in the area since clan members stopped attacking each other for long-forgotten reasons.

When Alan Peters was brought into the biggest room in the station from its only cell, he seemed bewildered. The experienced local officer had decided that handcuffs were not needed and the pair of them came into the room like a father and a problem son out on a visit together. After introducing them both, Wilkie followed the agreed plan and charged him with murdering Maxwell Robert Garvie 'while acting along with Brian Tevendale and Sheila Watson or Garvie'. After a long pause during which Geddes thought the man might even be deaf, Alan replied, 'No, I did not shoot him.'

With no legal adviser present, Wilkie suggested the suspect might need one, but Alan then said he wished to make a statement, which the local officer noted as Alan spoke in a faltering, hesitant Doric burr.

He brought it up at work a few weeks before. He just said he was wanting to get rid of the bloke and would I come with him so that he could have transport. Well, on the night I picked him up at Mr Birse's house. We went from there to Stonehaven. No, we didn't, we went straight through Stonehaven onto the coast road and we stopped at a little pub and had a drink in there and then we went and carried on that road and we made for Laurencekirk. We stopped in Laurencekirk and had one drink there too. We went from there to West Cairnbeg and we parked the car on the road that runs along the back of the house. We went from there into the garage and Mrs Garvie let us into the house. Brian got the gun from the back of the door and we went through to the sitting room. We got a drink from Mrs Garvie and then she showed us to the room upstairs. We waited there until Mr Garvie came home and went to bed and when he was asleep his wife came through and told us. Then we went through, and Brian had the gun and he hit him on the back of the head with the butt of the gun and then he shot him with the gun. Then we tied him up in a plastic groundsheet and we took him down to the car, then Brian took his car to the airfield and I followed. We then took him to the place where we left him. I burned the groundsheet. I put some petrol on it and set fire to it. That's just more or less it.

Alan Peters had chosen to give what later came to be called 'a mixed statement' without legal advice. In it, he had both incriminated and exculpated himself to different degrees, accepting he knew that they were there to 'get rid of' a bloke, whatever that might give rise to; his defence team would have to show – and later would try to do so – that their client had had no idea what he had got himself into, a tall order given the very plain import of the phrase 'get rid of' coupled with his co-accused being in possession of a firearm and all the preparations that had been made beforehand. On the other hand, their client had at least said that he had done nothing to 'the bloke' and that his role in all of it was to provide transport.

But why did he say anything at all? Without the input of his voluntary statement – and before the forensic scientists had swabbed the back seat of the Zephyr – there was only a single source of evidence against him, and that came from

Sheila. Peters had been told he didn't have to speak to the police as a matter of fairness, the only drawback to keeping his mouth shut being that his silence at that stage might lead to the jury questioning whether he was telling the truth in court, having said nothing before; his counsel could easily have explained all that to the jury.

Evidently, had he not said anything, he might have bought himself more freedom, more time to live a lie, more time to wake up with night terrors about the gurgling sound Max Garvie's throat made as he lay trussed up in the back of the car on the way to be buried under stones on the grounds of the castle at Lauriston, more time to have nightmares about being hanged in Craiginches like that Burnett boy only a few years before.

Geddes and Wilkie took him back to Bucksburn in their car, making no comment in his presence about what he had said to them. Yet, on a human level, it's almost always impossible for some sort of dialogue not to take place, particularly on a long journey. The difficulty for the police is that, when the case goes to court, it often sounds like a trap for the unwary prisoner to incriminate himself when he says something that can be used against him, so the plan is usually to keep any conversations general and free of chatter about the reason the prisoner is in custody.

Wilkie asked Alan how he was feeling and how he liked living in Fort Augustus, and Alan again took an age to answer. Both CID men separately wondered if the man was the full shilling, yet, when he spoke, he sounded fine and was probably just slow at catching on. Without making eye contact with Wilkie in the rear-view mirror from his seat in the back, Alan said he didn't really like living there, then he clammed up. Wilkie asked him what was it he didn't like and Alan said he missed his old job and his own family. The boy certainly seemed to be an open book.

Then he sighed and started to speak again. 'I wanted to go to the police and confess ...'

Geddes was about to caution him, but he couldn't stop him from continuing. 'Maybe I didna mean confess. What I mean is tell them what Brian did. I was just the driver.'

'So, what stopped you from going to the police?' Wilkie took the chance of asking.

'I dinna really ken. It was just that I was scared in case if I gave Brian away, I would be frightened for the rest of my life. Brian's a good friend, but after what he did at thon place, I was worried if the same thing would happen to me if I told you.'

As they wound their way slowly eastwards, Geddes wondered if the prisoner's recently uttered words might be admissible in court. If they were, they could be significant – he said he would be frightened of *Brian* for the rest of his life. Not *Brian and Sheila* or even *them*, but Brian *on his own*. Wouldn't it have been more natural for Peters, consciously or not, to have used the plural if there had been a pre-conceived plan of action between the lovers? Perhaps, Geddes reasoned, that would depend on whether this disarmingly unguarded young chap in the back of the car was privy to it. *I know if I was Tevendale and was planning to murder somebody, I'd tell him nothing beyond the bare minimum he needed to know.*

Back at Bucksburn, Alan was lodged in a cell to await his first court appearance whilst the duty sergeant called a solicitor for him. Never having been in any kind of bother before, Alan had no idea who he should instruct, let alone what to say to him beyond what he had already told the police.

Wilkie and Geddes then compared notes.

'Peters really is the perfect patsy. Somebody like Tevendale could get him to do anything he wanted,' Geddes said.

'So how much of what he told us is true? Has that man got the wit to make all that up?' Wilkie wondered.

'You mean "wanting to get rid of a bloke" and "needing transport"?'

'Yes,' Wilkie said, 'if he's that frightened of Brian Tevendale why would he volunteer that? Surely that's the sort of thing that Brian would tell him to keep quiet about?'

Geddes agreed. 'That and Tevendale hitting Max with the gun butt, then shooting him. Some friendship. If Alan Peters is being truthful about agreeing to help Brian, what was in it for him, apart from grief?'

Wilkie looked at his watch. 'I told Mrs W that I would try to make it back in time to see her mother and sister, but I'm already two hours late, so no need to rush now.' As he spoke, he approached a filing cabinet that had handwritten cards with alphabetical sequences printed on them, opened a drawer marked 'W-Z', then reached in and pulled a half bottle of blended whisky out. 'So, what about Sheila letting them into the house and pouring them a drink before Max got home? Surely that puts a new slant on it.' As Geddes considered the words, Wilkie retrieved two glasses from his desk drawer and poured two large measures, passing one to his colleague.

Geddes agreed that Sheila letting Tevendale and Peters into the house added a new dimension to her involvement in the plot. 'It does, but you've got to wonder why she even mentioned Alan Peters in her statement if she's that mixed up in it. Would she not have been better off saying nothing or just mentioning Brian on his own so it would have been his word against hers if they fell out in court? Now she's letting them into the house when they could easily have let themselves in and then pouring them a drink before they shoot her husband. Surely nobody's going to believe that bit, are they? I've been in the house and the last thing you would do is hang about in the sitting room. It looks out onto the parking area and the lawn and, anyway, what would-be assassins are not going to go straight into hiding? Where does Peters get that from? It *must* be made up.'

Wilkie was not so sure. 'I agree it sounds ridiculous, but, as we often find out, so does the truth. What did you make of Sheila going through to the spare room upstairs to tell them Max was asleep?'

'We'll now have to go back to West Cairnbeg to check some of the details he's given us. So much for Brian's "Sheila did it and I moved the body" nonsense. One thing's for sure, though, Alan Peters's story helps nobody. He's actually dropped all three of them well and truly in it.'

Chapter 23:

Sheila had never been able to settle into the prison regime, but fully understood why she was there.

Being awakened from a deep, tranquillised, mid-May sleep, then failing to stop her husband from being brutally and fatally attacked might be excusable in a stranger's eyes when little or no blame could be attached to her, but keeping the whole thing quiet was obviously not. The decision *not* to take decisive action by calling the police as soon as Brian and a stranger called Alan had driven off that morning had never really been consciously made, as she imagined that Brian had done it solely for her and she couldn't let him down.

Poor, deluded woman – but worse was still to come!

Of course, any delay – even a short one – in contacting the authorities would look hugely suspicious to someone not fully acquainted with all that had been happening in her life, and the gap of three silent months made it look as if she had been complicit in the original, horrific act. What had begun as stupefied inactivity had turned into mouldering months of miserable anxiety, leaving her alone with increasingly resentful thoughts. Briefly working in the East Neuk bar beside Brian before her arrest had not given her relief from the nightmare of Max's killing. All it had done was buy her time to distance herself from the murder, although each extra minute simply added weight to the prosecutor's likely argument that silence after the event was just as culpable as planning before it would have been. And now, being bound to Brian because of a dreadful, shared secret had not made her love for him any stronger, rather it had frozen it, like a dying songbird buried under a fall of snow, waiting to be discovered when the thaw came.

It was the prison officers' change of shift when Laurence Dowdall's black and cream-coloured Bentley pulled into the car park at the prison. Limousine aside, he had come a long way since those early days and was now able to contribute more hard-earned cash than promissory words at the firm's monthly partners' meetings. By the time he had parked it, word had spread amongst the prison staff who were coming on duty that the well-known Glasgow-based lawyer had arrived to consult with one of their guests, the debate being which one of the three currently lodged there for the murder of the 'Flying Farmer' he was there to represent.

Prison officers often while away long shifts by discussing the forensic chances of those who are assigned to their care, a sort of pre-trial assessment of the case along the lines of, 'Well, I for one don't think he/she would be capable of doing that' and 'To hell with the lack of evidence, believe me, I know what he's like!' It would be fair to say that the gossip about the Garvie case helped pass the time during those interminable back shifts and long winter nights inside its chilly Victorian interior. So far, the debate concerned the extent of Alan and Sheila's involvement in the killing; the book was closed on Brian once word spread about Alan Peters's explanation to the police. In effect, that made it the word of two accused against the word of one, that Brian, not Sheila, had pulled the trigger that ended Max's recent thrill-seeking exploits.

Meantime, the smart money was on Dowdall coming

to see Sheila and not the other two. Being the only female inmate at the old jail and having her own section of the prison, she had had a staff all of her own ever since her court committal a few weeks previously. She divided opinion, some feeling it was instinctively wrong that someone like her should be in prison, let alone an otherwise all-male one, whilst others saw her as the reporting officer did – 'as hard as nails'.

Some of the more curious staff stole glimpses of Dowdall as he signed himself in using a gold fountain pen. Even without counsel, he was a jailhouse box-office attraction on his own. The defence lawyer who helped convict the notorious Peter Manuel ten years before was renowned throughout the country, but there was more than a suspicion that he wasn't above playing up to his public image with the flash car, the wartime spiv moustache, the *strippet troosers*, the velvet collared Crombie coat and the immaculately polished handmade shoes. Down the years, a routine of working late and eating at the wrong end of the day had helped steadily widen his girth to the point where his wife was no longer able to widen *westcoats* or take out trousers or suit jackets, having run out of available material; on the other hand, the Dowdalls could now afford to be less frugal, although old habits – particularly ones learned in times of want – sometimes stubbornly persist.

One of the staff told Sheila of Dowdall's arrival and she instinctively thought of applying lipstick she no longer had access to as she considered what it was appropriate to say to him. *How much are you meant to say to your solicitor? Is it right to tell him the truth or does he not want to hear that? Is it true that some defence lawyers are unscrupulous charlatans who advise, then concoct the best bespoke defences to answer the essentials of the prosecution case?*

Dowdall was already seated in the small, stale-aired interview room by the time she was escorted to the door by a stern female warder, who unlocked the prisoner-side door and silently ushered her in. Meeting him for the first time, she felt that Dowdall looked intimidating as he sat writing the date and venue on his yellow consultation pad, and her first instinct was to keep quiet rather than open up to reveal all the intimacies of the case to some high-flying stranger who would no doubt pretend to be non-judgemental, all the time inwardly thinking she was as 'guilty as thon Delilah', as someone from her Sunday school class once said to her.

After all, that was what *she* felt.

At least there was no screen between them and there was a shared table, even if – as was almost always the case in institutions throughout the land – it bore the signs of previous occupants who had somehow managed to scrawl and carve their names on it.

Dowdall's first meeting strategy hadn't altered down the years, and he pretended not to hear her entering the room until he had apparently started writing up the preliminary details of the meeting. After a few moments of allowing her to study him, he looked up and smiled.

'Good afternoon, Mrs Garvie,' Dowdall said as he offered his hand. Sheila responded uncertainly, briefly touching his outstretched fingers. 'Please bear with me for a second whilst I finish completing my paperwork.' He smiled as he scribbled the formalities, giving her a further opportunity to assess him. From where she sat, his oversized glasses reflected the yellow page as they sat squarely on his prominent nose. As Sheila dutifully thought that she detected a faint whiff of expensive male grooming, after-shave or hair oil perhaps, his jet-black jacket contrasting with his bright yellow and blue Paisley-patterned tie and pristine white collar; Dowdall's performance was designed to allow his new client time to adjust and feel at ease more quickly.

He had thought about the best way to act for his new client on the journey north and decided that Sheila Garvie was no ordinary client in no ordinary case, and lots of patience would be needed to build a bond between them as the basis of a successful working relationship.

Looking up slowly, he removed his glasses before rubbing his eyes and speaking again. 'Please don't be nervous, I only intend to say "hello" today so that we can meet and know each other better the next time.'

She nodded. 'Yes, that's ok,' she heard herself saying. Then she prattled on nervously about being the only woman in the place, giving Dowdall time for *his* first impressions. She was a handsome woman alright, which could work either way with a jury, the women maybe seeing her as some sort of sex-crazed *femme fatale* and the men perhaps instinctively siding with her because of her good looks. He had seen this before, something he called 'the Madonna attitude', whereby women were either paragons of virtue or shameful tarts, with no credit allowable for anything in between. Or might it be the other way round, the female jurors seeing a wife and mother subjected to appalling treatment whilst the men might think she used her obvious charms to ensnare her young lover to brutally murder her unwanted husband and free her from a ruinous marriage?

Mastermind of a deadly murder or victim of fate?

Time would tell.

She was flustered, thinking this was her big chance to set things straight and nervous about not doing herself justice. She stopped talking and became tearful, as if she had blanked reality out until then and realised the gravity of her situation for the first time. Dowdall reached forward and briefly placed his hand on hers, 'Now, now, my dear, I'm here to help you, so let's not be upset. As I often say to clients, we'll get on much better if we're both relaxed and you're able to tell me the truth.'

Despite her upset, Sheila took comfort in his words. 'I'm afraid I'm terribly confused, Mr Dowdall. This might sound a bit, well, naive, but is it alright to tell you the truth, I mean everything? I never imagined I would be sitting in a place like this charged with murdering Maxie. He was such a good man to begin with. Then he became – how can I put it – dissatisfied with his life and needed to live on the edge all the time.'

Dowdall wrote as she spoke, then stopped, thinking it might inhibit her. He would write it up later in the car before he drove home and let her speak freely just now. She continued, telling him how much she missed her children and how selfish she had been in confiding in – and burdening her mother with – the news of 'Maxie's' murder. Dowdall sat back and let her flow, letting all her anxieties come to the fore as he sat there benevolently nodding like some kindly cleric hearing a supplicant's devotions or a trusted family doctor patiently listening for recognisable symptoms before pronouncing a cure.

As he had promised, the meeting was short, but it did seem to put her mind at ease about the need to tell him the full truth. He smiled as he said, 'I have heard this all of my professional life, but have never been able to work out why it ever entered anyone's head as a good idea to tell a pack of lies to the person tasked with preparing an accused's defence. Not only do lies cause unnecessary complications, but the truth is the most direct route to acquittal if innocence is genuine.' She had listened to his words and been gratified by them, even nearly smiling at one point. 'I can assure you, Mr Dowdall, I am completely innocent of being in any way involved in Maxie's murder.'

Dowdall was on the verge of assuring her that he would do his utmost on her behalf when she voiced an unsettling afterthought that stopped him from speaking.

'I also have to qualify that, though. I *am* guilty of allowing Brian to think he might be doing the right thing by ridding me of Maxie even though I never asked him to do so and had no idea it was going to happen.'

Later, reclining in the Bentley's padded leather driver's seat, Dowdall began to record the details of the first of several meetings between them:

Nervous and upset, nevertheless comes across as a credible person caught up in a deadly situation between two dominant, competitive men. Expressed concern for the welfare of her children, her mother and – curiously – her co-accused Tevendale, in that order. That might be significant, as she seems to feel responsible for him doing what he did to her husband. Will have to explore that next time. LD, Craiginches Prison Aberdeen, 18 September 1968.

Chapter 24:

Dowdall's visit had both a reassuring and an unsettling effect on Sheila. Lying on the shaky, makeshift camp-bed that the prison authorities had had to requisition in order to accommodate her, she felt an empty, pessimistic sensation in her heart about how all of this was going to pan out. Not being *au fait* with how the criminal law system works, she imagined she had blown her chance to somehow convince her solicitor she was actually innocent of the charge of murder. He seemed such a nice, understanding person, but was that just a bedside manner honed from long experience? Did he *really* understand how brutalised she felt after all the mental and physical torment that Maxie had put her through? Probably not.

Mr Dowdall said he would be back, so she would make sure she was in a better frame of mind next time to tell him everything that had been going on.

How could she – or anyone – fully explain how she came to become attached to Brian Tevendale? Instead of cherishing her and protecting her from harm, her husband had cast her into the arms of another man who had given her

141

the love, comfort and protection she needed. Only Maxie could describe what was going on in his head when he turned into the drink and sex-crazed monster he became, but that wasn't possible after Brian had done what he did to him in the master bedroom in West Cairnbeg, that poor frightened Alan character looking distressed, as if he wanted to be anywhere but helping bundle Maxie's body down the stairs. *Mr Dowdall needs to know this, though. I have no idea what Brian did to my husband. Did he shoot him or simply stun him with the rifle butt, then finish him off outside? Even now, I honestly don't know he's really dead! What if Brian and Maxie have concocted a devilish scheme to get me convicted of Maxie's murder and he's going to wait until I'm serving a sentence of life imprisonment, then he'll magically reappear to say it's all been a ghastly mistake? That's just the sort of thing he would take great delight in doing. That would have Maxie's seal of approval. I can hear him laughing about it now and saying, 'Well, how was prison for you, Miss Frigid Sunday School? Have you learned your lesson? Do you know now how important it is for you to look after your husband's needs – I mean* all *of them?'*

Sheila's despair knew no bounds. Here she was lying in a male-only jail, separated from her children and charged with organising and overseeing her husband's murder when all she had wanted was for him to stop abusing her. Could she get any lower than this? Imagining the entire nightmare might be a giant hoax and pinning her faint hopes that Maxie might still be alive and able to tell a jury the truth had to be a sign she had hit rock bottom, a real low point she needed to reach before her spirits lifted again, like the hot wax rising from the base of that lava lamp Maxie was so proud of showing off.

Before he became briefly obsessed with Trudy Birse, he would make Sheila sit beside him whilst he watched what he called 'the spunky stuff' inside the lamp rise up, then sink to the base again.

I suppose he never really grew up and life for him was like being a puppy, exploring everything and anything that might come his way with a brief, fleeting interest until he got bored with it, like a toy, then it was left after he'd played with it, lying half-chewed on the ground, ready to be picked up by a passing adult tidying up in his wake.

Who was to know that the handsome, cocksure young man, ten years her junior, the man-boy who was cheeky enough to ask them for a lift that June day at Bannockburn, would end up saving her and condemning her in one fell swoop?

As soon as Maxie set eyes on Trudy, I already knew some of what was about to happen. He was going to turn her head with glimpses of the sort of life that all the trapped wives and mothers out there foolishly think they deserve and are missing out on. Champagne, oysters, sleek-fast cars and flying up to touch the clouds convinced her she was destined to live like that, the poor, shallow woman. Whilst he was doing all the sordid things he could do to her – only so he could come home and taunt me with them – she had no clue she was just being used like that puppy toy.

Did he have a conscience about it? It would be easy to say no, definitely not. Maxie must have been born without one. Yet, what made him even things up – in his mind – by throwing me at Brian? Was that really what it was all about and his fling with Trudy was just a diversion, a ready-made cover story for his desire – no, his need – to be cuckolded?

I remember everything about that Saturday night and how I listened in on the upstairs extension on his call to her and the date they had made to 'have a tumble', as he put it, her laughing like a daft wee lassie being propositioned by a horny classmate for the first time, half thrilled, half terrified. I don't think he knew I had listened in, but he came straight upstairs to tell me he was going up to Aberdeen that night,

143

oh, and I was going out with young Brian, he told me, almost as an afterthought. That was it. Settled. No argument. Then off he went in his new Cortina, the fast one, the ones he read about that the police can't catch and Brian drove up in the Jag, all worried how I'd be about it all.

I actually pitied the lad that night as he fumbled with the notes Maxie had given him – £100 Brian told me later, £100 for a couple of rounds of drinks in a plasticky lounge bar in a local hotel! – and, God bless him, he acted all Hollywood, shouting 'Waitress!' at that wee woman behind the counter, who rightly ignored him, so he had to get up and order at the bar like everyone else. I could tell he was nervous and just a bit self-conscious about us being out together, as if somebody would recognise us and would tell on us, so I took time to let him know it was alright and he could relax. It's been like that ever since, I suppose, me soothing him and feeling responsible for all he's had to do in this terribly complicated situation. I'm sure he killed Maxie for me because he had started hitting me and threatening to slash my face so that no man in his right mind would even think of 'putting his dick near me', was how Maxie put it. He had such a way with words, that poor, dead husband of mine.

Looking back at it now, that must be when I started to have feelings for this nervous, faltering, dangerous younger man, when he showed me consideration and was so gentle in bed, unlike the man I married, who grunted instructions like 'do this', 'touch this', 'lie like this', all so he could use and enjoy my body as if it was a tired old car he wanted to drain every last mile out of before scrapping it. The way it was going, one of us was going to die, so it's better it was him than me – God forgive me for that last awful thought! At least I can relate to the children – my poor bairns! This is going to break my heart – unlike Maxie, who loved telling our eldest she ate too much and was fat and made her feel bad about herself just when she needed him to be nice towards her, or at least to stay out of things like Father did with me, leaving Mam to try to cope with the great mystery of what makes growing girls do the kinds of things they do. Father sometimes said that God made boys stupid and girls only part-time stupid so that lots of babies could be born and the human race could continue, and him just a stonemason!

That Saturday night, Brian tried his best James Bond on me, bless him. He even ordered a Martini for himself, then drank it in one like a tiny pint of beer, thinking I'd be impressed, totally clueless about how women can see through men's little deceptions, though I liked him for trying. His stories about his special forces service seemed tired and clichéd. They must have worked for him with some of the teenage girls in Aldershot and maybe even back here, but I smiled just to let him know I was not going to believe any of it as I'm too old to have to listen to it. Still, it was good that he tried. I knew I would be safe with him even after we both had some drinks. On the way out he opened the passenger door for me and closed it gently, making sure I was settled in my seat and that there were no straggling coat or buckle ends about to become trapped in the doorpost. Not that Maxie ever opened the car door for me to get in, he just got in and fired the engine, then roared off whether I was in or half in the car or not.

It was only after we left the hotel that Brian mentioned to me that Maxie had told him to wait for him at the Flying Club and to be there at 11 p.m. That meant both of us. We were meant to drink ourselves insensible with all the money Brian had been given and then end up sitting together at a pitch-black airstrip in Maxie's beloved Mark Ten Jag. By the time we got there, Brian had maybe realised that older, married women were unlikely to be swept off their feet by constant false tales of heroism, and he slowly began to reveal the appealing, exposed side of his nature, the one I eventually fell for. I still remember him trying to hide his emotions when *he talked about his father. He coughed, pretending his voice hadn't wavered, as he told me about the fire that destroyed the Bush Hotel. Disabled as he was with debilitating war wounds, the Major still managed to climb out the bedroom window on the first floor and save the family from smoke asphyxia or incineration. A genuine hero to the end. A tough act to follow.*

It was getting close to midnight and there was no sign of Maxie. I had been distraught when he so blatantly arranged the date with Brian's sister, but that night made me think that life could go on even if Maxie announced he was leaving the children and me and we had to begin again without their father and his money, should it come to that. Just as I felt that we had played my husband's warped little game long enough and was about to ask – no, tell – Brian to drive me back to West Cairnbeg, the front passenger door beside me burst open. For a second or two I thought I was going to die with fright thinking there was somebody about to shoot us or do us harm – isn't it funny, my dying thought would have been, 'How will the bairns manage without me?', and right now they have to – but inevitably it was Maxie, fresh from doing whatever he desired with the sister of the polite young person sitting beside me. He had to be disappointed, though. He had evidently driven up behind the Jag, parking a good few hundred yards away with the Cortina lights off for all of that time and then had drunkenly weaved a silent path in the darkness towards his favourite car, hoping he would be greeted by the sight of his wife and his recent protégé entwined together in a crazy, impassioned sexual liaison. He must have been disappointed to realise that his well-planned little ruse had failed.

As they drove back the short distance to West Cairnbeg in the Cortina 1600E, Max insisted on finding out what his wife and the other man *had been up to* in a scenario he himself had engineered. Concerned for her safety for the first time in their marriage, Sheila tried her best to fend him off with short, aloof answers, but she knew he wouldn't settle for anything less than selfish, emotionless, snorting sex once they arrived home. It was only now she knew he would not be making her life hell anymore that she began to appreciate what had really been going on in her husband's peculiar mindset.

Chapter 25:

West Cairnbeg Farmhouse and The Royal Hotel, Stonehaven,

Wednesday, 25 September 1968

As was his usual practice, well before the indictment had been served, Dowdall contacted both the local Procurator Fiscal in Aberdeen and Crown Office in Regent Road, Edinburgh, to ask for a provisional list of witnesses likely to be called by the prosecution. Most other agents simply waited until the final list was known so there would be no wasted effort in speaking to witnesses who might have little to add to the case, but, based on experience, he had developed his own method of guessing who might be important when the case came to trial. As he drove north to meet and precognosce Mrs Edith Watson that day, he thought back to the Manuel case and how crucial it had been when he personally took statements from some of the witnesses, although his close liaison with the police in that case had relaxed their usual reluctance over telling a defence lawyer anything that might help his client, usually always obviously guilty in their eyes.

In that case, Dowdall had represented a William Watt, who had been charged with murdering his own wife, daughter and sister-in-law in a Glasgow suburb in September 1956 after the police reckoned he had broken off a fishing holiday to travel through the night, staged a break-in at his own house, shot his wife once, his sister-in-law twice, knocked his daughter unconscious before shooting her as well, then

148

driven back to Argyllshire, arriving back before first light. When Dowdall met Watt in Barlinnie Prison, Glasgow, he immediately felt the police and the prosecution had got it completely wrong and he set out to test his instincts by speaking to a ferryman who alleged he saw Watt travelling over the River Clyde – one possible route he might have taken had he been travelling on the night in question. The witness was strangely confused about the details of his police statement and Dowdall was eventually able to persuade the authorities that the real murderer was Peter Manuel. That led to the release of Watt from Barlinnie, where, it turned out, Manuel was also lodged, having been sentenced for a break-in committed six months before the triple murder.

Apart from providing a proper service to his clients, Dowdall also liked to assess how people came across when he was speaking to them face to face. Important matters such as eye contact, verbal responses and attitude could not be properly gauged on the pages of typed foolscap that constituted police statements and, anyway, his client's mother, Edith, was obviously going to be an important witness at the trial.

The whole story had unravelled in mid-August after she told Dougie Scrimgeour, then DS Geddes, what her daughter had revealed to her about Max's disappearance that fateful day in May.

Dowdall's secretary, Evelyn, had been in touch with Edith to find out where and when it suited her to meet Dowdall, and Edith had explained that she continued to look after her grandchildren at their home in the farm until the outcome of the trial; Edith also said that it would also suit her if Dowdall came at a time when the youngsters were at school, so they wouldn't know he had been there. It was obvious to Dowdall that his client's mother made her grandchildren's welfare her top priority.

Leaving nothing to chance, his secretary had also marked

out Dowdall's best route on an AA handbook, which he stopped and studied after leaving Arbroath. Arriving at West Cairnbeg in time, he pulled the Bentley into the long, sweeping driveway, crunching the gravel under the tyres, just as Maxwell Garvie must have done for the last time on the night of 14 May. Dowdall stepped out of the Bentley and stretched his limbs before parking behind the Cortina 1600E and noticing the double garage at the end of the driveway. The small, fussy figure of Mrs Edith Watson appeared at the newly opened front door, her hands clasped together in a characteristic desperate, wringing gesture and her grey hair pulled back in a matronly style. His first impression of the little woman was one of a no-nonsense, practical individual who nevertheless appeared pleasant enough; on later learning of her Spiritual leanings, he was at a loss to figure out how that fitted in with his first impression of her. That was what the job had taught him – be prepared for people doing surprising things and never judge them by their appearances.

Once inside the farmhouse, Dowdall was able to study her more closely as she spoke. She looked world-weary, but, despite her diminutive size, she came across as a determined yet reasonable lady, the sort of person who, in different circumstances, would have made an ideal juror in the case against someone charged with murder, the sort who would rigidly stick by the terms of the collective oath to return a true verdict according to the evidence. In a way, she had already demonstrated her integrity by going to the police about what her daughter had told her, but Dowdall now had to try to understand what drove her to take such commendable but drastic action.

Edith told Dowdall she knew what had been going on between Sheila and Brian and between Max and Trudy. Edith and Sheila's father, William, had done all they could to stop it, not just for appearance's sake, but so that the Garvies might patch things up between them, above all, so that the children might not suffer through their parents splitting up. She deeply regretted getting her daughter into bother by going to the police, but as it was the right thing to do, she knew she had no choice but to do it. She had done her best to stop Sheila from seeing Brian, but she seemed to be infatuated with him and, after Max had 'gone', she continued to advise her daughter to stop seeing her lover, which led to rare tension building up between her and Sheila. Both Sheila *and* Max had told her about Max's incessant demands for *rude* sex – as Edith put it – with Sheila, and both knew Trudy was happy to oblige him in that respect. Max had told her about that, so keen was he to patch things up, since he regarded his mother-in-law as holding the key to marital reconciliation. She had organised the meeting in her house in Stonehaven that had led to Max completely splitting from Trudy, but later found out that her daughter Sheila had kept seeing Brian despite promising she wouldn't. Edith made it clear she disliked Brian, as there was something about him she distrusted. No harm to him, but Sheila had to realise that he was bad for her and the children, and, after Max had gone, Edith had carried on looking after the youngsters, getting them to school, cooking their meals and washing and ironing their clothes only because she wanted to help them survive this awful time, and *not* to make it easier for Sheila to see Brian, as she did three nights a week in Aberdeen.

Dowdall wondered what it was that made her crack three months after Max had been murdered. Edith explained that Sheila abruptly announced she was thinking of moving to Aberdeen to be nearer Brian; Edith said that her patience had simply run out at that stage. She felt that she could suffer nightmares and keep a confidence as well as anyone, but her daughter's plans had changed everything. Now the children would have to be uprooted from the only home they had known all their lives and that would not do. Should it look as if Sheila was actually going ahead with the move, that would change everything, and Edith would then be withholding a horrendous secret from the police so that her daughter could simply change partners. That had never been the reason she kept quiet about what she knew for three agonising months, as it was always about keeping what remained of the bairns' lives at their home in West Cairnbeg.

So, there it was. Sheila's news had been the final straw and Edith's decision had to do with the welfare of the children, not revenge or hatred or retribution or anything else that folk round about said about her. Edith had clearly lived her life by rigid, easy to understand rules that should not be breached by anyone and Sheila, above all others, must have known that.

Dowdall asked her about Sheila telling her that Max 'would not be coming back' and Edith said that when Sheila had told her that, it was obvious her daughter had no idea where her husband's body was. After Sheila said something about tidal currents, Edith reckoned that her daughter was guessing that it might have been dumped in the sea.

Dowdall then came to the crucial bit.

'Was there anything in what she said that made you think Sheila had anything to do with the murder?'

The lying witness bends the truth to what they *wished* had happened whilst the truthful one tells it as it actually did, regardless of the consequences. As Dowdall waited with his pen poised, Edith thought carefully. Eventually, she shook her head. 'I really can't say. She certainly gave me the impression it wasn't just Tevendale on his own who did it, but knowing her, I think she might have said that to stop me from doing anything about it. She told me that she had 'a strong man' at her back and, when I asked if it was him, she nodded her head. She must have known that, had she said that Tevendale had killed Max on his own, I would have gone straight to the police. Believe me, Mr Dowdall, it was sheer hell keeping such a dreadful secret, but I would have for her sake.'

'So, apart from Sheila planning to move to Aberdeen, was there anything else that made you change your mind?'

Tears started running down Edith's face. 'If Sheila had stopped seeing Tevendale after the murder, I would have taken the secret to the grave with me for my beautiful lassie's sake!'

Dowdall let that sink in. 'I'm sorry, Mrs Watson. So that I fully understand what it is you're saying, did you think Sheila had something to do with Max's murder?'

Edith became business-like again, wiping her tears on a floral hanky she kept up her sleeve for such occasions after removing her little round glasses. 'I honestly don't know, Mr Dowdall. I suspect Sheila wanted me to think that she did, only to protect Tevendale. I know what my lass is like. She's loyal like me and most likely loved Max to begin with, in her own way. I had a bad feeling about him from the start, though, and when I woke up on 14 May, I sensed something was going to happen. That's my birthday you see, and when Sheila phoned me to wish me happy birthday, she sounded that dreamy way she sometimes gets.'

Dowdall tried to make sense of the information. 'You mean she sounded upset?'

'That and more. The real problem for Max Garvie – and he knew it – was that my daughter can't be false. Once he'd made her go with Tevendale, he must have known the marriage was over and there was no way back for him. She told me that Max played a game with her body, tossing a half crown to see whether he or Tevendale would sleep with her that night. My poor girl! Max told her that was all she was worth, 2 shillings and sixpence!'

According to her police statement, Max too had spoken openly to his mother-in-law, something that puzzled Dowdall. 'Can you assist me with this please, Mrs Watson? You've already been kind enough to have told me about the *rude* sex that Max wanted, but did he often confide in you in confidential matters?'

Edith nodded. 'He was like a little boy at times. He told me some things that went on between them I really didn't want to hear about. Things some American friend had told him were all the rage in the States, things that I never knew could or should happen to a wife. Understand this, Mr Dowdall, I'm not crying for Max Garvie or Brian Tevendale or even Sheila now, although I feel guilty about having to go to the police. I'm just sorry for those poor wee bairns and want to protect them from all the terrible things that can happen to them out there, the sort of things that happened to my lovely girl.'

So that he might understand the layout of the house, Dowdall asked Edith's permission to have a look upstairs. Edith led him up to the first floor and pointed out which room was what. Then she had the courtesy to leave him and go back downstairs again, telling him that she would probably be in the kitchen making the bairns' dinner. Dowdall sketched the layout of the first floor, carefully noting the locations of the bathroom, the children's bedroom, the master bedroom and the spare bedrooms. The landing at the top of the stairs opened out to a series of doors to the various rooms, as well as some cupboards that stored linen and towels. Turning right at the top of the stairs brought him to a corridor where the bedrooms were. Two doors to his left, another facing him and one to his right. Dowdall went into the master bedroom first. This was where the murder had occurred, and Dowdall ran what Sheila had told the police over in his head. On Max's side of the bed, nearer the door, there was a wash-hand basin with a mirror above it and a pull-down string above that, which presumably lit the strip light it was attached to. He could picture the now deceased head of the family standing there shaving, wearing a vest and trousers with the braces dangling down at his sides and shouting irascibly at one of the children to hurry up in the bathroom just along the corridor. Elsewhere in the spacious room were two large mahogany wardrobes, a tiled fireplace with a trace of ashes in the grate, a wicker chair and a bedside cabinet still with copies of *Country Life* and a few Mills and Boon type books on it, surely originally at Sheila's side of the now empty bedstead, which stood two feet proud of the wall. Expensive-looking blue and cream coloured flock wallpaper with a floral theme adorned the walls.

From his knowledge of the case, he knew that the furniture in the room had been moved at least twice since the murder over six months before, once by his client herself and a second time by the police when reconstructing the crime scene. He had an issue with the first part of that theory. How could she have moved the heavy wardrobes by herself? It just might have been possible if she had emptied them first, but his guess was that she had needed a certain young man's help to do so and would have to be persuaded to admit as much in line with the quasi-religious vow of silence she had elected to undertake to protect him.

Standing at the wall to the right of the wash-hand basin, he could see the outline of where the headboard had rested against it, etched in an impressed patterned outline of its upright, curved shape. A few feet above and to the left of the outline was a row of small nicks in the wallpaper, tiny white patches where the plaster of the wall showed through.

Despite Brian using a pillow to muffle the sound of the rifle's discharge, Max's lifeblood had obviously sprayed out onto the wall above and behind him, the spattering forming an almost perfect arc on the expensive wallpaper he alone had so carefully chosen. Or did the gruesome splatter get there when he was being bludgeoned into unconsciousness before he was shot? However it came to be there, Sheila had gone to the trouble of wiping away any marks she could see after noticing them when moving the furniture. It all sounded so

155

calculating in the cold light of day, yet it was all so slapdash with no pre-planning or realisation that forensic technicians would pick up on things that could not be seen by the naked eye, things that experience would tell them they should look for and had found, as evidenced by the miniscule slits in the wallpaper.

A cursory look around the spare room door confirmed that anyone lurking there with intent to commit murder would clearly run the risk, in the dark, of bumping into the various items stored there and would obviously draw unwelcome attention to themselves by the noise it would make.

A quick visit to the children's room next door to the main bedroom raised definite doubts about Sheila's involvement in the plot, though, in Dowdall's logical mind. Would she really have agreed to running the risk of them hearing the sounds of violence that brought their father's life to an abrupt end? Or was she beyond caring after years of torment?

Descending the stairs, Dowdall made his way to the other side of the house, where Edith was busily engaged in supervising bubbling pans and a pressure cooker with a continuous wisp of steam rising above it. It was all so curious. Both of them sought justice for the same person, one her mother and one her lawyer, but the closest to her by far was the very woman standing in front of him, fussing over a large Raeburn, yet she was also the reason why it had all come to light.

He thanked her most kindly for all her assistance, then asked for one more favour. Would he be able to have a proper look at the double garage from the inside? Edith undid her apron, moved some pots from the heat and led him through to the washhouse from the kitchen. Noticing a Yale lock on the connecting door from the garage to the house, Edith was able to tell him that it had been installed *after* the murder at Sheila's behest, as she had felt scared living in such a big, insecure house; from Dowdall's viewpoint, that also meant that entry could be gained to the house through the garage *without* a key on the night of the murder. And no-one inside the house had had to 'let someone in' that night either, as Peters claimed.

As he left, he detected a predictable air of despondency about this anxious, prematurely aged grandmother, as if she wanted to beseech him to make everything right again between mother and daughter. In return, he wanted to tell her one thing only – he would do his best, of course, but there were no guarantees after a jury had been empanelled that they would come to the 'right' decision, as that depended entirely on which side you were on. Instead, both Edith and Dowdall remained silent, apart from the usual pleasantries exchanged when parting.

As Dowdall sat filling in his notes in the car, Edith came out onto the driveway, clutching a piece of paper. Dowdall opened the door of the car and he could see she had been crying again.

She presented him with a letter from Buckingham Palace. It seems that Edith had tried to use what little Royal connection her family had – after their stay on the Balmoral Estate when William had been employed there some years before – by asking the Queen to help Sheila. Dowdall read the letter, then looked across at the desperate woman who had done the right thing by going to the police, then had taken the pathetic step of seeking the Monarch's help. Unsurprisingly, Her Royal Majesty had declined to become involved.

As he drove north to Stonehaven, Dowdall thought about what Edith had said. She had to be a truthful, credible witness, so what could be taken from her likely evidence that would help Sheila? He would meticulously note down all the points in her favour once all the facts were known, starting with who would come up with a plan to shoot their husband when the children were sleeping in the room next door and why would Alan Peters allege that Sheila had 'let them into' the house when there was no need to do so?

Dowdall arrived at the Royal Hotel in plenty of time, so he ordered a pot of tea and a sandwich as he sat at a window near the door. Along with everyone else in the lounge, he noticed Trudy as she walked in. A tall, blonde, short-haired woman wearing a mini skirt, she strode confidently towards him, her hand extended in anticipation of introducing herself. 'Gertrude Birse,' she announced in a loud voice, so that others might hear her and realise a celebrity was amongst them. 'You have to be the lawyer from Glasgow.'

Dowdall shook her hand, acknowledged his name and asked if she wanted some tea. Trudy shook her head, then asked if she was entitled to expenses for turning up, always a bad sign in his experience, when a witness makes that their top priority. Close up, he was struck by her brash confidence and boyish features. As she spoke, she looked around her as if trying to involve people at nearby tables in the conversation she and Dowdall were having. Uneasy with her brazen manner, Dowdall suggested they move to the empty seats at the foyer. Trudy looked a bit mystified, but agreed. In his haste, he left a cup of tea and a half-eaten sandwich on the table, Trudy glancing over her shoulder to smile at two men gawping at her nearby. Dowdall instantly disliked her.

He noticed that her behaviour changed when there was no audience to impress and she settled back in her chair as she answered his preliminary formalities. 'Yes, Gertrude Birse, maiden name Tevendale. Married to Alfred and have three children. He's a policeman with Aberdeen City police. Well, he was until recently.' She wrinkled her nose disapprovingly when she said her husband's name.

She had met the Garvies when they came to her house in

Aberdeen and Max had made it clear he was interested in her. She knew her brother Brian had already been sleeping with Mrs Garvie, so Max was *justified* in doing the same with her. Dowdall decided not to ask about her husband's reaction to his wife and a complete stranger flirting before his eyes, then embarking on a prolonged sex-based relationship with each other. As she spoke, Trudy was warming to her story and was obviously out to shock this apparently staid, older man, not realising that he had heard many a sordid tale down the years and hers was just another one of them.

'Max and I became lovers quite quickly and his wife could hardly complain after what she was doing with my brother. Anyway, I was able to satisfy him in ways she couldn't.' She paused, expecting him to seek further sleazy details, but Dowdall was too experienced to fall for it; no doubt she would tell him without him having to ask.

He was right. She spoke again because she had to.

'Because of that, we were adventurous in bed, and I think he appreciated it because he told me he had had more pleasure from me in two weeks than he had from her in all the time they were married.'

Dowdall deliberately kept his head down, writing what she said.

'I take it you'll have to know what it was he liked?' Dowdall continued writing without looking up. She persisted despite the lack of any encouragement on his part. 'I suppose I'll have to say it in court anyway. He wanted back passage sex and, because I was falling for him, I was able to give it to him.'

Dowdall remained outwardly impassive despite the words she had just uttered. *Because she was falling for him, she was able to give it to him.* Where had she learned that line from? She paused again and Dowdall briefly looked up from his notepad in time to see her wiping a non-existent tear away, as if rehearsing for her big moment in court.

'I'm sorry. I get upset thinking about him now and what she did in revenge.'

Dowdall kept his cool. 'I see. You think *Mrs Garvie* acted in revenge?'

Trudy was in full broken-hearted-victim flow. 'Must have. My brother would have done anything to please her. She's rich and ten years older than him. He was under her spell.'

It occurred to Dowdall that Max's two women could not have been more different. Trudy was as shallow as Sheila was deep. Before he spoke, Dowdall quickly banished a fleeting image of a lovestruck teenage version of Trudy on all fours with Max fiddling about behind her. 'When did you find out what had happened to Mr Garvie?'

Trudy play-acted again, wiping her eyes and blowing her nose loudly at the mention of her lover's murder. Her voice became quiet as she spoke. 'I'm not sure now. It's been a dreadful time for me, thinking of him and whether he suffered in his final moments ...'

His rising impatience was tempered by his objectivity. 'So, you can't be sure, then?' he asked trying to sound business-like and practical.

Trudy ran her hand through her short, dyed blonde hair as she gave the impression of searching for accuracy in her answer, as if rehearsing again for her starring role in the trial to come. 'As I've said, it really upsets me to think of him. Whether he loved me or not, I was devoted to him ...'

Dowdall decided he no longer wanted to give her a platform for her blatantly false performance, so he closed the notepad and replaced the top on his fountain pen. Realising their time was coming to an end, she blurted, 'I remember now. Brian told me the next morning.'

Dowdall closed his briefcase. 'Oh, you mean on the Wednesday? Was that in your house?'

'Yes, must have been.'

'So, who washed the dirty clothes Brian and his friend were wearing and what happened to the mattress from West Cairnbeg?'

Trudy was taken aback by his unexpected directness. 'Suppose it must have been me. I mean, it *was* me who washed Brian's clothes, oh and I think Fred got rid of the mattress.'

'Fred? Your policeman husband?'

Trudy was becoming sullen. 'Yes, my policeman husband,' she repeated flatly.

'Did you and Brian not go to West Cairnbeg and pick the mattress up on the Thursday, so you must have known about the murder very soon after it happened?'

This was not going as she had imagined, from being the glamorous star witness she thought she was going to be to having to face awkward questions. Trudy looked at her watch. 'Are you going to be much longer? I have an appointment with my solicitor ...'

'Sorry, that's all for now.' Dowdall packed the notepad in his briefcase.

'For now? So you might want to speak to me again?'

'I might. You don't mind, do you? It's so I can give my client proper advice.'

She got up, picked up her silver clutch bag and strode out of the hotel without speaking.

Dowdall drove southwards wondering how much damage an unpredictable witness like Gertrude Tevendale or Birse could do. What was her role in all of this? Her claim to be head over heels in love with the murdered man had to be bunkum, unless she had somehow managed to bypass all the milestones of life, the ones that a married mother of three children had no option but to recognise on her journey, the ones that tell her she needs to be realistic about her position in the lives of those around her and that teenage dreams were exactly that. Unless Trudy had managed to skip large swathes of the sort of learning necessary to ensure proper progress through life, she was playing out some fantasy about her allure to the opposite sex or was on an egotistical exercise to make sure she was the centre of attention. It would have made more sense if her docile-sounding husband had chosen to ditch her after the way she had behaved, but, seemingly true to form, he had meekly accepted her publicly known infidelity, then welcomed her back into hearth and home once it was all over. The riddle Dowdall might need to solve in time for her cross-examination by counsel was what her eccentric conduct had to do with his client, who clearly bore no ill-will towards her husband's erstwhile lover. It was to be something that would not be resolved until after the court case was well and truly over.

Alan Peters's voluntary statement and Brian's fictional rifle-grabbing scenario between Sheila and a sexually rampant Max aside, it occurred to Dowdall that he was in the unenviable position of acting for a client the prosecution alleged had actually done very little apart from murder by acquiescence. She had then helped build a case against herself by continuing to do nothing apart from covering up for the actions of others. The case was well and truly in the territory of the old adage that it's much harder to prove a negative than a positive, that the client *hadn't* done something rather than *had*. Previous experience told him that juries instinctively preferred cold, hard facts to belated, lame sounding explanations as to why no action had been taken when perhaps, in hindsight, it should have been.

All would become clearer – if never perfectly clear – in the end, but not necessarily at the conclusion of the trial.

Chapter 26:

HM Prison Craiginches, Aberdeen,

Tuesday, 12 November 1968

After several visits involving many miles and hours, Dowdall felt he had eventually gained Sheila's trust. The scepticism some 'first offenders' have for their legal adviser had disappeared. Talking to a stranger about domestic violence, threats of unwelcome sexual advances and sleeping with another man who had replaced a murdered husband in her affections was never going to be easy for her.

Dowdall knew that, so he had deliberately taken his time in introducing her to her leading counsel, Lionel Daiches QC. The other issue was that Daiches's diary was always full and finding time to travel to Aberdeen from his base in Edinburgh was difficult, so Dowdall arranged to pick him up outside Queen Street Station in Glasgow to drive him to Craiginches in Aberdeen. An outsider might puzzle over that arrangement. Surely it would have been easier for Daiches to have taken a train to Aberdeen and *then* been picked up by Dowdall, but what counsel said was rarely questioned; anyway, it was a three-or-four-hour opportunity for Dowdall to explain the finer points of the evidence against their mutual client. Unlike some counsel, Daiches sat in the front seat as the instructing agent drove north, rather than masquerade as aristocracy in the back, as at least one other had done to Dowdall when he picked him up at his home address.

They had worked together on cases before and Dowdall's

meticulous preparation had proved a valuable platform for Daiches's flowery rhetoric. As with many who chose constant court work as a profession, there was something of the actor about him; his overuse of obscure words and theatrical references was sometimes effective for the entirely wrong reasons, such as jurors acquitting an accused person on the basis that what they could make of the evidence was just too complicated for them to arrive at an appropriate decision. Daiches was a confident, dapper man who always wore striped trousers and a bowler hat – even when off duty – and he habitually carried an umbrella lest the weather be 'unpropitious'. To say it was raining outside would have been *passé* in Lionel's company. Those who got to know Daiches grew fond of him, but only after they realised his dismissive manner was his way of dealing with an overload of information, which, once digested, allowed him to relax and reveal an impish, self-deprecating sense of humour buried under decades of critical comparison with his intellectual younger brother, who was a prolific writer and professor of English literature.

Sheila later wrote that he *'was most distinguished-looking with beautiful silvery hair groomed to perfection'.* But, she added, *'he would appear more at home in a film set than in a court room'* and although charming, he *'lacked Mr Dowdall's warmth of personality and kindness'.*

By the time he arrived at the prison that day, Dowdall had discussed all the details of the evidence against her with both the client and counsel, and had decided it was necessary to lodge a notice incriminating her co-accused, in effect saying they, and not she, had murdered Max.

The other notice under discussion was more difficult; how far should they go in attacking the dead man's character? Starting from the premise that no-one should speak ill of the dead, they had to consider one aspect of the case very carefully, namely, what effect it would have if one of the defence teams went out of their way to show that the victim of the crime had acted like Max had actually done. Would the jury think allegations of sexual licence, drunken excess and domestic violence were overblown and possibly exaggerated when the man himself was not present to answer them? Another factor, of course, was the accused woman herself willingly engaging in an extra-marital affair with a co-accused, no matter how disinclined she had been to embark on it at the start. It would prove to be a fine balance requiring a lot of consideration.

At the consultation, Dowdall suggested they had no option but to give notice to the court that an attack on Max's character was necessary, the caveat being that it was up to Daiches to judge how far to go with it. It was worded:

Dowdall for the Second-named Pannel, Sheila Watson or Garvie, hereby gives notice that it is intended on behalf of the said Second-named Pannel to attack the character of the deceased Maxwell Robert Garvie in respect of his unnatural and perverted sexual practices.

When the notice was first typed up by Evelyn, Dowdall's secretary, she felt obliged to question its forthright terms, instead suggesting it be muted in some way such as 'in respect of sexual practices to which the Second-named Pannel had not consented', but she was overruled by a majority of two to one, the two having the added distinction of being seasoned legal practitioners. Evelyn consoled herself with the thought that she had at least tried to improve the notice and that her employer applauded and encouraged her input as a means to keep him – if not their senior counsel – grounded.

Sheila had the chance to study both men as they went over the legal details and evidential subtleties that might develop in the case. Dowdall was intense, focused and knowledgeable, whilst Daiches listened attentively as he occasionally ran a manicured hand through his hair and rubbed his chin as if seeking out unshorn stubble missed in that morning's no doubt fastidious ablutions. She realised how important it was that her leading counsel – the one who would be asking questions and addressing the jury – had as deep a knowledge of the case as the solicitor she had come to rely so much on already had. Perhaps sensing her thoughts, Dowdall broke off his conversation with counsel to explain to her that Daiches spent all his time in court and at this early stage necessarily knew less about the case than he did, something that would undoubtedly change before the trial, Daiches nodding and smiling at her as if to endorse Dowdall's words.

They moved on to what they called the Crown's 'batting order'. Sheila imaged a green and pleasant village cricket pitch with gentlemanly players insincerely applauding opposition efforts. Was that what it was like in the High Court of Justiciary? Once again, Dowdall seemed to anticipate her concerns and explained that the Crown could decide the order the accused appeared in on the indictment. 'Why would that matter?' she asked.

Daiches remained slightly aloof, still pushing his hair back at the sides and checking that his beard hadn't grown since he last checked, as Dowdall explained the implications.

'I, sorry, we, think the prosecution have made it a priority that you are to be convicted. With Peters's name first on the indictment, he will have to give evidence, should he choose to do so, before you do and we can expect him to say that you let the pair of them into the house, gave them a drink and told them when your husband was asleep.'

Sheila was indignant. 'Why would the prosecutor do that, Mr Dowdall? I knew nothing about what Brian was going to do that night and that poor boy Alan is terrified of him. He'll do anything Brian says, starting with even driving him to

West Cairnbeg that night.'

Dowdall was as patient as ever. 'I know, Mrs Garvie, I know. The point is that if Peters gives evidence, then you give evidence, that means that Tevendale can then add his tuppence worth, which also contradicts what you say happened. Your version is sandwiched between theirs and the last thing the jury will hear is that you were at least part of the plan.'

Sheila was dismayed to hear her legal team's pessimistic angle on this potentially important aspect of the case that she was unaware of. 'Is there not a rule about what order the accused appear in, such as age? And can the Crown act in this way? It's unfair.'

'Yes, they sometimes put the accused in age order, in which case your name would be first,' Dowdall explained, 'but alas there is nothing we can do about their choice of order.'

Daiches then spoke, illustrating the point by waving a copy indictment just above desk height. 'Mr Dowdall and I discussed your case as we travelled here and we are both of the mind that the prosecution team is going all out to convict you. They must be truly confident about snaring Tevendale already, so have to work out the best way of catching you as well. That the Solicitor General himself is conducting the case indubitably implies that they are intent on securing convictions in respect of all three pannels.'

For the first time, Sheila realised how different senior counsel was from her solicitor. His accent was plummy and he had much of the showman about him. Why use five words when ten could suffice, indeed?

'They are attempting to turn you into Lady Macbeth,' he continued, 'with Tevendale as Macbeth and you giving him the courage to perform the evil deed.'

Sheila had to react. 'There was no need for me to persuade Brian to do anything. The two of them hated each other. Maxie had Brian attacked twice. Brian talked of ways of killing Maxie either in his plane or his car. I was in the middle. Some plot! Maxie wasn't even meant to be going to Stonehaven that night and his plans changed at teatime when my brother phoned the house. If what Mr Dowdall tells me is right, there is no evidence of an outgoing call that night to tell any co-conspirators about a change of plan, so surely that supports what I said to the police as soon as I found out Brian said *I* had shot Maxie?'

'Ah, yes, but they are going to say that because you spent three months covering up what Tevendale and his accomplice did, it makes you a *socius* in the crime and prior involvement can then be inferred by the jury.'

Daiches's words had an effect. She paused as she considered them. 'Mr Dowdall has already mentioned that, and I realise that aspect of the case has to be explained. I'm certainly guilty of feeling morally responsible for what Brian did. He did it not just for himself, but for me as well, because of the man Maxie had become and because I had allowed Brian to fall in love with me even before I fell for him.'

'And what was your reaction to what Tevendale said to the police? Does that alter your view of how this case should be approached? For instance, he says you called him after you shot your husband accidentally?' Daiches deliberately chose more prosaic language to make sure he got his point across.

'That doesn't make sense. Had I shot Maxie accidentally, why would I not call the police or an ambulance?' Sheila protested. 'An accident is an accident.'

Daiches leaned forward with his arms outstretched to emphasise the importance of the point. 'So why not call the police after Peters and Tevendale left?'

Sheila was becoming uneasy about the way the consultation was going and had begun to feel as if her version was being doubted and questioned. 'Because Brian must have honestly thought he was doing the right thing by me and knew I would never let him down. He did it for me!'

Back in the Bentley, as Dowdall switched on the ignition and pulled the starter, he let slip a worrying thought. 'How much can be done for a client when *she* adjudges herself to be guilty?'

Daiches sighed. 'I do fear for her. Three irreconcilable variations on the events of one fatally memorable night on a rural Scottish farm. It really should be one for Lord Peter Wimsey!'

Two days before the trial started, members of the flying club Max had helped found at Fordoun unveiled a plaque in his honour. Whether their gesture would have been made *after* the evidence in the case began might be questioned, but following the trial's conclusion, on 11 December 1968, neighbouring farmers and suppliers organised a petition to 'clear Max's name' after the 'slurs' of the trial had tarnished his reputation. Part of it read:

We who have been friends, neighbours, business associates and employees of Maxwell Garvie over a considerable number of years, wish it to be known that we deplore the character assassination of one who contributed so much to the general good of the community of which he was a respected member.

Does anyone *really* know anyone else?

Were Evelyn's misgivings correct and had the attack on Max's character gone too far?

Chapter 27:

Aberdeen High Court, Union Street, Aberdeen,

Tuesday, 19 November 1968

Sheila awoke from a fitful sleep when the cell door opened and a peak capped female warder brought in a powder blue suit that Edith had handed in a few days before. 'Yer mother seems to think yer going on some fashion parade, *Mrs Garvie*,' she said in a smug voice. 'Well, she's wrong. You and lover boy are in the dock today!'

It was not an attempt at humour.

Sheila had only recently dozed off after hours of listening to a powerful wind outside and watching a pitch-black night turn into a hesitant grey morning through the small, frosted glass window high up in her cell. Just before waking, she had been back in West Cairnbeg, sitting at her knitting machine looking out towards the garden where her girls were drawing bees and mayflies, all busily making the best of their short lives. Instant reality brought a heavy heart with it and it was now time to face the nightmare she dreaded.

A breakfast of lukewarm tea and a greasy Lorne sausage on a dry roll over, she changed into her court suit. Mr Dowdall's advice had even extended to how she presented to the jury. In his own clumsy, paternalistic way he had explained that it was really up to her how she looked, but 'in his humble opinion' there was a danger the women on the jury might instantly dislike her if she looked too *chic*. Sheila knew what he meant and appreciated his words, but she valued his legal experience more than his knowledge of the female mind and *haute couture*. She had already decided that *any* change of outfit during the trial was likely to make the newspapers – along the lines of 'Murder Wife Shows Off Wardrobe in Dock' – and so settled on wearing one suit throughout the whole case, although that, too, would probably lead to snide comment.

The same warder appeared in her cell at exactly 8 a.m. 'Right, *Mrs Garvie,* fashion show over, the Black Maria's waiting over at B Hall for all those lucky enough to take their chances before juries today. Your travelling companion today is Big Jess Cameron, but she's up for breach and police assault again at the Burgh Court. She's definitely not in your league!'

As Sheila clip-clopped down the metal stairs in her heels, some prisoners shouted messages of encouragement whilst others wolf-whistled before she disappeared from sight. Sheila took her seat in the rear of the prison van alongside a female guard and the other prisoner, who simple-mindedly broke into a wide, toothless grin before she reached out and touched Sheila's hand, calling her *Mrs Garvie* and wishing her luck. It was all so alien to her, and she felt numb inside.

Sheila herself later described the scene as the van drove along Union Street on its way to the court:

I could see the excited crowds gathered in the streets around the courthouse as I arrived. Hundreds of people had queued for hours on that cold, damp winter's day in the hope of getting a seat on the public benches. The hostile, disapproving eyes of the women and the gaping, eager faces of the men etched their reflections on my memory as they pushed and jostled for better positions to see this disreputable woman who had brought shame and disgrace to her family and had defamed the very soil of the Mearns.

There was only one case set down for the Aberdeen 'circuit' on 19 November 1968 before the Honourable Lord Thomson and that was *Her Majesty's Advocate against Alan Peters, Sheila Watson or Garvie and Brian Gordon Tevendale,* all designated as Prisoners in the Prison of Aberdeen. They were indicted that –

They did on 14th or 15th May 1968 in the farmhouse occupied by Maxwell Robert Garvie at West Cairnbeg, Kincardineshire, assault said Maxwell Robert Garvie and did strike him on the head with the butt of a rifle or an iron bar or other similar instrument, discharge at him a loaded rifle and shoot him on the head and did murder him and you Brian Gordon Tevendale did previously evince malice and ill-will against him.

The archaic sounding appendage to the charge – evincing malice and ill-will – was added to allow the Crown to lead evidence of warnings made by Brian about Max having an accident whilst driving or flying.

'Circuit' justice began with the Stewart kings hanging criminals or opponents as they travelled round the country and *Her Majesty's Advocate* v *Peters and others* began with vestiges of times long gone, the judge inspecting a kilted Guard of Honour from the city's Scottish Infantry Depot, outside the court building in Union Street.

This was 'circuit' justice as it used to be, miscreants answering for their crimes in unsettling, imposing settings and judges 'protected' from potentially vengeful locals by detachments of troops.

The queue for admission by the public had begun at 6.45 a.m. that morning and by 9 a.m. the police decided to erect barriers as a crowd of more than a hundred had appeared. When the doors of the court building eventually opened, a further two hundred prurient, scandal-loving members of the public had to be turned away.

That seventy-five prospective jurors were in attendance when only fifteen of them could be selected for service seemingly reflected the no-nonsense approach the authorities were taking. Even with each party's legal objections taken into account, there would still be plenty judgemental citizens to go round.

After bright lights were switched on to combat the gloomy November light from outside, trumpets sounded in the courtroom as the Macer, Mr Gibson, entered carrying the High Court Mace followed by Lord Thomson and a chaplain whose task was to seek divine guidance in the pursuit of justice. In a sombre voice – and in what amounted to a plea for judicial redundancy – he prayed unrealistically that 'the day be hastened when all violence and strife are banished from our land,' something still awaiting unlikely fulfilment.

Brian was the first to appear out of the trapdoor from the cells below; he seemed unimpressed with the scene that met him, not even looking around the courtroom as he took his seat beside a policeman in white gloves with a drawn baton in hand. Sheila was next to emerge. Dowdall's judgement about the importance of her appearance proved to be correct. It wasn't just the women on the jury who would take an interest in what she wore. The rows of journalists noted she was 'hatless' when she emerged from the cells below to instantly become the centre of attention. Had she actually worn a hat to climb the sixteen steps from the cell area to the dock, that, too, would have been worthy of comment. The vestiges of a link still existed in the public mind between a woman's virtue, respectability and hat-wearing, and Sheila had inevitably failed the first test. The signs of a fallen woman were everywhere if you knew where to look for them.

Alan Peters appeared last, and, by contrast, he seemed

pale and unsure of himself. He looked around and blinked uncertainly beneath his boyish, fair quiff. Glancing in the direction of the unempanelled jurors, Alan's lead counsel, R R Taylor QC, noticed them staring at the accused, him hoping they were noting the stark contrast between the erstwhile lovers' apparent nonchalance at facing a murder charge and the gawky, nervous adolescent-looking young man sitting in pole position in the dock.

Taylor, an academic lawyer drawn into the drama of High Court cases, had appeared for the last man to hang in Scotland, Henry John Burnett, in Aberdeen five years before. He had resolved to learn from the trauma of that experience, as if exorcising that awful memory by continuing to act for accused in murder trials. He had lectured in International Private Law at Edinburgh University and, as he held a doctorate, was addressed as 'Dr' throughout the case, at his own insistence. He was regarded as a cold, unemotional operator, although his representation of accused in serious criminal cases perhaps suggests otherwise, particularly as he had offered his services to the Poor Roll administration. A tall, austere man with a large, pointed nose that supported small half glasses, Taylor resembled an inquisitive blackbird in his long black gown with his head cocked to one side as he listened to witnesses' answers.

As his client maintained his innocence and said that *both* Sheila and Brian committed the murder, Taylor was set for a clash with the flamboyant Daiches, who would undoubtedly charm and flummox the jury in equal measure with classical and Shakespearean references. Accordingly, and so that he could appear to be spontaneous when the need arose, Taylor had secretly brushed up on the literature Daiches was known to favour when addressing the jury. The client's instructions were clear: Tevendale had used Peters, *suborned* him, even. Had the Bard not used that very word – 'suborned' – in the Scottish Play? That was bound to get a mention and was something to keep in reserve for when Daiches embarked on his inevitable literary tour. Suborned; 'induced to commit an unlawful act'. 'Induced'? Well, maybe not. More 'enticed'.

Enticed with a false pretence of friendship.

K J Cameron, Advocate, acted for Tevendale, and was on his own with no support apart from his instructing solicitor. As junior counsel, acting for a murder accused – particularly one who was clearly guilty – was highly unusual. Senior counsel had given the client advice he had not liked along the lines of putting his hands up to actually killing the deceased, but Brian Gordon Tevendale was not for pleading, even if it dragged his co-accused down with him – or perhaps *because* it would. Senior's parting shot to Cameron was that it was a hopeless case and that Tevendale would be convicted unanimously, barring the miracle of a legal submission about fairness succeeding. That Aberdeen CID had threatened Tevendale, then beaten him up so much that he falsely confessed to moving the dead man's body before leading them directly to it in an impossible to find hiding place was such a flight of fantasy that the judge would have to be deluded to uphold the submission as well-founded. So good luck, young Cameron, you are on your own.

The original prosecutor – called the Advocate Depute – was hastily superseded by the Solicitor General once the 'facts' of the case became common currency around Crown Office. He was a dumpy little man who could appear deceptively friendly, his red cheeks contrasting with the snow-white hair that curled from underneath a misshapen court wig, dark brown with age. His jolly laugh and appetite for socialising belied a ruthless court persona.

Being neither a solicitor nor a general, he was tenacious and forceful, unsuccessful opponents sometimes saying his doggedness was down to him compensating for his lack of height and his squeaky, high-pitched voice. The holder of the office was known universally as the Sol-Gen, but Ewan Stewart baulked at the lack of respect implied in the shortened title and made it known that he would take disciplinary action against any Crown employee who was reported as using his truncated description. Some said he was the holder of the Military Cross, which might have meant that he *earned* the respect of those who met him, but in practical terms the suffix MC QC somehow did not work like that, with people tending to find authority figures who demand acknowledgement for their achievements as more tedious than admirable. Others claimed the letters stood for 'Master of Ceremonies'.

His approach to the case was, as Dowdall and Daiches had anticipated, to go all out to snare Sheila Garvie rather than Alan Peters, Brian Gordon Tevendale as good as convicted in advance. That counsel for Peters had lodged a notice incriminating both Sheila and Brian was obviously good news for the Crown, as cut-throat defences always are. Now there would be at least *two* counsel prosecuting her. Both Dowdall and Daiches were grateful that Tevendale, at least, had refrained from claiming his co-accused had pulled the trigger.

During the trial, the many members of the press who were present were obviously keen to take full advantage of the lurid details they knew must emerge, one angle being that nothing – including Max – could get in the way of Sheila's love for Brian. It was reported that the two accused lovers were keen to marry regardless of the outcome of the case, and that an application for permission to do so was being, or had been, lodged with the Scottish Home and Health Department; no such request was ever made.

It was what was to be reported *after* the trial that helped

176

shape people's perception of the truth.

And by that time, of course, the jury had returned their verdicts.

Chapter 28:

The Evidence, The First Days, Aberdeen High Court,

Tuesday, 19 - Wednesday, 20 November 1968

Geddes had served in the Gordons beside the Macer, Mr Gibson, in the last year of the war. 'Gibbie' and he had together seen the destruction of Caen and the devastation that world conflict had had on German cities. Unlike Geddes, the unflappable Gibbie had hardly seemed to notice either the suffering war brought or the euphoria of final victory. Back home in Aberdeen, Geddes had joined the police whilst Gibbie had gone back to being a heating engineer so, he claimed, he would never have to wear his ill-fitting demob suit.

In his world, Gibbie saw things simply. Nothing was complicated and all things usually fitted together. People were either good spuds or basket cases, men were either trustworthy or vagabonds, whilst women were in three categories, skelfs, sumphs or bonny. When genuinely surprised, he was in the habit of borrowing his fisherman cousin's phrase: 'Well, bugger me through ma oilskins!'

Geddes followed the trial in the press even before he gave evidence about going to see Sheila Garvie at West Cairnbeg and Edith's momentous visit to the office on 16 August. After that, occasional evening meetings with Gibbie in a pub just around the corner from the court helped fill in the real story about what was going on. That they met in the East Neuk Bar was more to do with convenience than irony, since it was there that both Brian and Sheila had served customers earlier that year.

When Gibbie originally told him that he had applied to be a Macer, Geddes doubted his friend's suitability and judgement. Tall and slightly awkward as a young private during the war, Gibbie had expanded comfortably in middle age, the trimmed but full moustache adding an air of Edwardian firmness to his overall appearance. Moving to Edinburgh had been the easy bit, as Mrs Gibson came from Leith, but the idea of Gibbie consorting with lawyers and judges had made Geddes uncomfortable, Gibbie responding by pointing out that he was perfect for the job as 'naebody' would 'ken' what he was really thinking. How would those learned judges and counsel cope with Gibbie's earthy sense of humour and forthright views? The answer, Geddes later discovered, was that they did so effortlessly, some even seeking his opinions in a roundabout, conversational way on the evidence they had both heard. 'What did you make of the complainer then, Mr Gibson? Do you think the jury believed her?'

'They'd have to be damned fools if they did,' he answered on one notable occasion just before a unanimous acquittal.

Not that Gibbie wasn't above joining in the theatre that High Court trials sometimes became. Daiches himself occasionally recounted the impression Gibbie had made in one memorable case when he asked the Macer for Crown label ten; Gibbie had solemnly retrieved the label – an ornate handled sword in an equally ornate scabbard – and showed it to the witness. Daiches normally finished the story, 'When I requested Mr Gibson unsheathe the weapon, he did so in the manner of Achilles slaying Troilus, the sudden withdrawal of the sword causing a prolonged ringing sound as he held it vertically in front of his face whilst standing to attention. Needless to say, the jury were awestruck with the imagery of the scene, Mr Gibson appearing before them in the manner of a warrior from *The Iliad*.'

After the first week of the Garvie trial, Gibbie's summary of the evidence was succinct. 'Before you were called,' he said to Geddes, 'there were one or two gey funny things. The first witness knew Garvie from them both being in thon SNP – the ones that imagine that whisky and oil are going to make us free of the English! Can you imagine anyone falling for that? Anyways, the mannie met Garvie the last night he breathed air in God's own country. It turns out, he said something awful strange just before he drove home in that racing car of his, just afore he left the Marine. He told him he was driving home to West Cairnbeg because he had to go as he "couldnae keep them waiting". Now, Geddes, you're the bobby, not me, what in the Lord's name does that mean? You know the case, what would Garvie say that for?'

Before Geddes could offer a view, Gibbie had gulped most of the malt whisky that had awaited his attention for much longer than Geddes had anticipated, and then answered his own question.

'If you want my opinion, he was up to something. A man like Garvie drove home most nights three sheets to the wind and here he was, after two drams, off to make sure he wasn't keeping them waiting? So, who's he not keeping waiting?'

Geddes had puzzled over that too, earlier in the enquiry. Was it a rendezvous with someone? Was it a grubby love tryst with a couple of desperate streetwalkers in a lay-by on the way home? Had he arranged to meet some others who didn't show up, just as *he* hadn't, to meet Sheila's brother William? Whatever it was, it was unlikely to have been concern over seeing his wife and children before they went to bed. He had left the pub at around 10.15 p.m. and, barring drunken accidents, it would have taken him twenty minutes to drive back to West Cairnbeg. For what it was worth, Sheila claimed he arrived home *after* 11 p.m., so had he waited somewhere in vain for someone who failed to show up, then simply gone home? Why would a twenty-minute trip take close to an hour?

Gibbie continued to hold court in a quiet corner of the bar. 'Alec – the mannie that runs the spare parts centre – he got Garvie's car started at Fordoun Flying Club. Imagine! A flying club at Fordoun! You'd think it was Biggin bloody Hill or somethin'! Anyways, when he gets it started, the choke's well out an' the wipers are on.'

Gibbie stopped to take a second, final gulp from his glass. Geddes thought better of telling him about information to come, about young Tevendale dropping the 1600E off at the airfield; instead, he went to the bar and ordered another round of whisky.

Drink replenished, Gibbie moved on to the evidence of the dead man's sister. He reckoned the whole court, even the shorthand writer, could sense the bad blood between Mrs Kerr, the sister, and Mrs Garvie, the wife. The two women had fallen out in 1964 and had not made up since, with the result that Max had visited her and her husband on his own and what she knew about the Garvies' marital problems came from what her brother had told her. She said she knew about Sheila having 'a gay old time to herself' by going about with other men. Gibbie had thought it an odd thing to say, as he had understood Mrs Garvie had slept with only one man – Tevendale – 'as if that wasn't bad enough'.

'Mind you, after the lovers ran off to Bradford together, Garvie said she would get bored with Tevendale and he would take her back then.'

Geddes wondered about that. 'It was Max's idea they got together in the first place, so you might think he had no choice. Is that what the sister said – he would take her back?'

'Yes, the man must have been awfully mixed up. One day he's wanting her to sleep with someone else and the next he's greetin' about her running off with him. The sister, Mrs

Kerr, was all for Max telling her she wasn't getting back, but he said he would always take her back, and that's what happened. Can you imagine? Could you take your wife back after she ran off with another man?'

Geddes coughed to avoid answering, the image of the ultra-sensible, tweedie Irene Geddes having a lover being unlikely, the idea already strangely floated by Essie at an earlier stage in the enquiry. Should Geddes be worried about her living a double life or was the whisky having an unusual effect, he wondered?

Gibbie carried on. 'Well, getting back to the dead man's sister, Mr Daiches showed how much Garvie had tried to make out to her that he'd never done anything wrong. Mrs Kerr, Garvie's sister, answered "no" to all the questions he threw at her – like was she aware that her brother had actively encouraged Tevendale to sleep with his wife, did she know her brother gave Tevendale money to take her out, did she know her brother and a policeman's wife were going away with Tevendale and Mrs Garvie for weekends of sex and did she know about strange goings-on at West Cairnbeg? He saved the best till last, though. Waving a sheaf of papers about, he asked about Garvie's interest in photography and the poor lassie thought she could maybe answer one of his questions with a "yes". Oh aye, says she, I knew fine well he liked photography, she says, he took a great photo of my house once! Of course, she'd walked right into that one and had no idea Garvie was taking dirty pictures of his wife and apparently showing them to everyone in the pub. Mind you, she did manage to get it in that she had reported her brother missing before his wife did! Well, as you'll know, that Mr Daiches is some man for the big gestures, standing with his hand on his hip and getting the cleaning lady, Mrs Smart, to agree with him that the master bedroom wasn't a "Bluebeard's Chamber". The woman, like everyone else, clearly had no idea what she was agreeing to!'

Gibbie looked at his watch, then stood up to order more drinks. He came back from the bar with one for the road for each of them as 10 p.m., closing time, loomed. 'I've just got time to tell you about that poor wee woman, Edith Watson. Does she not just stand there when Mr Stewart, the Solicitor General, asks her a couple of questions? He asks her again in that funny, whiny wee voice of his and the poor wifie just stares at him. She's got a hanky in her hand she dabs her eyes with all the time and she's got a brown velvet hat on and a heavy cream coloured coat on as if she's going for a walk on the beach on a stormy day. Of course, you'll know it was all because of her that they got caught. When she was called to give evidence, Tevendale snarled "Judas" at her as if *he* would be likely to know the scriptures, but there was no need for him to get angry at her. She was angry enough with herself and already knew fine well what she'd done might get her own lassie a life sentence. I said to His Lordship Mrs Watson couldnae be faulted for doing the right thing and he agreed. But she just stood there with her mouth open as the Solicitor General started to get annoyed at her for not speaking. Then she comes away with a low moaning sound, starts sobbing loudly and collapses. Big Geordie Buchanan and the rest of the court squad had to pick her up and then she was taken away in an ambulance, the wee prosecutor shaking his head as if she's putting it on to avoid giving evidence, but he's wrong, because the next day she speaks up fine about what Mrs Garvie told her the morning after Garvie was done in.'

'That's the bit I don't get,' Geddes said. 'If Sheila Garvie had been involved in plotting to kill her man, why bother telling her mother about it?'

'You know, the judge sometimes likes a good blether after court and that's exactly what he said too. And another thing, Mrs Garvie thought her man's body was in the sea – well, that's what Mrs Watson was told and there's no reason to disbelieve anything she said. So how come Sheila Garvie didn't know he had been buried at Lauriston?'

'I've thought about that too,' Geddes said, 'and I'm not sure that proves anything, really. She might have told Tevendale not to tell her where the body was just so she could say she wasn't part of the murder plot.'

'Aye, that could be right, but did you know why Edith Watson went to the police after three months of total silence? I mean the real reason? Because of Garvie!'

To begin with, Geddes was puzzled. The way he remembered it, Edith had come clean about the murder because Sheila had told her about moving to the city.

'Let me explain,' Gibbie continued. 'That's why the poor woman has to be telling the truth. You see, before he was killed, Garvie said to Edith that she had to promise him that if anything happened to him, *she* was to look after the children and they were to have nothing to do with Tevendale. Then, on 15 August does Sheila Garvie not turn round and tell her mother she's thinking of moving to Aberdeen, obviously to be nearer her lover, and that's when Mrs Watson cracked and went to you lot at Laurencekirk!'

Geddes understood what he meant, but didn't really think Max's wish that Edith become the children's guardian was the real reason she turned up at the office that day, it was more to stop them from having to leave West Cairnbeg. *Interesting how some people see things so differently from others when they've heard the exact same words being spoken.*

A loud hand bell sounded as the barman shouted 'Gentlemen, that's ten o'clock! Time's up! Your lovely wives are waiting to give you a goodnight kiss afore they're off to bed! Pay no heed to the curlers and face cream and just think of her the first time you saw her!'

Gibbie drained the whisky and placed the empty glass on the bar, then spoke to the barman on the way out. 'Ye

know you're not making going home any easier for these
poor men!'

Chapter 29:

The Evidence, Day 3, Aberdeen High Court,

Thursday, 21 November 1968

Unlike Essie, Irene Geddes did not think her husband's fascination with the Garvie case was because he had an unrequited crush on Sheila. She understood how enrapt her husband could be when he was involved in a big case, so was not too surprised when he arrived home just before she went to bed with *The People's Friend* and told her Gibbie had reserved him a seat at the trial the next day, one of his days off.

The following morning Geddes got up as if he was on an early shift and was washed, shaved and suited before she got out of bed. 'Today should be interesting,' he said as he brought her tea and buttered toast to her side of the bed. 'There's going to be some medical evidence and Trudy Birse is being called.'

Mrs Geddes's policy was to be attentive when he was like this, not because she wanted to seem that interested herself, but because she knew it helped him get over his obsession with a case more quickly. A comment here and there might make it sound like she was more engrossed than she was. 'Of course, did I not read somewhere that Mrs Birse's husband resigned from the force after his role in the case came out?'

'Yes, PC Alfred Birse, now ex-constable. I daren't tell you what his colleagues used to say the "PC" stood for, being married to Gertrude Tevendale, but the first word's "poor".'

186

After he left, Irene thought about how her husband became so absorbed in his work and was glad for him, despite her complaints about the long hours he put in. Not many of his work colleagues would use one of his valuable free days to sit in on a trial. *I should maybe make more of an effort and really listen to him when he talks about his work.* With that, she finished her toast, sipped her tea and settled in to read her magazine.

Geddes was in a side door of the court, courtesy of Gibbie, by 8.30 a.m. and was seated by 9 a.m., just before the sweetie-eating hordes arrived to claim their ringside venues.

The day began with the Solicitor General announcing that one of the jurors was ill and moving to continue with fourteen, something generally popular with the defence as the Crown still had to persuade at least eight of their number to convict.

Then, a colleague of Geddes's, a fellow Detective Sergeant called Henderson, gave evidence about test firing the .22 in the West Cairnbeg farmhouse. When the rifle was fired with the door closed in the master bedroom, Henderson had heard nothing whilst standing at the bottom of the stairs. Geddes wondered exactly what that proved. At best, it might mean the sleeping children in the bedroom next door would not necessarily have heard their father being murdered, but, unless the accused had carried out a similar test before the fateful night and knew about the muffled acoustics, it all seemed a bit pointless. After all, when the older children were spoken to, neither of them had heard anything, so carrying out the rifle firing exercise almost suggested *their* credibility was also being tested, although, at four years old, the son was deemed too young anyway, and wasn't questioned. The same officer spoke about the photographs taken outside and inside the farmhouse, the evidence led by the Crown's assistant, Mr Morton, who had originally been scheduled to conduct the trial himself. What the photographs showed was that access to the interior of the house *could* be gained through the double garage at the end of the driveway that ran along the front. The 'magic eye' that was meant to allow Max to operate the garage door remotely from his car eventually stopped working, so it had to be opened manually, which it could easily be from the outside. Once inside the garage, a doorless aperture on the right led into the area that housed the central heating boiler, then there was a door that led directly into the washhouse; by the time the police photographer took the images that were presented to the jury, that door had a Yale lock fitted to it, although evidence to come was to show that it had not been there on the night of the murder. Once through the washhouse, there was a passageway that led directly to the kitchen and the front of the house.

The photographs from upstairs showed the master bedroom directly to the left at the top of the stairs, the children's room just a few feet away to the right; the view from the entrance to the master bedroom showed three further doors to the right of the top of the stairs and the bathroom door beyond them at the far end of the corridor.

Geddes was aware that his CID colleagues had spoken to the Garvie girls, who could have been competent witnesses in the case, but they were unable to add anything of note. Seeing the upstairs layout again reminded Geddes just how close they had been to the sinister events of that night. He also imagined Sheila hiding inside the locked bathroom door at the opposite end of the corridor from where Tevendale and Peters were engaged in ending Max Garvie's life, then her kneeling outside the children's bedroom, clinging desperately to the door handle.

DS Henderson was then asked about a search he conducted of Brian Tevendale's room at Birkhall Parade in Aberdeen. As if the Crown needed to present more evidence against him, the Detective Sergeant confirmed he had found two live and two spent .22 bullets and, intriguingly, a book wrapped in an expanding bracelet with 'B G Tevendale' engraved on it along with his former address in Stonehaven at Jacks Buildings. The book was called *Death Trap* and the officer managed to remain impassive as he confirmed the title. The assistant prosecutor then enquired about the book's contents and instead of consisting of typed pages, the officer opened it to reveal it had been hollowed out to conceal a hypodermic syringe and a bottle of clear liquid that someone either in Police Headquarters or in Crown Office presumably decided against having analysed. Was Brian diabetic? Was he a drug user? By not having the liquid tested, the jury – and Geddes again – were left to speculate why that evidence had been led at all. Geddes had also heard about a letter Brian had sent to Sheila that showed his bizarre thought processes, although she had refused to 'betray' Brian by handing it over. It would have been good, admissible evidence against him, as he likened himself to the Four Horsemen of the Apocalypse; as Conquest he had 'won' her from Max, as Slaughter he had killed him, as Death he had left his body to rot underground. Famine would be living apart from Sheila should he ever be jailed for murdering Max. *Little wonder*, Geddes thought, *that Brian's original counsel despaired of his client's impulsive boastfulness.*

Dr McBain, forensic pathologist, was called next, and the Solicitor General resumed the lead. Geddes had heard that those medics who are not involved in that particular field often struggle to understand why anyone would choose to spend their time cutting up dead people rather than treat the living. The long-lasting, macabre impact of the Burke and Hare trial must have had something to do with it, Geddes thought as the doctor took the oath; that said, Geddes had heard an explanation from more than one casualty surgeon that the departed were much better patients than live ones and far less likely to cause trouble. The pathologist came across as perfectly normal as he explained how he had crawled into the culvert at Lauriston in August and had seen the decomposing body of 'a muscular male'. He and a colleague had later carried out an autopsy on the body and had concluded that death was due to a gunshot wound to the back of the head to the left of the right ear, the bullet fracturing the skull before embedding itself in the dead man's brain. It seemed a single, low calibre slug had ended his life. *You might think Tevendale would have fired another just to make sure,* Geddes reflected, a second disfigured piece of metal also found at autopsy causing him and others to consider that maybe two bullets *were* fired, the second incredibly following the exact same path as the first.

He looked towards the dock. Brian was listening intently, like a medical student eagerly soaking in anatomical knowledge; Alan Peters might as well have been sitting on a bus in Union Street as he sat staring downwards, his hands clasped together. Sheila, though, had gone a greyish white and was gulping nervously. As the witness went on to explain that the brain had been removed for further examination, the Solicitor General stepped back and appeared to check something in his notes. He then looked across at the witness and asked him to have label number fourteen in front of him. Gibbie carried a large cardboard box from the production table and placed it beside the witness box. Looking at the jury, the prosecutor then asked the witness to remove the contents of the box in order to illustrate what he had just described. Dr McBain reached in and lifted a yellowing, grinning skull, which he held up to show where the fracture had occurred.

Loud gasps came from the public benches. Geddes looked at the dock again and noticed Sheila quietly dabbing her bloodless face with a hanky as she stared fearfully at the spectre. Dowdall turned in his chair and spoke to her, then conferred with Daiches, who immediately stood up and asked for an adjournment due to his client 'feeling indisposed'. His Lordship seemed reluctant to interrupt proceedings, asking, 'What *now*?' before allowing 'a short adjournment'.

As she descended the sixteen stairs to the cells below, a policewoman held Sheila's arm to steady her. Geddes went back over what he had just seen. The doctor had been clear enough. He had even demonstrated on the back of his own head where the bullet had gone in and roughly where it had come to rest. He had gone over all he had done in detail and had explained the cause of death, so was it really necessary for the prosecutor to have the witness lift Max's skull out of the box? It seemed to Geddes that the Crown had deliberately set out to shock the court or had pandered to the press to produce a headline along the lines of 'Murder Victim's Skull Comes Back To Haunt Accused'. Did the Solicitor General have a hint of a smile on his face when Daiches's client felt 'indisposed'?

Just before midday, Gertrude Tevendale or Birse was called as the next witness for the prosecution. Gibbie led her in, announcing her name before she took the oath to tell the truth. She was wearing a new two-piece suit, which was dark brown with white flecks, the jacket collar a brown velvet and the skirt above the knee, showing her long legs. Her blonde hair had recently been styled into a small bouffant with a short fringe and had been lightened from its original mousy brown. In repeating the oath, she appeared eager to get on with things. Geddes imagined her as an overconfident teenager going for her first job interview or a pools winner about to divulge her spending plans to the press. She seemed energised and not the least bit nervous. When the judge warned her that she need not answer questions that tended to show she had committed adultery – in line with the law – she

191

readily agreed that she would do so. *Why wouldn't she? This is her big moment,* Geddes thought.

As the Solicitor General crossed the room to begin his examination in chief, Geddes noticed her exchanging a hurried, knowing glance with her brother in the dock. She quickly settled into routine answers to formal questions in a loud, clear, confident voice.

She had met the Garvies for the first time the night they came to her house in Birkhall Parade in August of the previous year, and she was out flying with Max the following day. The Solicitor General edged carefully towards what had developed between the two of them. 'Now, Mrs Birse, please tell the court about your relationship with the deceased from that time on.'

Trudy appeared to brighten up on the mention of Max. She smiled broadly at the jury. 'Max? He was a lovely man. Very attentive towards me. We became lovers almost right away, on the Monday, I think, after we met on the Friday. He explained that, as his wife Sheila was seeing my brother Brian, we were meant to be together.'

She paused as if unwilling to go on, lest she cause any upset. *That, of course, is the last thing she wants to do ...*

'Not wanting to be the cause of tension between them, I wondered if his wife would object to us, well, being lovers. Max said she couldn't possibly complain as she was having a good time with Brian. We went to hotels in Edinburgh and Glasgow some weekends, Max and I in one room, his wife and my brother in another.' Trudy paused to allow the effect of her words to sink in with the jury. 'He told me she was frigid towards him and that I had given him more pleasure in two weeks than his wife had done during their entire marriage!' She sounded almost self-congratulatory, as if she had decided to embark on a one-woman crusade to spread sexual happiness to cuckolded husbands.

Pleased with the witness's performance so far, the

prosecutor moved on to the next, logical stage. 'So, you and he became lovers. Did the deceased mention any, ehm, practices, that he said he would like you to perform?' The Solicitor General, not the witness, blushed slightly.

Trudy nodded eagerly, anxious to tell her tale. 'Yes. He liked anal sex and I allowed him to do it. His wife would not. You see, I had fallen in love with him and just wanted to please him, that was all.' It struck Geddes that her explanation sounded hollow, as if it came from the 'below the waist' section of a girl's magazine like *Jackie: 'The poor besotted creature was so in love!'*

She told the court that, when the four of them spent the night in West Cairnbeg, Max insisted she leave his bed and let Sheila know she had to take her place beside him in the morning, something Sheila hated doing. Trudy was *not* asked how she felt about it, but had she been, would no doubt have reverted to being the starry-eyed teenager she was hoping to portray.

Like Geddes, Dowdall watched Trudy's performance with a mixture of embarrassment and trepidation. What was she going to say next?

Eventually, she said, Max had come straight out with something that had been bothering him when he asked Brian what his feelings were for Sheila. Brian said he loved her. Then he asked Sheila how she felt about Brian, and she said she loved him. Sheila said that Max had used them all and she could not be expected to give Brian up just like that. Trudy mentioned 'The Conference' at Edith's house, which ended with the announcement that the foursome was over. 'And how did you feel about that, Mrs Birse?' asked the prosecutor.

For the first time, Trudy reached into the inside of her sleeve and produced a small blue hanky, which she held in possibly hopeful anticipation of tears to come. 'Both my brother and I felt we were treated unfairly as we had no say in the decision to end the foursome.' She reached towards her eyes, the hanky extended as she spoke. 'Max then told me he was not going to see me again and Brian was to stop seeing his wife, but Sheila phoned me to say she wanted to carry on seeing Brian. After that, the three of them – Max, Sheila and Brian – met again and Max demanded she choose between them. She chose Brian and Max was very angry and said he would shoot her between the eyes.'

Asked about Bradford, Trudy said she had arranged accommodation for Sheila and Brian and had driven them there, but was unhappy that Sheila had just upped and left her brother by himself. After Brian returned, he had been attacked twice in Stonehaven, both times successfully defending himself. Realising the witness might be difficult when it came to the next bit, the prosecutor took his time. 'And do you recall your brother saying anything about those attacks?'

Trudy looked at Brian as if to reassure him that she was not going to let him down. 'Yes, he told me that both times he was attacked, the men said they were just passing on a warning from the Skipper, which was what Max liked to be called.'

'And tell the court how your brother reacted to those attacks. For instance, did he make any comment about Max?'

Trudy looked momentarily pensive. 'Yes, he did. He said that Max would have to go.' She waited until the Solicitor General was about to move on to a different chapter of evidence before she added, 'I know my brother. When he said those words, he was only joking.' Trudy clearly knew she had to stick to what she's told the police or there could be consequences; she also seemed to know the way round facing those consequences by sticking to the script, then adding asides like Brian 'only joking' about Max 'having to go'.

She had met Alan Peters in February of that year, as he and Brian used to do home jobs on people's cars. 'Did Peters seem to be afraid of your brother in any way?'

Trudy looked puzzled. 'You mean was Alan frightened of Brian?' At first, she looked astonished at the notion, then she scoffed at it in a vacant, forced laugh. 'No, he was *not* frightened of Brian!' she added emphatically.

The Solicitor General moved on to the events of 14 and 15 May when Alan had called in at her house at 7 p.m. so he and Brian could go to work doing homers; she next saw Brian the following morning about 8 a.m. At that, she began to quiver dramatically. *Time for her to turn it on*, Geddes thought.

Catching her breath in between great long sobs, she gasped words out. 'Brian sitting … reading … saw dirty clothes on floor … asked what he had been up to … he said … was nothing to do with me … then he said …' – she gave out a great wail at this point before finishing the sentence – 'and he said, it's been done, it's over, Max is dead!'

Geddes studied the jury. Were they falling for this? He noticed the judge trying to look impassive, but his face made him look like he was watching a film he had no time for. Gibbie, though, remained stoical as ever.

The prosecutor paused for effect, hoping the court would understand that time had to be allowed for a witness genuinely recounting a traumatic event.

She sniffled to a stop. He continued. 'And did your brother say anything else, Mrs Birse?'

'Yes. He said, "it was either him or me" … I remember that clearly, "it was either him or me", that's right.'

She began to quiver again. 'I was worried in case poor Max had suffered in any way, but Brian assured me he had not.'

Despite trembling, her voice sounded much clearer. Geddes concluded she had forgotten one of her special effects. She dabbed her eyes, then spoke again, adding something no-one had expected, something not in her original statement to police, although the indictment had been worded to take account of it. 'The Sunday after that, the two of us were driving home from West Cairnbeg when Brian told me that Alan had struck Max with a steel bar and Brian honestly thought Max was dead when he shot him.'

As a serving policeman, Geddes realised Brian's latest attempt to squirm out of what he had done – if believed – could be successful; you cannot kill someone who is already dead. Not only that, here was his sister doing him the favour of giving evidence on his behalf, thereby saving him the inconvenience of having to answer those difficult questions such as 'why has your story changed so much – you previously said Sheila had killed Max and now you're saying it was Alan?' So that's what the Tevendales were up to – the sister visiting the brother so they could concoct a defence for him, taking advantage of the rule that what an accused has said about the crime is not regarded as hearsay.

What she said next was even more brazen. Her little-girl-face on, Trudy went into more detail about what Brian had told her had happened. Even the prosecutor looked surprised when she said that Sheila had let Brian and Alan into the house. The colour drained from Dowdall's face. She had clearly forgotten to mention this vital piece of information before. And there was more. Sheila had poured them drinks as they waited for the victim to arrive! Like all those round the table, Geddes was astonished that Trudy had waited until now to let the world know that the victim's wife was involved to the extent of casually pouring drinks in the front room at West Cairnbeg just before Max arrived home.

Trudy went on. 'And then Brian and Alan waited in a spare room upstairs for Max to come home. Sheila went through to tell them when poor Max was asleep ...'

As this was the first time anyone had heard about Sheila's

supposedly direct role in the murder, all eyes and ears were on Trudy. The jury were scribbling to keep up. Daiches and Dowdall were deep in whispered conversation and the Solicitor General did his best to pretend that what Trudy was saying was perfectly predictable and not coming as a major surprise. 'So, Mrs Garvie not only let her two co-accused into the house, she poured them drinks before the deceased arrived home?'

Trudy nodded, seemingly thinking back to what she had been told by Brian. 'Yes, that's what my brother told me. Oh, and it was Mrs Garvie herself who told me she had gone through to the spare room to tell them when Max was asleep.'

His case against Sheila unexpectedly improving by the second, the prosecutor went back over Trudy's words. He got her to confirm that Sheila had either been present when Brian talked about her letting them into the house, pouring them drinks and telling them when Max was safely asleep, or that she herself had said it. Daiches and Dowdall could see what was happening, the rule being that what an accused says in the presence of a co-accused can, of course, be evidence against them depending on how they react to it. In this case, not only was Sheila apparently going along with what Brian was saying, but she was seemingly boasting about it herself.

According to Trudy, anyway.

Geddes too was coming to terms with this unpredictable turn of events. He realised that Brian Tevendale's evidence – given through his sister's mouth – was now exactly in line with the statement Alan Peters had given at Fort Augustus.

Trudy continued. 'As I was washing the clothes I had seen Alan Peters wearing the night before, Sheila phoned, then appeared at Birkhall Parade.' She said that Sheila was upset and her face was drawn and white-looking; she asked Trudy if her brother had told her about what had happened.

Dowdall wasn't alone in thinking another barb was on its way. Trudy said that she knew 'a little' about it and Sheila had then said, 'It had to be done. I couldn't take it anymore. There was no other way.'

Geddes studied the jury for signs they were being taken in by Trudy. It was hard to tell, most of them still writing her words down. Those on the public benches were easier to gauge. Whilst most of them listened intently, some were clearly sceptical. Was that because of the way she was giving her evidence? In between bouts of apparent upset, she seemed to be enjoying herself, loving every second of being well and truly in the limelight, as Dowdall suspected she might.

According to Trudy, Sheila had driven her home the day after the murder and had mentioned a mattress that had been messed up and torn and that she needed to replace without attracting attention; it was then, apparently, that it suddenly occurred to Trudy that she might be able to help out. It turned out that, by coincidence, she and Fred had been discussing changing the mattress on their bed, which was too short, so she and Brian had driven to West Cairnbeg that night with the replacement mattress and had taken the soiled one away with them, eventually being reimbursed the £18 by Sheila they had had to pay for a new one. Fred and Brian had then taken the bloodstained one to the Dancing Cairns dump, where it was burned. Sheila had also asked her and Brian to burn Max's clothes, which was duly done. Once again, Dowdall realised that Trudy was twisting the facts to give Sheila the sort of lead role he was confident she never had at any stage of the whole crazy scheme.

When Daiches rose to cross-examine her, he was keenly aware that, for some reason, the witness was out to do his client no favours. Almost from the start of his questions, Trudy became needlessly combative. When Daiches mentioned that the children had watched *The Avengers,*

198

which started at 10.30 p.m. on 14 May, Trudy responded by asking him if it was appropriate that children be up so late at night. Geddes could hear comments from the row of spectators behind, a female voice loudly whispering, 'Well, that's rich coming from her! Did she not just abandon her bairns when she was out galivanting at weekends with her bit on the side?'

Trudy freely offered details about her and Max being lovers for the first time, sharing vodka and making love one afternoon when her husband was at work and the children were at school, then meeting again later that day and making love again in Max's car. Geddes was puzzled regarding why she was apparently keen to be so forthcoming about a part of her life that most women in her circumstances might naturally be far more reticent about. Looking wistful, she added, 'It was the start of a very nice relationship,' and in a faraway voice went on to describe her 'deep feelings' for Max.

Referring to the night Max had arranged for Fred to be set up with the young girl from Edzell whilst he and Trudy retired upstairs, Trudy conceded that she had not seen her husband until the following day, having spent most of the night with Max in the master bedroom. Daiches probed what her police officer husband thought about it and Trudy drew more subdued gasps from the public when she admitted that she 'knew what was on Max's mind' and that Fred was not too keen to go. She claimed that her husband didn't know that she and Max had become lovers by that time. Daiches then applied more pressure on her.

With an innocent, curious look on his face, suggesting total naivete on his part, he suggested to her, 'It must have been perfectly apparent in the romantic candlelight that Sheila and Brian had gone upstairs to discuss more than philosophy. And you went upstairs to go to bed with each other?' The proposition brought giggles from the spectators.

One trial observer, Paul Harris, would later observe that, '*no doubt, the onlookers felt that the hours of queueing for a seat had not been wasted.*'

Trudy answered that she had 'warned' her husband that 'this would happen', meaning the couples pairing off to spend the night together.

Daiches described the scene, mentioning candles flickering in their sockets, romantic music playing and Fred left alone with his much younger blind date, and then put it to Trudy that Max had organised and controlled all that night's activities.

Peering at Daiches, Trudy eventually agreed. 'He organised what happened, but "controlled" is a bit strong. Looking back now, Sheila must have been involved in it too. They must have talked about it and she must have approved it.'

Daiches then asked her about any complaints Max had voiced to her about Sheila 'as a wife'. Trudy appeared puzzled at first, but seemed to recover quickly. Effecting a pained expression, she went on to reveal pillow talk between her and her dead lover. 'Max once told me that Sheila was very frigid and that, no matter what he did, she was unresponsive to his lovemaking.'

Geddes mulled that over. He knew plenty of men like Max who began married life as clueless beyond a very basic visual attraction to their new wife, but who eventually cottoned on to the fact that their initial caveman approach was no guarantee of marital bliss; most of them had been able to work out that the longer term involved something other than further cajoling or bullying.

Having taken an oath to God, Trudy continued to look as if her telling the truth was a necessary but personally harrowing experience, something that the circumstances of love had tricked her into doing. 'Max eventually told me that his real aim in encouraging Sheila and Brian to get together was to try to make her a better lover for himself,' she continued by way of explanation, as if the murdered man had been motivated by altruism rather than lust. Conversely, she also confirmed that Max had shown her colour photographs of a naked Sheila posing not only in the living room at West Cairnbeg, but on sunny, clearly foreign, beaches.

Daiches was clearly going all out to dispel any lingering doubts the jury might have about the depths the dead man was prepared to plumb to achieve gratification for himself. On the other hand, Trudy was employing a curious combination of being patently partisan against Sheila whilst attempting to create a maiden-helplessly-in-love image with her answers.

Touching on the result of 'The Conference' at the Watson house in Stonehaven, Daiches asked her whether she had wanted her relationship with Max to carry on. Trudy confirmed that she did, but, looking sad, added she had 'just suited Max sexually'. *The perils of puppy love!* Geddes mused to himself.

Turning to the morning of 15 May, after her brother had told her that Max was dead, Daiches pressed her on whether she had assumed that 'someone had killed him'.

Trudy swallowed hard and began to weep, barely managing to utter that she 'really didn't know what had happened', presumably a reference to her supposed state of knowledge the morning Brian returned from murdering Max. Geddes assumed she forgot to add 'at that stage'.

For some, Trudy's willingness to help her brother and, apparently, Sheila after the murder was a source of puzzlement; why no period of reflection on her part or sisterly advice about the necessity of coming clean about what had happened, instead of just blind denial doomed to almost certain discovery and punishment? On the other hand, Fred's involvement in the cover-up was surprisingly not questioned as much as Trudy's was, primarily due to his automatic obedience to his wife as opposed to any loyalty to his chosen profession.

Turning to Trudy's evidence about Sheila talking freely about the night of the murder, Daiches suggested that Sheila had never said anything about letting Brian and Alan into the house.

Trudy began shaking again.

When she finally spoke it was to say that it was 'the most dreadful thing that had happened to Max' and that she found it difficult to 'speak calmly' about it.

Asked about her previously typing up an account of the evidence she was going to give at the trial, she said it was 'at the request of solicitors', but could not explain why that account made no mention of the later discussions about the events of the night of the murder she alleged Sheila had engaged in or started. What she was unable to reveal was that the solicitors concerned were unconnected to the criminal trial itself and had an entirely separate interest in the case. Trudy's machinations would become clear after the trial was finished.

She was able to say, however, that her aim had been to shield those responsible. If that was so, Daiches pointed out, she had failed to shield Alan, whom she said had struck Max with a metal bar, and Brian, whom she said had shot him. It was a fair point and Trudy must have been close to forgetting her previous pronouncements on the case as well as being tempted to prematurely reveal her hidden agenda, yet to be unveiled on a public desperate to hear more shocking details about the case.

As she was not for altering her testimony about Sheila's seeming inability to keep quiet about her role in the murder, Daiches eventually sat down as if exasperated with her.

Brian's counsel, K J Cameron, who had not asked many questions so far, rose to his feet. All eyes were on him, wondering what he could possibly explore with this witness that would make matters better for his client. It soon became clear that was not his task or intention. Obviously acting on his client's instructions, he then made it worse, much worse, for Sheila. Given that the press had previously reported Brian and Sheila's supposed wedding plans, the tenor of his counsel's cross-examination soon dispelled any prospect of it happening, whether true or not.

'Please tell the court, Mrs Birse, how you got to know about Maxwell Garvie's murder?' Cameron began.

Trudy dabbed her eyes again, the mention of her lover's death seemingly still too painful for her to think about even after all those months.

'Well, my brother Brian told me he was dead that morning when we spoke in Birkhall Parade.' She began to quiver again.

Cameron consulted the list he had composed earlier and ticked the questions off as he progressed through them. 'Apart from your brother, did anyone else say anything about it in your presence?'

Trudy outwardly composed herself in time to answer. 'Oh yes. Sheila – Mrs Garvie – mentioned it several times when she spoke to me both in front of my brother and at other times when we were on our own. Most times it was when Brian was there, though.'

'Please remind the court what she said or what was discussed in her presence on those occasions,' Cameron continued.

On the home stretch now, Trudy finished strongly, addressing the jury directly. 'Sheila – Mrs Garvie – was there when Brian told me she had let him and Mr Peters into the house. Oh, and she was also there when he mentioned them having drinks before poor Max arrived home that night and, now that I think about it, it was Mrs Garvie who said she had waited until he was asleep before she went through to the spare room to tell Brian and Alan the coast was clear.'

'Thank you, Mrs Birse.' Cameron was about to go back to his seat at the table when Trudy continued speaking, causing him to pause halfway across the well of the court until she finished.

'I should say Mrs Garvie was sometimes not happy discussing it and would try to change the subject, saying things like "let's not talk about it" and "I want to forget about it", but then other times she just opened up and went into detail about it.'

Evidence over, Trudy strode confidently from the witness box to one of the few vacant seats in the court in the front row. Gibbie glanced impassively towards Geddes, a gesture from the Macer he interpreted as 'Now, that was some performance!'

The Solicitor General called Fred as his next witness, then the judge addressed Trudy just as she sat down.

'Mrs Birse, perhaps it would be reasonable if you simply left the courtroom if your husband is giving evidence next.'

Trudy looked puzzled, then annoyed, as she stood up and left with everyone present watching her depart, some of the women commenting on the shortness of her skirt. It was a public court and Trudy had been revelling in her vastly expanded fifteen minutes of fame, which was now curtailed. Counsel round the table conferred as to whether the judge had the power to ban someone from the trial without explanation. The quickly reached consensus was that he had. But why had he done so? Had he decided that her very presence in court might influence her husband's evidence? After all, she was clearly able to control every other aspect of his life. Gibbie later told Geddes that that was exactly what the judge thought too.

There was speculation about how Fred would come across. In her evidence, Trudy had described him as a man who preferred his own fireside after coming off a shift and the puzzle for the public attendees was how two such different

204

characters could have met and married. 'For goodness' sake, he even put up with her going away for dirty weekends whilst he worked shifts and looked after the kids!'

As expected, Fred was stolid and slow in his answers. For a serving police officer to have turned a blind eye to what had happened was generally regarded as scandalous, yet he replied to all the prosecutor's probing questions in the same impassive way. 'I did not think my brother-in-law was serious when he told me he was going to kill Max ... I thought he was joking when he said he was going to blow up his plane or his car by remote control ... I decided not to ask Brian why my wife was upset about something that had happened the night before on 14 May ... Yes, my brother-in-law gave me a pair of boots and a rucksack to get rid of on 15 May, which I did, and we burned a bloodstained mattress and some clothes a few days later in the dump ... Sheila asked me how to get rid of fingerprints from a gun and I told her to use an oily rag ... Yes, I did help conceal a murder and I did tell CID officers a lie when I said I knew nothing that would have assisted the enquiry ...'

The court was also shown a couple of photographs of Fred at the local authority dump holding up the twisted, skeletal interior springs of the mattress that he and Brian had publicly incinerated in May. In them, he is seen standing facing the camera, partially bent over, holding part of the coiled metallic mass in his right hand, his left hand down the seam of the leg of his police uniform and his legs slightly buckled at the knees, giving him an almost comic bow-legged appearance. Fred's biddable nature obviously knew no bounds. His wife had told him that she was going to have an affair, then she instructed him what to do when her lover was murdered by her brother and, finally, he posed obligingly when ordered to do so by his bosses during his last few days as an Aberdeen City policeman.

Despite all he had done, Fred somehow managed to

garner sympathy from the public benches, mainly, it was said, because they had seen Trudy in full, frightening flow just before he was called as a witness. He even retained some dignity in their eyes regardless of his spinelessness and lies; the Crown had considered his actions carefully and chosen to use him as a witness rather than have him charged with perverting the course of justice. In the circumstances, charging and prosecuting him would have been a pointless gesture in a unique situation, merely a warning to henpecked policemen whose brothers-in-law had committed murder.

After Fred had completed his evidence, the Birses left the building together, she with her left hand entwined in Fred's right arm, he with his gaberdine folded over his left arm and the Major's wife on the outside wearing a musquash coat and dark leather gloves, all three of them resignedly progressing through the inquisitive crowd around them, some of them jeering and hissing at Trudy, Fred protecting her from worse as they made their way along Union Street. Their return for the verdicts a few days later would only allow the public another opportunity to vent its feelings towards her and the next time it would be more intense and unpleasant.

For now, the big question was whether the jury's views reflected the public mood in the streets of the granite city.

Chapter 30:

The Evidence, Day 3, Aberdeen High Court,

Thursday, 21 November 1968, 5 p.m.

Daiches and Dowdall sat dejectedly in the little interview room deep in the basement of the court building. For comfort, Daiches had removed his wig, which was lying on the battered wooden table in front of them, and had slackened his collar and his senior's fall, which now sat below his collar like a loosened, rumpled, angularly-shaped tie. Dowdall took his jacket off, removed his glasses and rubbed his eyes as Sheila's legal team awaited a brief meeting with her before she was driven off to Craiginches Prison.

'I have rarely seen anything like that, Lionel. I personally precognosced Mrs Birse and she never once said anything about our client mentioning letting the other two into the house, them having drinks before her husband came home, or her telling Tevendale and Peters when he had dozed off. It's almost inexplicable.'

Daiches sighed. 'Unless, of course, Mrs Birse was out for some sort of misplaced revenge against her former lover's wife. "*Revenge, the sweetest morsel to the mouth that was ever cooked in Hell!*" Scott's *The Heart of Midlothian,* if I'm not mistaken.'

Dowdall had become used to his chosen senior counsel's penchant for literary quotations and sometimes suspected they had a bearing on how his thoughts were directed, the facts of any given situation moulded to fit with an appropriate bookish reference. Dowdall continued, 'And young Cameron reinforcing it by confirming our client said things like she let them in. I went personally to West Cairnbeg and Mrs Edith Watson confirmed that anyone could have got into the house in May! It was simple, you just came through the garage!'

Daiches, too, had been dismayed when counsel for a co-accused had seemingly gone out of his way to make matters worse for a fellow accused. 'I had a word with young Cameron about that. You were correct – his client specifically asked him to do that. The conundrum is this; how does our client being convicted of murder assist either Tevendale or Peters? It's not as if the judge can give them a sentence less than life imprisonment if they are convicted of murder, regardless of whether our client is acquitted or not.'

Keys rattled outside the door, which then swung open, allowing a very tired-looking Sheila to enter. Being a stickler for form, Daiches quickly donned his wig, did up his collar and adjusted his fall as she took her seat, the wig leaving a small sheen of sweat on the table.

Dowdall spoke first. 'Mr Daiches and I have been discussing the surprising nature of Mrs Birse's evidence. She said certain things today which no-one could have anticipated and which she certainly never said to me when I spoke to her.'

Sheila appeared too tired to answer, but nodded to acknowledge his words. Then she took a deep breath before speaking. 'Obviously, you know much better than I do, but could she not have been asked about that? I mean, if she has never said these things before, surely the jury should be told?'

Her legal team were surprised. Despite her jaded appearance, the client was not too tired to come up with what appeared to be a decent point in her defence.

Daiches answered. 'There are certain rules which have to be followed concerning what a witness has previously said before trial. Put simply, when the police take a statement from a witness, that person can be asked about what they said in it, but they can't be asked about a precognition, which is sometimes described as what the office apprentice *thought* a witness said. Our best way of dealing with this situation is for you to give evidence – which you are clearly going to have to do anyway – and to convince the jury Mrs Birse is lying. Have you any idea why she is doing that?'

Sheila shook her head. 'None at all, same as Fred. They helped us after what Brian had done, even giving me their mattress and taking the old one away. Incidentally, what Fred said about me asking how to get rid of fingerprints was not quite true.'

'Not quite true?' Dowdall repeated. 'In what way?'

'I've pitied Fred ever since I've got to know him. He's got no say in anything that goes on in his own house and, well, he's got no confidence in anything he says or does. He really has a sad existence. I remember the "oily rag" discussion because it was so unlike him to have the gumption to bring something like that up, or even to start a conversation. It was as if he was doing it under Trudy's orders, even the way he began.'

'In Birkhall Parade, I presume?' Dowdall asked.

'Yes, it was about four days after Brian had killed Maxie. No-one had mentioned what had happened, although it was obvious that both Trudy and Fred knew all about it, after what they had done to help out, moving the mattress and burning his clothes. Suddenly, Fred turned to me and asked if I knew how to get rid of fingerprints. Brian and Trudy were there, sitting on the sofa across from me. I told him I didn't, and he suggested using an oily rag to wipe down the barrel of the rifle Brian used to kill Maxie. It was out the blue and it was Fred who brought it up. I never asked him about fingerprints because I've never had any reason to do so.'

As with Trudy's evidence, Daiches had been somewhat caught on the hop when such an unexpected and possibly damaging piece of information emerged and Fred's 'oily rag' story came into that category.

Sheila continued. 'Fred's advice got me thinking. It was as if he had been prompted to say it and, because my mother had moved into West Cairnbeg after Max was gone, Brian was *persona non grata* there. She made that clear.'

Dowdall removed his glasses and rubbed his eyes again. 'I'm sorry, my dear, it's been a long day and I'm not sure I'm following this. You say it was Fred Birse who first mentioned how to clean fingerprints from a rifle barrel, you never asked him. Am I correct?'

'Yes. He told me about it.'

'Out of the blue, as you put it?'

'Yes, as if he had been told to.'

Daiches was puzzled. 'So, you thought about it afterwards. What made you think, though, that Mr Birse had been told to say it, presumably by his overbearing wife?'

'Because Brian had no access to West Cairnbeg after my mother appeared there and he wouldn't be able to wipe the rifle clean himself. The Birses – and Brian – were trying to make sure his fingerprints did not appear on Maxie's rifle, even though he could have explained their presence by him sometimes going shooting with Maxie in the past. I may be wrong, but can fingerprints not be discovered years later?'

Dowdall confirmed that, depending on the surface they were deposited on, they could virtually last an eternity.

The conversation appeared to inspire Daiches, who then embarked on a short lecture to demonstrate his knowledge of the subject. 'Ah, dactyloscopy, one of my favourite studies. Fascinating how it took until relatively recently for it to become a useful forensic tool. You know the ancient Chinese signed contracts, as it were, by the parties appending their fingerprints? Unlike here in the west, they understood the exclusivity of an individual's fingerprint ridges, which left unique fatty deposits that they couldn't later deny.'

It had been a difficult day and the client looked exhausted. Dowdall thought it appropriate to curtail the meeting and so searched for a courteous way to do that. 'Well, Mrs Garvie, I think that's about enough for today. It's a pity that fingerprints don't feature largely in this case given Mr Daiches's encyclopaedic knowledge of the subject.'

'That's perhaps not strictly true. I agree fingerprints don't feature largely in the case, but suggest that my knowledge of the subject is less than encyclopaedic'. Daiches's new lease of life was coming at an inconvenient time. 'The complete absence of fingerprint evidence in this instance *does* have a bearing on the outcome.'

'How so?' Dowdall kept it deliberately brief.

Daiches looked at Sheila rather than Dowdall when he answered, there being little point in impressing someone whom he knew well and who had sought his services out above all others. 'It strikes me that when Mr Birse informed you how to remove them from your husband's rifle, not only was he doing so at his wife's and brother-in-law's behest, but at that early stage his suggestion demonstrates important issues in this case. Firstly, that Tevendale was already planning to impeach you for murdering the deceased.'

Sheila was taken aback. 'But that was only a few days after Brian killed Maxie! Surely that can't be right?'

Daiches tapped the table with his right index finger to emphasise the correctness of his theory. 'It has to be. Following your joint arrests, he seems to have lost no time in convincing some senior CID officers that you were the one who pulled the trigger.'

Dowdall was intrigued. 'And what does that have to do with Fred Birse's oily rag advice?'

'If my theory is correct,' Daiches explained, 'Mr and Mrs Birse were implicated right up to their necks by that stage.

Not only must they have been aware of Tevendale's scheme to blame you, but they must have been confident you would trot obediently back to West Cairnbeg and would do as they said, thereby removing all traces of Tevendale ever coming into contact with the rifle.'

'What was the point?' Dowdall asked. 'As Mrs Garvie says, Tevendale's fingerprints on the rifle could be explained from previous occasions.'

Daiches again spoke directly to the client. 'They were confident that you were so much in their thrall that you would unwittingly comply with helping establish Tevendale's pre-existing defence. After you eventually told the police what had actually happened, and following Peters's apprehension, it became clear that Tevendale's chances of acquittal were narrowing, so Mr Birse's information about oily rags was turned on its head.'

'What do you mean?' Dowdall asked.

'That's the bit I still don't fully understand, but it's the only real explanation. As Conan Doyle wrote, "*when you have eliminated the impossible, whatever remains, however improbable, must be the truth*",' Daiches said.

'You mean that Tevendale was planning to implicate Mrs Garvie from the start?' Dowdall asked.

'Yes, and once Tevendale's prospects looked gloomy, both he and the Birses seemed determined to ensure that you, Mrs Garvie, went down with him, hence Mr Birse's falsehood that it was *you* who asked *him* how to get rid of fingerprints!'

The three of them sat silently thinking about Daiches's theory, which now looked like being correct, as shown by Trudy's evidence. Sheila hated the thought, but it now seemed likely that she had shielded a lover who had always planned to blame her as soon as he could.

Sheila managed a weak smile, then said, 'Poor Fred! Once he cut up the boots and burned the mattress he had as good as lost his job!'

Picking his papers up from the table, Dowdall marvelled at his client's ability to express compassion for another during what must have been the worst time of her life.

Chapter 31:

Day Six of the Trial, Aberdeen High Court,

Tuesday, 27 November 1968

Just before Aberdeen became known throughout the world as Britain's oil capital, it experienced a brief, undeserved reputation for being the nation's centre of sleaze, courtesy of the Garvie case.

Day six of the trial dawned and media interest continued to grow. Not wanting to miss out on the feeding frenzy, editors throughout the land pushed reporters hard to come up with *any* new angles on the scandalous story that was unfolding. Anything would do.

The *Scottish Daily Express* passed on the vitally important news that Max's naturist club in Alford, Aberdeenshire, had been broken into and certain selected pages had been ripped from the visitors book. The police presumably restricted their enquiries to former patrons of 'Kinky Cottage' anxious to erase all record of their attendance in its confined space. Or did the culprit commit the offence in order to blackmail free-thinking neighbours suspected of involvement in such an alien activity for that part of the world? Or was it an out-of-town journalist reacting to editorial pressure? Some of those, caught up in the maelstrom of scandal, short-circuited their enquiries by assuming that 'Kinky Cottage' was actually the Big Hoose at West Cairnbeg and reported as such, despite the two properties being fifty miles apart.

The same journal, the *Scottish Daily Express*, completely

threw caution to the wind when it reportedly unveiled an anonymous witness who had seemingly spotted the Garvies sitting together in an unnamed hotel in Stonehaven. Max was drinking heavily, and Sheila was sitting wistfully beside him as he repeatedly played Hank Snow's 1952 hit *Married By The Bible* on a jukebox – the lyrics of which bemoan that a solemnly sworn church marriage can be dissolved by a legally obtained, secular court decree. The 'witness' was also able to pinpoint the exact date of the fictitious encounter to 13 May 1968, the day before Max vanished.

The final Crown witness was a detective constable who corroborated what Brian had said about Max's apparent disappearance. He told the court that, whilst the police had kept an open mind about it, no suspicion had been attached to Brian Tevendale at that time and they were keen to follow up any possible leads. Brian had volunteered to the detective that he thought that Max had possibly gone off with a woman and had mentioned Ireland or even Hamburg as potential destinations.

Daiches wondered why the Solicitor General – never one to accuse of failing to think ahead – had kept that witness to the end. He was to get his answer when the prosecutor turned to what Brian was found to have in his possession after he had been arrested on 16 August.

With one eye on the jury, the Solicitor General asked the witness to have before him Crown label number 51. Gibbie, the Macer, solemnly retrieved a folder from the production table and handed it impassively to the detective constable. The operation was stage-managed for maximum effect, the jury anticipating that an important adminicle of crucial evidence in the case was about to be revealed. With equal solemnity, the witness slowly unravelled the two wind-around cords at the front of the file, then obediently refrained from going any further until instructed.

'Please proceed to carefully remove the contents of the folder, Detective.'

The witness held the outer edges of the file apart and looked inside before tentatively placing a hand into it and removing a polaroid print. As if forewarned of the unfolding performance, the witness held the picture side out towards the court for a brief second or two, the press benches straining furiously to catch a glimpse of the subject matter, one or two of them later boasting of catching sight of its bawdy content.

'Take care, Constable, to ensure that you hold them appropriately, and now take them out singly, then place them face down on the witness box after you yourself have looked at them,' the prosecutor ordered.

As if handling gelignite, the officer did as he was instructed and eventually assembled a row of white cards with black edges in front of him like he was playing a game of risque patience with them.

'Now, please confirm firstly that these are items that were found in the third pannel's wallet when he was arrested on that date.'

'They were,' the officer verified.

With a note of disdain in his voice worthy of clerical disapproval, the Solicitor General sought further clarification. 'Can you now confirm that *all* of these items are intimate prints of the second-named pannel posing whilst naked and wearing no clothes *whatsoever*?'

Daiches struggled to stifle a smile at the prosecutor's choice of emphasis in the question. *All* of them were snapshots of his client in the nude at the time. Worse, she had no clothes on *whatsoever* in the course of posing naked. As gossip at the Faculty of Advocates was as vibrant then as it ever was, Daiches had heard that the prosecutor had been in the habit of personally keeping hold of certain court productions, these included, for security purposes. How sanctimonious was he going to get? Daiches recalled being ushered into the prosecutor's room at the start of the trial when he had been granted a brief sight of them, the Solicitor General holding them up individually for a second or two before hastily stuffing them back into their folder and instructing the Crown junior to place them back in the safe. Rather than concentrating on the lascivious aspects of the snaps, as others had appeared to do, Daiches had been struck by his client's unforced, natural smile at the camera, as if she was not only enjoying posing for them, but was appreciating being the centre of the camera operator's attention. In light of what was happening now, he was glad the prosecutor had adopted the ridiculously cautious approach he had, otherwise the jury might catch a glimpse of another, less troubled and more compliant side to her marriage to the deceased than he, as her counsel, was hoping to portray.

Eking the situation out to its full extent, the prosecutor then got Gibbie to gather up the snaps, place them back in the folder and hand the folder up to His Lordship on the bench. The imagination of some of the jurors now working overtime, the judge took a peremptory glimpse at them individually, then replaced them and handed the folder down to his Clerk, who passed them back to the Macer.

The Solicitor General then advised the bench that the Crown case was now closed.

When later comparing views on his tactics, both Dowdall and Daiches expressed surprise at the prosecutor's concept of finishing his case strongly, something seasoned campaigners always strive to do. Both of them thought his approach misguided, unless he regarded attempting to shame a woman trapped in a bad relationship as likely to achieve a strong, convincing finale to the Crown's evidence.

In truth, though, Daiches feared the questions that were likely to come from the first accused's counsel to his client rather than the probable cross-examination from the prosecutor.

The judge briefly explained what was happening to the jury. 'Ladies and Gentlemen, that is all the evidence you are going to hear from the Crown. Let me find out from Dr Taylor what the position is regarding his client.'

Taylor stood up. Tall and unsmiling, he answered abruptly, then sat down. 'Call the first-named pannel Alan Peters to give evidence on his own behalf.'

Peters looked around, unsure of exactly what was required of him at that stage. One of the white-gloved dock escorts stood up and squeezed by him, then raised the bar of the dock and beckoned him to join him in the well of the court. Peters rose unsteadily to his feet like a child frightened of entering a darkened room and made his way tentatively across the floor and into the witness box, followed by the police officer, baton still in hand, who sat in a chair nearby lest the prisoner attempt an improbable breakout.

The judge stood up and put him on oath, Peters temporarily forgetting which of the two was his right hand and cancelling his left – which had ascended to his midriff from his side – in favour of his right as he repeated the words uttered by His Lordship.

Taylor stepped briskly over to the lectern at the side of the jury box and, without wasting time, began firing questions at his client. 'Are you Alan Peters?'

'Eh, yes … sir.'

'What age are you, Peters?'

'You mean just now?'

Taylor tutted. 'Yes, right now!'

Peters was flustered already. 'I'm 19, no, 20.'

Taylor led him through meeting Tevendale at Aberdeen Motors, them doing homers together at night, that he got married to his wife Helen in July and both of his co-accused were present at the wedding.

Whether Taylor's style was deliberately designed to do so or not, the overall effect of the brusque treatment of his

218

client was to engender the court's sympathy for the man anxiously trying to answer his lead counsel's questions. One of the assembled onlookers audibly mumbled 'Gie the laddie a chance!' as Taylor stormed on.

Regarding the night of 14 May, Alan claimed to have no idea what was going on and thought he and Brian Tevendale were going to work on some vehicles that night to earn extra money. He went to Mrs Birse's house at 7 p.m. that night and, by arrangement, picked Brian up. Brian put a rucksack in the Zephyr's boot, but Alan said he didn't know what was in it. After driving around, going to two different pubs and stopping for petrol, Brian had directed him to park at the rear of the farmhouse at West Cairnbeg, somewhere he had never been to previously. It was around 10.30 p.m. that night and they went through the garage and he had seen a white car in it; once through the garage, Mrs Garvie let them into the house, then made them drinks as they stood in the front room. Brian had taken a rifle from an outhouse and had loaded it with bullets from his pocket as they waited. Mrs Garvie then showed them to a spare room upstairs near the master bedroom and later came in to let them know that her husband was asleep. Brian and he had gone into the main bedroom, where Mr Garvie was lying asleep face-down on a pillow. Brian then struck the back of his head several times with the butt of the rifle and shot him once. They then wrapped the body up, carried it downstairs and put it in the back of the Zephyr, after which Brian drove Mr Garvie's Cortina to a nearby airstrip and Alan picked him up there in the Zephyr; they then took Mr Garvie's body to Lauriston, where they changed into different clothes before burying it in a stone tunnel. Then they changed back into their suits.

And something else.

After Brian had killed Mr Garvie and he and Brian were still in West Cairnbeg, Brian kissed Mrs Garvie on the lips, then she got changed into a nightdress and she and Brian

219

'disappeared somewhere for half an hour' before he and Brian left. The reporters' shorthand was being thoroughly tested. '*Killing Max had sexually thrilled Sheila and Brian!*'

They got back to Mrs Birse's house sometime between 6.30 a.m. and 7 a.m. Brian made them both a cup of coffee, but Alan was sick after he had drunk some of it. Alan had then left for work.

Before he married Helen in July, Alan had stayed with her in a caravan and Brian and Mrs Garvie had visited him there before the wedding to tell him that the police had been to see them about Mr Garvie's disappearance. 'They said I was not to say anything if the police came to see me,' Alan revealed.

Taylor asked Alan why he didn't go to the police himself; Alan told the court that what stopped him was that he was afraid of what Brian might do to him if he did.

He then spoke about the wedding again. Alan had asked Brian to be his best man before 14 May and Brian had agreed. Brian and Mrs Garvie had been witnesses at the wedding and a dinner was held at Mrs Birse's house with both her and Mr Birse present.

Some of the women on the jury began pitying Helen well before they heard from her; there she was on her 'big day' surrounded by everyone involved up to their necks in, or covering up, a murder she knew nothing about.

Daiches rose to cross-examine Alan and made his way to the lectern just as it was approaching 4 p.m. Not one to miss a theatrical opportunity, Daiches had just asked his first question when the Town House clock outside struck the first of four loud bongs. With several seconds between each strike, Daiches ostentatiously stood back from the lectern and mouthed counting each one as he checked the accuracy of his expensive-looking wristwatch. Dowdall watched his senior counsel with a mixture of wonder at his scholarly presence and doubt as to whether his flamboyancy would impress an earthy Aberdeen jury.

'Now that the famous Town House clock has reminded us of the exact hour, Mr Peters, might I begin by asking you about your choice of best man for the nuptials?'

Alan looked blank. He was genuinely bewildered. Taylor rose to capitalise on the situation in the jury's presence. 'Might my learned friend refrain from using anything but plain language when asking questions of my client, M'lud? I seriously doubt if he understands what 'nuptials' actually means.'

One or two of the jurors grinned whilst others pitied the feckless, uncomprehending *loon* who stood before them awaiting their solemn judgement. *If it's all an act, it's a damned good one*, Dowdall thought.

Before the judge had time to consider the point, with his hand outstretched and his palm held upwards, Daiches retrieved the involuntary gaffe. 'No need, M'lud, I shall rephrase the question. Mr Peters, please tell the court how it was that you chose Mr Tevendale to be the best man at your wedding?'

Peters stood, blankly staring into space, for a while. Then he seemed to remember the answer. 'Aye, I mentioned that Helen and I were gettin' hitched like and he agreed to be the best man.'

'Did you not have second thoughts about that arrangement after the events of 14 May?' Daiches paused to emphasise the care he was now taking in making sure that the witness understood his every word.

The feud with Taylor was hotting up.

'What I mean by that is after Mr Tevendale had murdered Mr Garvie, did you not feel like changing your best man?'

Once again, Alan took his time to answer. Dowdall wondered if Taylor – or someone else on his legal team – had explained to him how important it was that he thought *carefully* about his answers to his own and other counsel.

Not that the jury would notice, but was he really thinking about what he said in reply or was he only trying to give that impression?

'Aye, I ken what ye mean now. If I'd told Brian he was no longer my best man, he might have taken it the wrang way.'

No matter what Daiches asked, Peters remained calm and resolute in recounting his version of events. He denied inventing parts of his story and stuck to what he had said in examination in chief, insisting that Mrs Garvie was involved in meeting them and tipping them off when it was the right time to murder her husband. Restraining himself from using words like 'embroider' or 'embellish', at one point, Daiches's dramatic side re-emerged when he asked Alan about him helping bury Max by 'feeding his warm body down the hole like a worm'. It was all in vain. Alan Peters stood his ground and would not be shaken, even about seeing the white car in the garage when it simply wasn't there. He was either genuinely gullible or finely accomplished in employing his native Aberdonian cunning when in a tight corner. Not a bad thing in front of a jury selected from the city and areas around the northeast such as Banchory, Buckie and Fraserburgh.

There were, of course, no questions from Brian's counsel.

Employing his quick-fire technique gave the Solicitor General no advantage with this witness either. No matter how rapidly the questions came at him, Alan used the same, effective, stoical routine when answering, taking all the time *he* needed to think about the answer, if indeed he *was* thinking in those interminable, silent gaps.

As Daiches and Dowdall had predicted, the prosecutor's top priority was to convict their client along with Brian. His first barrage of questions all related to Alan's supposed links to her *before* the murder, but he failed to dislodge Alan's contention that he had never met Sheila prior to that night in West Cairnbeg, although he had seen her and Max in the Marine Hotel bar before that.

Then, he tested Alan's apparent inability to tumble to what was really happening on the night of 14 May. Alan flatly denied realising there was any connection between Brian's announcement at work he was 'wanting to get rid of a bloke' a few weeks before, and their staggered journey to West Cairnbeg; he claimed to be equally clueless as to why the pair of them met up and meandered aimlessly in a southernly direction, right up until the purpose of it all was startlingly revealed in the master bedroom at the Garvie's farmhouse. The packed public benches were undeniably on Alan's side, but the consensus from the many reporters was that the 'daft laddie' defence was receiving yet another tired old outing.

Once his client had completed his evidence, Taylor called Mrs Peters. Dowdall noticed the effect her first impression clearly made on the jury. Heavily pregnant and only eighteen years old – the only one of the wedding party not to know about the shared dark secret that loomed like a thunder cloud over her happy day – she invoked sympathy before she had uttered a word.

Lord Thomson recognised her condition and, after he administered the oath, asked her if she wished to sit whilst giving her evidence. She declined. Discussing her appearance in stage whispers, two of the female spectators agreed she was a 'poor wee soul'. As with leading her husband as a witness, Taylor's clipped, unsmiling examination again served to increase feelings of compassion for this newly married lassie who was soon to be a mother as well. Was *nothing* ever going to go her way?

Helen came across as young and inexperienced but feisty in the face of adversity. She knew that her husband and Brian sometimes carried out car repairs at night and she had met Brian through that. She had also become friendly with the Birses, particularly Trudy, and had occasionally babysat for them to raise some extra cash. She met Sheila for the first time in the Birses' house, but thought she was a neighbour, having no idea that Sheila's husband had been reported as missing. In fact, after being told that Brian had recently been out on a date, she stupidly 'put her foot in it' a few days later when she asked him how it had gone. Sheila stood up and left the room, but Brian thought it was funny and laughed, and it was only after that she realised that his 'date' had been with Sheila.

She had noticed a change in Alan. He had become nervous and quickly lost interest in the things they spoke about, preferring to go to work rather than talk.

Taylor turned to asking her about her husband's character. Helen told of a dance where Alan was challenged to a fight. He began shaking and quickly left the hall by a side door. She confirmed that he would 'do as he was told' if someone with a gun ordered him to do something. *Who wouldn't?* Dowdall thought.

Completing his case, Taylor then called two other witnesses, the first his client's twenty-two-year-old schoolteacher sister and the second Alan's school headmaster. They confirmed that he was a cheerful, reliable, popular 'boy' who had had a good upbringing and had never been known to have been aggressive.

Taylor could now relax in the knowledge that he had successfully built a decent platform for an acquittal based on a snapshot portrayal of his client's character.

His next task was to ensure that his client's chances of being exonerated were increased at Sheila Garvie's expense.

Chapter 32:

Days Six to Eight of the Trial, Aberdeen High Court,

Tuesday, 27 - Thursday, 29 November 1968

Sheila then gave evidence for three court days, starting on the sixth day and extending into the eighth.

Daiches called his client and the dock escort went through the same routine as they had for the first accused Alan Peters, now back in the dock again, looking flushed and drained. Sheila stood up and waited for the escort to raise the bar that notionally divided her from the law-abiding members of the public, then she trod unsteadily towards the witness box in her fashionable high-heeled shoes and by now crumpled and creased suit, the same one that Edith had handed in with such a leaden heart to Craiginches before the trial started. Many observers in the court later agreed that she appeared gaunt and drawn even before the judge had administered the oath. *The oath*. The oath to tell the truth before almighty God, the same deity that she had taught kids about in Sunday school. Her voice sounded small and distant, but the judge deemed she had fulfilled her obligation to the Almighty and Daiches began with one of his characteristic flourishes.

Looking directly at the jury box but addressing the question to his client, he said, 'Well, Mrs Garvie, you have raised your right hand, now raise your left.' It was unscripted and unexpected. Sheila fleetingly imagined it might be part of some sort of secondary, special oath that somehow sealed and guaranteed her integrity. She raised her left hand to shoulder height, palm outwards.

'Now turn your palm inwards towards yourself.'

Sheila complied so that her wedding ring now faced the packed court.

Still concentrating on what effect the exercise might have on the jury, Daiches then asked, 'Have you ever had that ring off since the day you were married?' All eyes focused on the wedding ring, which gleamed conspicuously in the harsh court lights.

'No,' she confirmed reluctantly, now realising why her counsel had made the peculiar request.

Beginning her evidence with a blatant lie was a bad start.

After Max's murder, Sheila had removed the ring on several social occasions so as to prevent others who didn't know her from noticing she was married and asking about her husband. It had been an anxious decision taken before she and Brian had been arrested, since the gesture implied Max's departure might be permanent and would have been of interest to investigating officers. 'I see you've removed your wedding ring, Mrs Garvie. Does that mean you know your husband's never coming back to West Cairnbeg? Is there something you know that you need to tell me or one of my officers about?'

Trudy, for one, had noted Sheila's bare left hand at the Peterses' 'wedding reception' and had regarded the action as reckless. She concocted an excuse to record the fact in a photograph to satisfy herself, once again, of Sheila's ingenuous nature. Like charging her for a new mattress. *Does this woman have any common sense?* Trudy wondered.

Taylor and the Solicitor General were not alone in puzzling over the public pronouncement Daiches was trying to make. Surely this witness was about to admit to falling in love with one of her co-accused, then go on to outline the litany of abuse she had suffered at the hands of the deceased before confessing to maintaining a stony silence about his murder for an unconscionable three whole months? Was her counsel about to lead her down an entirely different route, one of everlasting devotion to her dead partner and desperate grief at his sudden overnight departure? None of that made any sense after what she had revealed in her voluntary statement and it was as if she was about to revert to her original, discredited tale of Max simply disappearing in the early hours of 15 May. Sheila was perplexed. Hadn't Mr Daiches himself insisted that it would be tactically sound for her to wear her wedding ring during the trial? Wearing it might invite hostile questions about prolonged, three-month-long hypocrisy from counsel round the table, but *not* wearing it in court would definitely give an impression of 'good riddance to bad rubbish'. She had been impressed by the level of detail her legal team had explored, but was now having misgivings about how much of that had been wasted in the very first question she was asked.

Once her evidence began, it became obvious that the opening flourish was a curious, empty, theatrical gesture that only served to baffle those members of the public who were about to pass judgement on her participation in her husband's murder.

She spoke of her children and her marriage, which had been 'normal' and happy until about 1962, when her husband had taken an interest in naturism. He had pressed her – and their daughters – to become involved in his latest hobby, but she had resisted, the stress of it all causing her to resort to taking tranquillisers, then to visiting a psychiatrist. Around that time, Max also began pressuring her to allow him to have 'unnatural' sex with her and for her to pose for pictures; he bought a plane and one of his flying acquaintances later told her he had 'seen more of her' than she thought, evidence that Max had been showing friends the posed nude photos, despite their agreement that they were for his eyes only. Up until then, Max had studied farming magazines, but these were now binned unread in favour of pornographic literature he ordered through the post. He started drinking heavily and wanting them to go out to meet younger, unattached people. Having met Brian Tevendale, Max invited him to stay over at the farm at weekends and on three separate occasions had left them alone downstairs with dimmed lights and music playing when he announced he was going to bed. After she went to bed, Max had asked her 'absolutely revolting' questions about what she and Brian might have been up to after he went upstairs.

Daiches asked whether Max had 'taken the view' that she and Brian had been 'intimate' in his absence and, slowly becoming accustomed to her counsel's extravagant style, she confirmed that it had occurred to her that that was what he was suggesting. After Max had taken Trudy on a flight in his two-seater plane, Sheila got upset when it became clear that he intended to carry on seeing her; she did not tell the court that she had listened to their conversation on the phone extension, but agreed with her counsel that she knew that Max had arranged to see Trudy again. When she questioned him about it, he simply answered that 'it was 1968' and people now did that sort of thing.

Listening to her evidence and seeing her deliver it in person, many present wondered if Max had been playing his dangerous game to try to make her jealous. If that was what he was doing, it should have occurred to him that there would be uncomfortable consequences; Sheila meekly accepting him back when he tired of Trudy was an unlikely outcome from the start. And, of course, there was just an outside chance that the 'other' woman might also suffer a reaction to being used, then discarded. Or – if Sheila was right and she had been pushed into Brian's bedroom *after* Max began seeing Trudy – could Max's peculiar desire to be cuckolded be explained as him evening things up in *his* mind at least, in a 'now we've both strayed' way that should prevent any repercussions? If that was how he truly thought, it simply made her a chattel he could do with as he pleased by enforcing his erratic will on her to suit his own selfish ends.

Concentration levels amongst the onlookers were intense when Daiches moved on to her relationship with Brian. Asking about the circumstances of how she came to be unfaithful to her husband led to the reply that she had 'fallen in love' with the other man after Max had forced her into Brian's bedroom. In the morning, Max was very pleased that she had done what he had wanted and had required to hear all the details of the encounter, something he would also demand after future liaisons.

The night Max organised what came to be known as the 'sextet' – a label coined by Daiches and eagerly seized on by the press – at West Cairnbeg, with a young girl provided for Fred, Sheila said Max was 'very excited' and at one stage considered putting a sedative in Fred's drink so he would not know what was going on, but, of course, Fred had driven the girl home, leaving Trudy upstairs in bed with Max. The jury must have a picture of ponderous, reliable old Fred dropping the girl back in Edzell, then going home to the love of his life – his fireside.

Sheila said that the real problems began when Max realised that she had developed feelings for Brian. Max's oversimplified solution to his self-created predicament was that she should simply stop seeing him. He protested that, as *he* had not developed any feelings for Trudy, Sheila should easily be able to ditch Brian. No doubt some of the jury must have thought that it doesn't really work like that.

Either way, Max had forbidden her to carry on seeing him and had told her that, if she chose Brian over him, he would 'put a bullet between her eyes'. Disregarding her feelings, she told Max that she *would* stop seeing Brian, then ended up seeing him by chance in Aberdeen and Max became very angry when he found out. Contrary as ever, Max then got in touch with Brian and they appeared to renew their friendship again.

Finding it difficult to cope, Sheila asked Brian to take her away and it was then that Trudy drove them to Bradford. Sheila only lasted a few days before missing her children and calling West Cairnbeg. Max held the phone away from him at one stage so that she could hear their son cry for her, after which she agreed to return home and Max picked her up at London's Heathrow airport.

At this stage in her evidence, Sheila was in her stride and Daiches was allowing her to talk freely and without interruption.

'Pray tell, what happened on your return?' he asked in his peculiar, theatrical way.

Sheila explained that things did not improve at home and one night she took half a dozen tranquillisers to 'isolate herself' from her husband, who then called the doctor to tell him that she had taken fourteen in an attempt at suicide; an angry Max then threw a glass at a radiator, picked up a piece which had broken off and held it against her face before pulling her out of a chair by her hair and forcing her arm up her back. She said she thought her shoulder might be broken and, as he was doing that, Max was demanding she call Brian 'a bastard', which she refused to do. She was screaming as he then threw her against a wall. Come April, he was taunting her by telling her that she needed treatment for her mental health and was still making demands for sex that she found unnatural.

By that stage, Daiches was concentrating on letting her tell her side of things and had seemingly given up on the sort of dramatic, pointless gestures he had begun the examination with. Dowdall noted the jury were listening intently. Daiches then turned to the night of 14 May 1968.

Now more accustomed to answering questions, Sheila

took a deep breath and related what she did that warm evening, having spent a day in the garden planting marigold seeds with her young son before Max came home.

He had arranged to take her brother's girlfriend flying, but that changed when William junior phoned to say that there had been a change of plan and the girl was now not coming. Sheila listened in to Max's side of the call and Max, unpredictable as ever, then told William that, in that case, he was going to an SNP meeting in Stonehaven instead and would meet him in the Marine after the meeting was over. Sheila confirmed that he had not told her about his amended plans for the night.

Max drove off in his Cortina, leaving her working on her knitting machine, her son playing just outside in the garden and her daughters spending time with their pony. With Max leaving in his car, there were no other available vehicles, the white Cortina estate being repaired at a garage in Laurencekirk and Max's Jaguar in an Aberdeen body shop after he had run it off the road into a field whilst driving home much under the influence. Max had all but used up all his chances with the local police and had been warned they would have to take an interest in his post-pub pastime of driving home heavily under the influence, so Sheila wondered if he was, in fact, setting her brother William up to drive him home instead by arranging to meet him in the Marine.

She made the girls' supper, then put her son to bed, reading him a story before he fell asleep in the children's room, next door to the main bedroom. Meantime, the girls were watching the television downstairs and had begged her to watch *The Avengers* there, which didn't start until 10.30 p.m.; she relented and together they all watched about twenty minutes of it before she sent them upstairs, agreeing they could continue watching it in bed and reasoning that she didn't want them up when Max got home in case there

231

was a drunken scene. Shortly after 11 p.m., she crept upstairs and, as all the children were sleeping, switched the portable television off, then put the light off, closed the door and went downstairs again.

Max arrived home about 11.15 p.m. He had been drinking, but said that the meeting, which had been in a different hotel, had run on, so he hadn't been able to meet up with William in the Marine. As he normally did, he poured himself a drink and asked her if she wanted one. She took a gin and orange, poured by him, as she almost always did when he asked her.

Max began going on about his 'anti-sex pills' – Soneryls, powerful sleeping tablets – that he had recently obtained more of from their doctor, something Sheila was disappointed to hear as she had specifically asked the doctor not to give him any more of them in view of Max's habit of drinking large amounts of whisky, popping Pro-Plus tablets and then flying or driving. The doctor had agreed to 'speak' to him about it, but it turned out that Max had been able to simply pick up another supply from the local chemist.

Max then switched to talking about sex and a row started. At one point, she went to the kitchen cupboard and found the tablets. There were still some left in the bottle, yet Max had somehow managed to persuade the doctor to give him more. She took two of them, went to the downstairs toilet, then went upstairs to bed around midnight; no-one had been at the house that night, the only phone call had been from William and the outside doors were all unlocked as usual. Before going to bed she made sure the light in the upstairs hall was on and had left the main bedroom door open as their youngest sometimes woke up during the night and came in beside her.

Max followed her upstairs, removed his clothes, climbed into bed and they had sex. Not love-making, she pointed out, but sex, after which she fell asleep.

The next thing she remembered was someone pulling at

232

her arm. She had no idea how long she had been asleep for, but was in a dreamlike state between sleeping and waking. Slowly focusing, she realised that the person beside her was too tall to be one of the children. Then she recognised Brian's voice urgently whispering for her to get up; she slid out of bed and, still in a trancelike state, was ushered out of the room. Because the light was still on in the hall, she noticed another person standing there, a fair-haired stranger, next to the curtain at the end of the landing at the top of the stairs just outside the main bedroom. Brian took her to the bathroom at the far end of the landing, pushed her inside and told her to stay there. It was then that she saw he was carrying a rifle, its barrel point downwards. She was confused, dazed and bewildered and must have locked the bathroom door, although she now had no recollection of doing so. She heard a door in the landing close, then terrible thumping noises followed by someone trying to open the bathroom door from the outside. Brian's voice then told her to unlock it and, after she did, he said, 'He won't worry you any longer …' and he told her to hold on to the handle of the children's bedroom door so that they couldn't come out.

Unlike his client, Daiches was relishing being in the glare of publicity; only someone who knew him as well as Dowdall did would know that his theatrics were part of his continual need to prove himself at this potentially dangerous, skating-on-thin-ice level of excitement. For Daiches, acting and defending murder-accused was as addictive as Soneryls were later found to be.

Once again looking directly at the jury, he stopped, appeared to consult his papers, then asked Sheila another question.

Hands expressively cupped on his chest, he said, 'Let us pause there if we may, Mrs Garvie, to take stock of the situation you found yourself in.' She looked relieved. 'Had you any idea that your bedroom was going to be invaded by other parties in the early hours of that morning?'

'No, I did not.' *Her answer sounded a bit too rote,* Dowdall thought, *but how else could she have put it?*

'Did you have any idea what these two men were going to do after you were bundled into the bathroom?'

'No, I did not.' *Routine again?*

'Were you fully in control of all your senses? In other words, were you completely *compos mentis*?' Daiches was still concentrating on the jury whilst firing questions at the witness box.

'Not at that stage, no.' *What else was she going to say?*

'And we pause at the juncture following you being released from the bathroom,' – both the prosecutor and counsel for the first accused looked at each other, briefly thinking of objecting to the word 'released' as unjustified in light of her evidence so far, but neither did – 'where you found yourself holding on tightly to the door handle of the children's bedroom. Were you standing up?'

Sheila shook her head. 'I was kneeling. I was kneeling and holding on as tightly as I could in case the children woke up and saw what was going on.'

'And what were you wearing? Had you had time, for instance, to throw on a dressing gown over your night attire?'

Allowing for the pressure she must have been under, Dowdall was pleased with how she was coping so far, but this was the friendly territory of examination in chief and hostile forces were waiting to ambush her. The next point, though, was good for her defence, having a snippet of unnecessary detail with a credible ring to it.

'No. Because I had been sleeping so soundly, I had no time to put my gown on and was only wearing a short white nylon nightdress. Whilst kneeling there, Brian put something round my shoulders.'

One or two of the jury glanced at the dock to gauge any reaction to that gratuitous but possibly telling detail, but there was none, Brian sitting looking forward rather than at Sheila. Alan Peters sat shamefacedly staring at the ground between his feet. Indifference and contrition sitting near to each other.

'You appreciate that the Crown are alleging that you must have known what was going to happen? Did you?'

'No, I did not. How could I, when I hadn't ever spoken to Brian about what was happening that night before he appeared and woke me up?'

'And obviously you now appreciate that your husband had been shot. You saw Tevendale with a rifle. Did you hear a shot being fired? Please think carefully, as the Crown are going to tell the ladies and gentlemen of the jury that you helped arrange an attack on him that couldn't have occurred without your connivance.'

Sheila sounded convincing, Dowdall thought, when she denied either knowing Max had been shot or hearing a gunshot amongst the 'thumps'. After all, none of the police heard a shot when the crime was being 're-enacted'. With the client's position being that she had absolutely nothing to do with the crime *before* it happened, neither he nor Daiches were able to drop subtle hints or even directly suggest to the prosecution that a plea to something less than murder might be negotiable; that said, no decent prosecutor was going to accept anything like that, given the terms of the first accused's voluntary statement.

Her evidence continued. From her kneeling position, she heard the sound of something heavy being dragged from the bedroom and being bumped down the stairs. Looking back along the landing, she saw the long weighty package wrapped in a groundsheet and for the first time knew that her husband was definitely dead. She remained where she was, trying to come to terms with the rapid but deadly events since she had been wakened.

Eventually, Brian reappeared and led her downstairs to

the sitting room.

'What happened then?' Daiches asked, with Sheila replying, 'I asked Brian how he thought they were going to get away with what they had done, and he said that they were going to bury the body miles away.'

'And did he say anything else at that stage?'

Sheila nodded. 'He said if I squealed to anyone about what had happened, he would make sure I was implicated and get twenty-five years in prison. Oh, and he told me to put the gun back in its proper place, which I must have done, but have no memory of doing.'

Was that threat of making sure she would be implicated now being enacted?

Daiches flicked through his notes. 'Are the ladies and gentlemen to understand that the two persons who share the dock with you then drove off into the night with your husband's mortal remains?'

'Yes. I heard a car engine start up, then drive off as I sat in a chair in the sitting room.'

'That left you alone with the children asleep upstairs. Tell the ladies and gentlemen how you felt at that moment.' It was not a question Dowdall would have asked. Knowing Sheila much better by then, Dowdall was concerned that it might provoke a response that was typical of her unvarnished honesty; his fears proved to be correct.

Sheila took the question to be a green light to unburden her innate sense of underlying guilt in the whole tragic episode. Looking up towards one of the harsh mock chandelier court lights that glared in contrast to the darkening skies above Union Street outside, she seemed to dredge painful recollection from her memory of that night. 'I felt morally responsible for what had happened because I had allowed Brian to fall in love with me as I had become emotionally involved with him.'

Daiches immediately recognised the possible damage the

answer could cause, but now had no option but to continue to pursue the line.

'Can you elucidate further for the benefit of the ladies and gentlemen?'

Sheila appeared relieved to do so. 'Yes. I felt that I might have unconsciously provoked Brian into the emotional state he was in that led him to do it.' Dowdall briefly studied the jury for signs they were ready for such uncharacteristic candour in the course of a murder accused's evidence. It was hard to tell. Most of them maintained that understated north-eastern inscrutability that often perplexes outsiders, although a few of the jury were busily scribbling down her every word, the butcher from Cruden Bay alone not appearing thoroughly absorbed in proceedings.

'Please continue, Mrs Garvie. As a result of how you felt, what did you do?'

'I was at a crossroads in my life that morning and had a choice which I only partially regret now. I decided that whatever happened, I would protect Brian because of what he had done for me.'

The pace of writing by counsel round the table had increased and Taylor, in particular, had a satisfied look on his face. Sheila's testimony had obviously given him new angles of attack in his cross-examination to come.

Daiches moved on and Sheila recalled the phone ringing when it was light outside; it was Brian calling from a phone box telling her they had left Max's clothes wrapped up in a parcel in the garage. She found it, then checked the mattress upstairs, only to discover it was blood-soaked. She said Trudy took them both when she visited the farmhouse later that week.

She denied ever speaking about Max's murder in front of Trudy or that she had any financial motive in claiming insurance money; whilst agreeing she would never have left Max to live with Brian because of the children, Sheila did accept that she would have left him if she had been able to gain custody of the children. She told the court about 'the course of deception' she had embarked on, of which she now had regrets. She explained that it had been in line with her vow to protect Brian, as was her behaviour after her arrest in August, including the 'private' meeting in the Inspector's office she had with Brian when they were both newly arrested. She described the police superintendent speaking to her around that time, telling her that all he wanted was a 'fellow confessor' to Brian, who had 'answered a damsel's phone call in distress'. Dowdall was hoping that the jury realised that although the superintendent was not a witness in the case, Sheila's evidence would strongly suggest that he and other officers had fallen for Brian's get-out-of-jail-free card and were judging her on that basis.

Sheila said that, on hearing that Brian wanted to speak to her after they had been arrested, she initially doubted whether such a meeting would be allowed in the circumstances, but, once it was surprisingly granted – and, of course, unlawfully recorded, Dowdall asterisked in his notes – Brian told her that he had *needed* to see her and would have 'confessed to assassinating President Kennedy' to achieve that. Dowdall mused that Brian's self-serving duplicity had been evident almost as soon as he had been handcuffed, if not long before that.

Throughout her examination in chief, Sheila largely stuck to what she had said to the police in her voluntary statement.

She was about to have a difficult time when cross-examined, though, particularly by Taylor, who rose ominously to his task clutching a sheaf of notes in his hand and a predatory appearance to his long strides towards the lectern. Squinting at her with one eye seemingly half-closed behind spectacles precariously balanced on the tip of his long nose, he began by quizzing her about the dates of certain occurrences. In the flurry of the opening exchange, he seriously challenged her contention that her husband had begun his affair with Trudy – possibly a major consideration in the circumstances of the case – *before* she succumbed to sleeping with Brian. He was able to do so on the basis of the diary Trudy Birse had kept, which, Sheila agreed, was possibly more accurate than her own memory alone. Once again, Dowdall felt that she was conceding too much too easily.

As for Trudy's allegations that she spoke freely about her involvement in the murder, Sheila pointed out that she was as anxious to shield Brian as Trudy had been. She explained that she had not spoken to Trudy about what had happened, as she had plenty on her mind in trying to shield Brian and simultaneously convince the outside world that her husband had simply disappeared. Indeed, she claimed that she had never discussed what had happened that night at any time with Trudy and said it was 'absolute nonsense' that she had let Brian and Alan Peters into the house that night and had supplied them with drinks, as Trudy had maintained in her evidence. In Sheila's view, Trudy must have had her own reasons for saying the things she did, but those reasons were 'unknown to her'; she told Taylor that was 'her best answer' despite Trudy and Alan Peters's accounts being so similar.

Taylor's cross-examination of her underlined how important it was in his view that convicting Sheila would help his client. Brian too had made it clear that he sought the same outcome, although presumably for entirely different reasons.

At one stage in Taylor's questioning, he had tied her up in such a carefully prepared, well-thought-out interrogation that she resorted to admitting that, as her options narrowed dramatically during the course of her marriage to Max, she had considered suicide, but stopped short of doing anything drastic. In the months following Max's murder, she said, it had been 'terribly difficult' for her, and she had not been sure how long she could live with the secret, although she was never going to betray Brian, no matter what happened.

She explained that her motive in making a will in June was to leave everything to her children, then to commit suicide. She said she would take her own life rather than betray Brian and, to that end, she got her mother to get her a bottle of tranquillisers, the idea being to take them all. She conceded that she had never taken them, but claimed that, if she had not been arrested on 16 August, she was not sure what she would have done about taking her own life. As for her husband's insurance policies, she knew very little about them and was not really interested in them. She and Max had had many problems, but money was not one of them, she explained, insisting that Max was 'a very generous man'.

Following in Taylor's slipstream, the prosecutor asked her if she had wanted her marriage to end. She said no. He then asked her what the purpose of her consulting with a divorce lawyer had been if what she said was true, and she lamely insisted that she had not wanted to bring the marriage to an end 'despite everything' and had become 'terribly confused'. He then questioned her about how Tevendale was found to be in possession of several nude polaroid snaps of her and she said she had found them in Max's study after he had been murdered. She had thought that her husband had destroyed them and, because she did not want them 'lying around', decided to give them to Brian. Alighting on that response, the Solicitor General then asked her, 'So, the answer is that after your husband's murder, you gave nude photographs of yourself to your husband's murderer?'

She could hardly deny it.

It was the ultimate low point in her evidence, Dowdall thought. It would be impossible for any jury member to understand that his client had spent the latter half of her married life fending off accusations of prudishness, had eventually succumbed to her husband's demands for her to pose for him, then had transferred all her hopes to someone else whom she had trusted. At least Brian hadn't shown them to his pals down the pub, like Max had. Or had he? In trying to save his own skin, Tevendale had shown himself to be unworthy of her trust.

The jury did not hear Brian Tevendale's voice at any time. Not that he hadn't spoken in court, which he had in the course of a legal objection taken by his counsel relating to alleged unfairness. The objection was based on Tevendale's claim that he had been assaulted by certain CID officers, had been denied the services of a solicitor and had been deprived of sleep before being interviewed. The proper procedure was followed and the court conducted a 'trial within a trial'. The process involved removing the jury and then hearing evidence from Tevendale himself. Following that, the court heard from the officers involved so that the judge could rule on the admissibility or otherwise of the significant statement to come – the one where he had said, 'Get a car. I will take you to the body at Lauriston.' Police evidence was that Tevendale had been cautioned after he said those words but then went on to say, 'Let's go. I didn't shoot him, but I will tell you about that later.' The police stoutly insisted that Tevendale had neither been assaulted nor coerced into making the statement, but there must have been anxiety at the back of their minds that their illegitimate tape recording of the meetings between the two murder suspects would surface. Yet that, perhaps surprisingly, was never mentioned.

Should leading police officers to the well-concealed location of a murder victim not be sufficiently noteworthy, a successful submission would, of course, also lead to the second, far more detailed voluntary statement Tevendale made at Stonehaven Police Office being thrown out. That was the one in which he described first meeting the murdered man at the Bannockburn outing in June 1967 and how he claimed that Sheila had shot her husband in the course of struggling with him whilst she tried to stop herself from being anally raped.

Those reporting on the case described Tevendale's witness box performance – even without the jury being present to weigh up and scrutinise his every word – as unconvincing, one going as far as to say that '*his performance was of such a nature that there can be little doubt why his counsel did not put him in the witness box in the presence of the jury*'. Just as significant was his counsel's reaction to the judge repelling the submission; when the same officers gave their evidence again – this time with the jury members present – he, perhaps wisely, elected not to cross-examine them.

Instead, the jury heard what Brian had told police after he had taken them to where Max's body was buried – that it was actually Sheila who had shot him in the course of a struggle.

Chapter 33:

The Advocates' Speeches, Aberdeen High Court,

Week Ending 29 November 1968

Once Sheila's evidence was over, the entire court's attention turned to Brian's counsel. He stood up and informed the court he would be leading no evidence on his client's behalf.

That came as no surprise to any of the legal personnel around the table, although the members of the jury might have been disappointed. The general view was that the case would settle on either the version espoused by Alan or that put forward by Sheila, and both pointed directly and unerringly towards Brian bashing Max insensible before shooting him. Had he given evidence, Brian supposedly could have claimed, as he did at one point in police headquarters, that Sheila had shot Max accidentally or, as he did when allegedly recounting events to Trudy, that Alan had killed Max using an iron bar before he, Brian, had shot him. Either way, the jury had undoubtedly heard too much from both Alan and Sheila to place any credence in any contrary claims Brian might have suggested.

Laurence Dowdall later pointed out that, by instructing his legal team to take objection to the admissibility of the statements he made to the police, Brian had gone down the exact same route as serial killer Peter Thomas Anthony Manuel's advisers had done at his trial in Glasgow's North Court ten years before. Like Manuel, Brian had alleged violence and intimidatory tactics by the police in order to make him 'crack' and lead them to where the body was hidden, and, as happened in that trial as well, the judge heard the disputed evidence without the jury being present, then repelled the objection. Unlike Manuel, however, Brian did not then sack his counsel and go into the witness box. What would he have said if he had? That Alan *and* Sheila were both lying when they said that he, Brian, had the gun when he went into the bedroom? That what he had allegedly said to his sister Trudy was a pack of lies that *she* had invented? Dowdall concluded that Brian had had no option but to remain sitting in the dock rather than take the short walk to the witness box both his co-accused had done. What Trudy had said in her evidence also strongly suggested collusion between the Tevendale brother and sister, so, in effect, for the jury to actually hear Brian's voice was virtually pointless, as he would not have added anything new to what had already been said on his behalf.

Nevertheless, Dowdall reckoned, one thing Brian could perhaps have done was tell the court about the one issue that continued to intrigue him, namely, what proof was there that there had been a plan in place, agreed to by both of them, to murder Max?

In light of his judicial silence at the critical moment, perhaps the safe assumption is that Brian would have simply reinforced what Alan had already told the court. Dowdall later commented:

Obviously, Tevendale had been properly advised by Counsel not to leave the security of the dock for the hazards of the witness box. Nonetheless, his silence was hardly the action of an erstwhile lover, since he must have realised he himself was doomed. Tevendale's silence had obviously shaken Sheila, but it was only later – when I informed her that I had been told that Tevendale was negotiating with a Sunday newspaper for the sale of love letters she had sent him – that her devotion to him was killed.

Dowdall also realised that her loyalty to Tevendale must have been genuine up until that point, which also illustrated just how malleable and trusting she really was, something that was central to her defence. Judging her by objective standards would probably lead to a life sentence, whereas an understanding of her deep sense of devotion, even to an unworthy creature like Brian, was going to be the key to any acquittal.

The trial resumed with speeches, after legal points were debated, and the Solicitor General rose to speak at 3 p.m. He suggested that the jury put aside any sympathy they might have felt for Mrs Garvie in light of the evidence they had heard. He went on to say that the evidence had been 'double-edged' because it might show that she had a 'very strong motive to seek her husband's destruction'.

The Solicitor General then made the claim that the deceased 'had never lost affection for his wife' whereas she had lost her affection for him in favour of Tevendale, with whom she had been committing adultery for some months, and that it was 'most probably' after she returned from Bradford that the murder was planned.

That statement caused Dowdall to look up at the prosecutor and the jury.

Where, he wondered, *is the evidence for the idea that Max never lost affection for Sheila? Does forcing your wife into bed with another man not point to a cold, blatant disregard for her feelings? And does the biblical sounding 'adultery' not apply to Max or is the prosecutor being selective or wilfully blind about that? Worst of all is the brazen assertion, plucked out of thin air, that Sheila 'most probably' planned Max's murder after returning from Bradford! That is patent speculation and Daiches is going to have to tell the jury as much.*

When the prosecutor continued his speech the next day, the court was again filled to capacity, most public seats taken by those who had waited from 5 a.m. that day, although it was reported that some had gathered outside the court to see Fred, Trudy and Mrs Tevendale arrive.

The Solicitor General resumed by comparing Sheila Garvie to Lady Bountiful as regards her attentions to Helen Peters; perhaps he felt the need to keep up with the theatrical or literary references when he made the comparison, Lady Bountiful being a woman who publicly carries out generous acts mainly so others see them. The serious point he was trying to make was that even if Sheila Garvie felt no revulsion for Brian Tevendale, she should have for Alan Peters, the 'assistant murderer', but instead she took an 'exceptional interest' in Peters by providing for the wedding, 'tending to the sick, delivering mail and replacing bedding'. The conclusion was, he reasoned, there was some bond linking all three accused, presumably the murder pact he claimed was in place.

Alan Peters had been essential to the plan, owning a car that would not attract attention in the way one of the Garvies' vehicles would have. The Solicitor General suggested that Alan Peters knew of some criminal purpose weeks before when he was told about Brian Tevendale wanting to 'get rid of a bloke' and must have been in no doubt after they were admitted to the house and Tevendale loaded the weapon in the sitting room. Despite that, he still carried on.

'Ladies and gentlemen of the jury,' he continued in his high-pitched voice, 'the suggestion that Peters had been coerced into taking part in the plot to murder the deceased is ridiculous and, although Peters is in a different category from the other two, having no underlying motive, he is plainly guilty of the crime'.

246

The Solicitor General then turned to the case against Sheila Garvie. He asked, 'Is Mrs Garvie the real brain behind the crime? She had everything to gain by its successful completion. She would get rid of a husband with whom, in her own words, life was hell. She would be free to entertain her lover while maintaining the standard of living to which she had become accustomed.'

He continued, adding that by her own admission she was a skilled liar, having deceived friends, neighbours and relatives about her husband's disappearance, and – eerily echoing the initial CID view when they wrongly thought she had shot and killed her husband – 'as hard as nails'. Her connivance in the events of 14 May was obvious as, if she was innocent, Brian Tevendale must have been 'banking on her' keeping silent. Warming to his task, the prosecutor added, 'He must have come thinking he could murder her husband and take the risk, not only that she would not give him away, but she would passively co-operate by standing by and doing nothing ... do you think that even a lover could come to his mistress's house and murder her husband and not get the normal reaction of any innocent person, namely to protect life, to save life, to do what they can for their husband, even if they disliked him as a man?'

Dowdall thought the Solicitor General had at last discovered solid ground and was beginning to make some sort of sense; Daiches would have to tread carefully when explaining Sheila's motives for doing absolutely nothing during and after the attack on her husband, forewarned or not.

The Solicitor General spoke for two hours and twenty minutes. Just before he sat down, he reminded the jury that it was 'not normal' for Sheila to stand silently by while her husband was being murdered in bed; Dowdall carefully noted that that proposition was surely based on her being in full control of her faculties *and* having some element of

247

control over events.

It was a powerful speech by the prosecutor. His priority had clearly been to concentrate on the separate cases against Sheila Garvie and then Alan Peters with surprisingly little said about Brian Tevendale other than to point out that his statement about Sheila shooting Max accidentally could not be true as no phone calls had been made from the farm that night.

Taylor then spoke for an hour.

He began by pointing out that Alan Peters had nothing to do with the sex lives of his co-accused, had never spoken to or met either of the Garvies and had never been to West Cairnbeg before 14 May. Having had no motive to become involved, he had been tricked into going out that night and, once out, Tevendale had known he could dominate him and rely on his silence.

He maintained that Alan Peters was the only one who went into the witness box and gave a truthful account and, as Tevendale did not do so, consideration of the statement he gave showed it to be 'rubbish'. Taylor maintained that Peters did not interfere with what was happening because he was afraid to do so. He asked the jury if any of them would have tried to stop Brian Tevendale whilst he was in possession of a loaded gun and, anyway, it was clear that Peters had been brought to West Cairnbeg 'not to do the deed but to assist in disposing of the body'.

Describing his client as 'a fly drawn into the spider's web', he suggested that he had shown himself to be 'a person of impeccable honesty, but weak-willed and easily influenced', and pointed out that it was Trudy and Fred who had disposed of the bloody mattress, submitting that this showed that Alan Peters 'had not been in the original plot'.

That observation made Dowdall think.

Was Taylor saying that Trudy and Fred *were* in the 'original plot' whatever that might be? So far, the jury had heard the Crown and then counsel for the first accused talk of 'a plot', the existence of which could at best have been an inference, there being no tangible proof of it otherwise. That Taylor should have made the observation at all might easily have led the jury to dismiss the crucial parts of Trudy's evidence on the basis that she had something to do with 'the plot'; the prosecutor must have been anxious when the 'plot' theory was mentioned in that context, Trudy's evidence being central to the case against Sheila.

Finally, Taylor asked the jury to accept that there was not a shred of evidence to implicate his client in the murder and that they should weigh that with his good character and his timorous nature. Dowdall contemplated Taylor's tactics and decided that sometimes counsel have to balance whether their client's feelings should be disregarded in favour of providing them with a proper defence, the likely ultimate result often being the deciding factor, and that a client's sensibilities must necessarily rank below the eventual outcome. Should Alan Peters be acquitted, he would surely excuse his counsel for any disparaging or unkind comments he had made in his speech.

It was now Daiches's turn to address the jury. In his account of the trial, Paul Harris wrote:

Those acquainted with Mr Daiches and his style expected a good performance and they were not to be disappointed. To begin with, he confidently predicted that once he had presented his client's case, the case against her would "disappear like the mists of a summer's morning".

Daiches's taste for the dramatic was obvious from the start. Describing Max as 'young, vigorous and brilliant', he said all that could be seen of him was in 'Crown label number 14, a brown hatbox'.

He described the marriage between his client and the deceased as ideal and happy for many years before it changed. 'Maxwell Garvie himself, driven by some curious fate or compulsion, started forcing his wife to join him in a course of conduct that led along a road which ended in tragedy and his own death. He was creating not only a permissive society in his own way – not only a foursome group, which he thought was in the best traditions of a modern, enlightened society – he was creating a Frankenstein monster which eventually rose up and slew him.'

He then likened the situation to 'Lady Chatterley with a tragic ending', Brian and Sheila's love crossing age and social differences. Whilst Max regarded Trudy as 'a mere convenience' – Maxwell Garvie cutting out that relationship 'as easily as a mini-skirted girl can remove her false eyelashes' – it was not so easy for Sheila Garvie to cut out her feelings for Brian Tevendale.

He asked the jury to reject the Crown's theory about Sheila being interested in Max's money. If Max's body had never been found, she would receive nothing and be unable to marry again for seven years; as such she would have been neither 'wife nor widow'. Moreover, it made no sense that the 'principal participant' in the plot knew nothing of where the body was disposed of.

Switching comparisons of his client's character again, he said, 'If she had done a Lady Macbeth act and let in the murderers to destroy her husband so he would never be seen again, then surely it follows that she would have satisfied herself that the place of concealment of the body was a place which was very secure …?'

He continued by moving on to events on the night of the murder when Max was meant to take his brother-in-law flying. That arrangement was changed in a way that 'any plotters' could not have anticipated, particularly as it changed after 6 p.m. Significantly, there had been no phone call to Aberdeen from West Cairnbeg to tell fellow conspirators of the change in plan.

Describing it as 'a monstrous proposition', he pointed out his client had read her son a fairy story when she put him to bed that night, the Crown saying she did so knowing his father was to be murdered 'before dawn rose the next morning'.

Turning to the evidence of the Birses, Daiches said their behaviour was an extraordinary feature of the case. Trudy claimed to have deep emotional feeling for Max, but chose to shield her brother. Why, therefore, should she protect the murderess of her lover? The answer was because she had no reason to believe Sheila had anything to do with it. In her statement, 'turbulent Trudy' had said nothing about Sheila being involved in the murder and, whilst being able to calmly recount the whole story of her 'incredible sexual relationship', she broke down when pressed about her statement. In other words, Trudy had shown how selective she could be when it came to what upset her. Dowdall was initially puzzled by Daiches's reference to Trudy 'protecting' Sheila, but then realised he was talking about her statement rather than her extraordinary performance in the witness box.

Daiches finished with John Donne's lines:

No man is an island entire of itself
Every man is a piece of continent, a part of the main
Any man's death diminishes me because I am involved in mankind
And therefore never send to know for whom the bell tolls
– it tolls for thee.

He added, 'And for all of us,' before demanding a verdict

of Not Guilty.

Having listened to many of his speeches before, and been entranced by Daiches's oratory and precision, Laurence Dowdall described the one delivered in the Garvie trial as unsurpassed and superb. He was convinced that the jury would have acquitted their client had they been asked to consider their verdict then, but another speech, then the judge's charge were still to come with a weekend in between.

Paul Harris, an observer at the trial, said Daiches's words made a deep impression on those present, but wondered if that was lasting or transitory; he was soon to find out.

Sheila Garvie, though, had doubts, perhaps trying to assess the impact of being called Ladies Bountiful, Macbeth and Chatterley in quick succession. She described her counsel's words as '*beautifully said*', but so '*airy-fairy*' that she puzzled what all of it had to do with her. She continued: '*Far from being practical and down to earth, it all sounded like a fine Shakespearean actor giving a perfect performance.*'

Perhaps ending with the poet John Donne's poetry might just have been a bit highbrow in the circumstances, although it might be thought that Daiches would have disappointed the legal personnel around the table had he made no literary references in his closing speech.

Kenneth John Cameron, for Brian Tevendale, was inevitably much shorter in his address and certainly less flowery. Dowdall reckoned his speech was brief because he knew his client had no chance of an acquittal. He had the impossible task of persuading the jury that they could not rely on the evidence of his co-accused, despite the one thing they had in common being that Brian was Max's killer. As the tenor of Trudy's testimony was to inculpate Sheila rather than exculpate her brother, Cameron's task must have sounded illogical to those about to pronounce on his client's fate:

252

'Please don't convict my client despite him not giving evidence and both co-accused telling you he murdered Max?'

In short, Brian's chances of acquittal were as remote as Max Garvie's of surviving beyond 15 May 1968.

Chapter 34:

Trial Verdicts, Aberdeen High Court,

Monday, 2 December 1968

Lord Thomson concluded his legal directions to the fourteen remaining jurors, most of whom seemed to be listening intently, on the morning of 2 December. They were told to go and consider their verdicts at 11.07 a.m., and it was assumed that they would be deliberating the case for possibly two or three days. They had to weigh up the two competing versions of the deadly events at West Cairnbeg on 14 into 15 May 1968. As the judge had put it, there was the Sheila Garvie account, in which she and the deceased had gone to bed around midnight after both of them had taken sleeping tablets washed down with gins poured by Max; some time later she had been wakened by Brian Tevendale and was taken to the bathroom just along the corridor, where she had locked herself in. She had seen Alan Peters in the hall and saw that Brian had a rifle. She locked the bathroom door, then heard 'terrible thumping noises', after which Brian had come to the bathroom door and told her she should stand at the door of the children's bedroom to stop them from coming out and seeing the two men removing their father's body, now wrapped in something that looked like a groundsheet for a tent.

Then there was the account given by Alan Peters. He had no idea what was going on and thought he and Brian Tevendale were going to work on people's cars that night to earn extra money. After driving around and going to two different pubs, Brian had directed him to park at the rear of the farmhouse at West Cairnbeg, somewhere he had never been to previously; it was around 10.30 p.m. that night and they went through the garage and he had seen a white car in it. Once through the garage, Mrs Garvie let them into the house, then made them drinks as they stood in the front room. Brian had taken a rifle from an outhouse and had loaded it with bullets from his pocket as they waited. Mrs Garvie then showed them to a spare room upstairs near the master bedroom and later came in to let them know that her husband was asleep. Brian and he had gone into the bedroom and Garvie was lying asleep face-down on a pillow. Brian then struck the back of his head several times with the butt of the rifle and shot him once. They wrapped the body up, carried it downstairs and put it in the back of the Zephyr, after which Brian drove Mr Garvie's Cortina to a nearby airstrip and Alan picked him up there in the Zephyr and they took Mr Garvie's body to Lauriston, where they changed clothes before burying it in a stone tunnel. They then changed back into their suits.

And something else.

After Brian had killed Mr Garvie and he and Brian were still in West Cairnbeg, Mrs Garvie had changed into a nightdress and she and Brian had 'disappeared somewhere for half an hour' before he and Brian left.

All the speeches by those round the table had been delivered on the Thursday and Friday of the previous week and the consensus was that the Solicitor General's was the most rambling, Taylor's the most effective, Daiches's the most dramatic and Cameron's the shortest by far. Taylor's gamble over using 'suborned' paid off when, as he rightly guessed, Daiches launched into sections of Shakespeare's *Macbeth* to contrast the roles that the lady of Dunsinane and the lady of

West Cairnbeg played in the act of inciting murder.

The judge's directions to the jury were as clear as they could be in the who-said-what-and-to-whom debate that counsel had become embroiled in. What he did say at the end, though, was that the jury should consider Trudy Birse's evidence 'very carefully'. Not 'carefully', but '*very* carefully'. Did His Lordship sense something in her testimony that the man on the Aberdeen omnibus had already detected?

Trudy herself, along with Fred, had defied public condemnation by returning for the verdicts. After the jury retired and the judge was off the bench, Trudy stood up to speak to her mother – who was seated away from her – and those in the public benches began booing her loudly. She seemed to care less than the police in the court squad, who immediately quietened the crowd. Aware she was again in the public eye, she spoke to her mother, then returned to her seat beside Fred, almost daring the subdued throng to react. None did, but it would be a different story outside the court building.

Two minutes short of an hour after they had gone out, the buzzer went. Against the odds, the jury had come to a surprisingly speedy verdict. Word spread and pressmen and onlookers dashed back to their coveted seats. Others stood in the passageway until it became choked with tense, excited observers anxious to see which side of the story their fellow citizens on the jury had plumped for.

Having invested so much time and effort into preparing Sheila's defence, Dowdall was unusually nervous as the trapdoor from the cells creaked open and the three prisoners emerged in dock order. Almost superstitiously, he dared not look back in the direction of his client in case it gave her false hope. All the experienced lawyers seated round counsel's table pretended it was just another case, just a routine verdict, as they sat waiting for the Macer and judge to appear, their impassive exteriors betrayed by their flushed pallors and unsteady handwriting.

The Macer called for the court to rise and the judge took his seat. Gibbie then spoke to the Clerk, who signalled the jury minder to bring the jury in. It was definitely a verdict the jury had and not one of those anti-climactic pre-verdict questions. As at the start of the trial, Alan Peters looked lost and Brian Tevendale almost defiant. Sheila Garvie, still in the same by now creased and tired-looking outfit, looked surprisingly calm, beyond any further help.

Lap of the Gods stuff now, dear Sheila. Be there for your kids or spend eternity in Mearns folklore as 'that black affrontit jade fae Stonehyve'.

In his days as a legal apprentice, Dowdall had been told there were two reasons why it was pointless studying jury members at this stage of a trial. Firstly, there was no truth in the old adage that they never looked at an accused if they were about to return a verdict of guilty and, anyway, they were seconds away from announcing their findings. Nevertheless, Dowdall noticed how often counsel – even experienced practitioners like Daiches, who was now running his hand over a non-existent beard and studying them as they filed into their allotted seats – still looked up at them, trying to gauge the outcome by their demeanour, their furrowed brows and any signs of upset. *They've been out for less than an hour in a case like this. Have they truly given it enough time and care? Are they about to deliver a true verdict according to the evidence? Or is it a true verdict according to their prejudice?*

The Clerk asked who spoke for them and the youngest-looking of them, a stockily built man in his twenties, stood up and said he did. He seemed unperturbed at the prospect of publicly delivering his and his fellow jurors' verdicts, the foolscap paper in his hand only trembling slightly as he awaited the next stage.

'Have you reached verdicts in respect of the pannels?'

'We have.'

'What is your verdict in respect of the first pannel, Alan Peters?'

'Not Proven.' Before he was able to say it was a majority verdict, the public benches erupted in chaos as a collective gasp emerged, quickly quelled by stern looks from Gibbie, the Clerk and the members of the court squad.

For Dowdall, all was immediately lost. The jury had chosen the Peters/ Tevendale version above Sheila's – *'they had preferred to free Barabbas'* was how Dowdall later described it – and he already knew the inevitable outcome for his client.

The Clerk seemed to take an age to enquire what the next verdict was.

'What is your verdict in respect of the pannel Sheila Garvie?' he eventually asked.

All eyes turned towards the spokesman, who now seemed to realise that the role he had volunteered for was more onerous than he had imagined, signs of perspiration glistening on his forehead.

Curiously, before he spoke, he dropped his right hand, which clutched the note of the verdicts to his side, as if he no longer needed it, having memorised its substance. Or maybe he disagreed with it.

'Guilty by a majority,' he announced flatly without any assurance in his voice that this whole thing had been properly thought through.

More gasps from the public benches. Daiches slumped slightly in his chair. The Solicitor General appeared impassive, recording the trial's outcome in pencil in one of the standard buff notebooks Crown Office sparingly gave out for every case, a stifled, almost imperceptible smile appearing on his face as he wrote.

'What is your verdict in respect of the pannel Brian Gordon Tevendale?'

The spokesman's hand returned to the front of his body at chest height and he began to read again. 'Guilty unanimously,' he pronounced in a different, more confident voice. The assembled multitude remained strangely silent in a confluence of confused disbelief.

The sound of the Clerk's clear, objective voice cut across the invisible barriers between palpable exultation and bitter disappointment and discontinued further speculation for the moment. 'Thank you. Please be seated as I record the verdicts before reading them back to you.'

The spokesman sat down and, during the minutes that passed before the Clerk spoke again, tears formed in the corners of Dowdall's eyes. *How can they have believed that Sheila Garvie conspired with Tevendale to arrange for her husband to be murdered in the bedroom next to their children?*

Removing his glasses, he ran his index fingers underneath both eyes to try to remove any signs of upset. After all, he and counsel would have to speak to their client and God alone knew how she would be.

Alan Peters was free, free to return to a life of dissatisfaction, perpetual rumour and ultimate insignificance.

Dowdall risked a glance behind him as Sheila and Brian were sentenced to life imprisonment by the judge, the only sentence he could impose for murder. Like Edith at her own wedding to Max thirteen years before, Sheila was standing up, clinging to the edge of the dock with both hands, eyes shut and positively unsteady-looking. After sentence had been passed, she opened her eyes and, even in her shock, was taken aback on seeing Dowdall's ashen demeanour.

She wished she could, but was unable to cry, having to concentrate on walking down through the trapdoor to the cells below.

A footnote in some newspapers reporting the verdicts was that the respective escorts had allowed Sheila and Brian an improbable final kiss before they were separated to begin their sentences; Sheila might have been easy-going in many respects, but most discerning readers must have recognised the '*Ae Fond Kiss*' headline for the journalistic licence it clearly was.

The press also carried the story about the reception Trudy, Fred and Mrs Gertrude Tevendale got from the crowds outside the court. Women with prams, old men with pipes and even a bus driver who stopped in the middle of Union Street and slid his driver's side window open wanted to know the verdicts. Some waited to see Alan Peters, but he never emerged from the main entrance, having been directed to and ushered out a side door from whence he disappeared '*back into obscurity*', as Dowdall later wrote. Instead, the restless mob were able to vent their mysteriously inspired pent-up anger on Trudy, Fred and Trudy's mother, Mrs Tevendale. Once again, Trudy seemed oblivious to the jeers that greeted her appearance and Fred quickly realised he had to try to get his wife and mother-in-law to somewhere safe. As he took hold of their arms, men dispensed with characteristic reserve and shouted that Trudy was a 'dirty bitch', and women that she was 'a whore' and 'a disgrace'. To begin with, the chasing pack consisted of about a hundred people, most of them old enough to have known better. Fred panicked and manhandled the two women into an office, which happened to belong to the *Daily Record*. Ironic, some people later said in light of what was about to emerge after Trudy's dealings with the tabloid press became public. By that stage, Fred frantically demanded the staff call a taxi to get them home; the staff obliged, but also phoned the police, as the multitude outside had grown to an estimated two thousand who were now blocking the flow of traffic on

Union Street. A recent but now former colleague of Fred's came into the office to find out what the cause of the hubbub was. He left without speaking when he saw the three of them standing beside a worried-looking receptionist and went back downstairs to instruct other officers to form a cordon in anticipation of the arrival of an unsuspecting taxi driver. When the unwary operative finally appeared in an old Riley Pathfinder it looked as if he was about to take cold feet and drive off until the officer stood in his path with his hand up, ordering him to 'Stay!'

After the three fugitives left the safety of the office and came downstairs again, the police linked arms and held off the mob, who shouted, 'Lynch them! Hang them!' as they jostled to get through the cordon; once they had made it inside the taxi, some of the crowd grabbed hold of the handles to try to open the doors as others banged on the roof.

It had been a frightening turn of events in that normally douce area of the city. What had happened had been less a harmless bit of fun and more a spontaneous demonstration of public aggression towards the passengers. But the Major's widow? Why were they attacking her? Because she was Trudy and Brian's mother? And Fred? Because he had helped burn some clothes and a mattress? None of the crowd were smiling and the police present reported that it was just as well that none of the three of them had been successfully abducted from the taxi, otherwise serious violence would undoubtedly have occurred.

Especially to Trudy.

That barometer of public feeling should have been warning enough, even for her. But, by that time, the *News of the World* had leeched onto the case and had decided to run a series under the heading *Death of a Nudist*.

And it was all about her, Mrs Trudy Birse, now *secret* diarist of the parish, the same one whose 'diary' had helped convict Sheila Garvie.

Chapter 35:

By the time Geddes arrived, the bar was busy. He had gone home to get changed from his usual work garb – dark suit, white shirt, plain polyester tie, light-coloured gaberdine and a dark blue Trilby with centre Crown crease. His wife called it his Maigret look, but, meeting with Gibbie again before he went back to Edinburgh the next day, Geddes had no wish to look like a CID man, particularly in the East Neuk Bar. He had changed into black lace-up shoes, dark grey slacks that strained against his expanding waistline and a light grey sports jacket that he'd had for so long that Irene had hand stitched black elbow patches onto it, giving him the look of someone unused to dressing casually, but determined to give it a try for a rare night out drinking with an old friend.

Gibbie was sitting at the bar by himself clutching a whisky, another one amongst the water ring marks on the bar awaiting Geddes's arrival. Several of the locals had begun talking about him, having become used to interlopers having the temerity to sightsee in their hallowed drinking den ever since Sheila and Brian had worked there just a few short months before. Geddes and Gibbie moved to seats in the corner, taking the bar's only water jug with them, where they had a slightly better chance to talk more privately.

'Well, what did you make of the verdicts?' As ever, Gibbie wasted no time, going straight to the point.

Having been part of the enquiry from the start, Geddes could hardly pretend he was the impartial detective interested solely in justice.

'I've got to say, I was surprised Alan Peters walked away. The helpless laddie caught up in something he knew nothing about was obvious nonsense. Doing homers in their suits? Really? I take it the jury must have believed all that stuff about him not knowing why he and Tevendale were driving about all night and having no idea why they just happened to find themselves at West Cairnbeg?'

Gibbie shook his head. 'I doubt that. Who could believe he wasn't in on it at least at the start of the night? No, the jury did what they often do –despite being told not to – they turned sympathy into an acquittal. Lucky boy – very lucky boy. Mind you, him being an Ebberdeen loon probably helped too. That and the way the evidence came out.'

'I'm sorry I missed what he had to say. How did he come across?'

An opportunity for Gibbie to be blunt. 'Thick. Deliberately thick. Thick and frightened. Frightened of Tevendale.'

'Who wouldn't be?' Geddes said as he added more water to his dram. 'I mean, would you want to cross Brian Gordon Tevendale if you didn't do what he wanted – especially after you had seen with your own eyes what he was capable of?'

'Aye, that's true, but some of us were saying that despite being worried about what Tevendale might do to him, the boy spoke up. He said he saw him clubbing Garvie, then shooting him. What I mean is, he didn't hold back, did he? About what Tevendale did, I mean.'

Geddes sat back in his torn, green vinyl-covered seat to think about it. 'So, Alan Peters was worried that Brian Tevendale might be acquitted and come after him, so he did what he wanted that night, yet he told the truth about him killing Garvie? Does that make any sense?'

Gibbie had no hesitation in answering. 'It does if you

think about it. Tevendale must have known that the Garvie woman was going to blame him, so there's one piece of evidence against him already. His main hope was that she would go along with the accidental shooting in the course of the attempted rape scenario that Tevendale said had happened, but she wouldn't. Well, you heard the recordings of what they said when they thought they were alright to talk freely. In fact, did some of your CID friends not fall for that?' Gibbie was clearly in a good, combative mood, tomorrow being what his judge called a *dies non* involving a travel rather than a court day.

'Aye, Wilkie did. He wanted to believe him. He really hoped the story was true, so he assumed she wasn't going along with the "struggle for the rifle" nonsense because she just wanted Tevendale to take the blame for killing Garvie *and* for dumping his body. Tevendale sold him the story really well and Wilkie saw her as a right whore who cheated on her man, then used her lover like she was Cleopatra or something. "Hard as nails she is", he kept saying after she denied she had done her husband in. It turns out the quean was right to stick to the facts, although that did her no good in the end.'

After seeing so many over-righteous cops giving evidence, Gibbie was enjoying hearing tales of insider police politics.

'So, when she refused to say she had killed her man – because it wasn't true – Tevendale realised he'd got one escape route left? Blame Peters!'

Geddes disagreed. 'You mean by getting Trudy to say her brother told her *Peters* had hit Garvie with a metal bar and was dead when Tevendale shot him? No. That's too far-fetched, Gibbie. What would the Tevendales know about the rules of evidence?'

During the trial, it had occurred to Gibbie that the CID had always been one step behind events, as normally happens in a complex enquiry, but had never quite caught up with real time in the Garvie case. 'Well, for starters, the Major was in the police and of course until a few months ago, so was Fred. Most of the people in here tonight would have no idea what could be used against them in court and what could not be, but you know and I know because of our jobs.'

Geddes was intrigued. 'So, what are you getting at here? Are you saying that Brian Tevendale tried and failed to blame the others and when he realised he was going down for murder he got Peters to do the next best thing?'

'I am. And that was to make sure that the Garvie woman went down for murder too!' Gibbie said emphatically.

Having criticised others in the CID for failing to see the big picture, Geddes had to stop and think. Was Wilkie's 'policeman's hunch' really just a hindrance to the truth and did he, Geddes, have the same problem? After all, he thought Sheila Garvie was overly loyal, but essentially truthful, just as much as Wilkie thought she was guilty as hell and Tevendale the pawn as much as Peters was.

'Let me get this right, Gibbie. You're saying Tevendale's last resort was to make sure Sheila Garvie went down with him? Is that what you're saying? Obviously, I never heard all the evidence, but you did.'

Pleased, and faintly flattered that his experienced CID friend was taking him seriously, Gibbie was encouraged to carry on. 'And, between you and I, so did the judge. This is mostly his theory, not all mine, although I think he's right as usual. We often talk frankly about cases and I never tell anyone else what's been said. This case is the exception.'

Geddes was thinking. 'Well, if you and the judge are right, Tevendale used Trudy *and* Peters to make sure the Garvie woman, as you call her, went down for murder. That could explain a lot. Her serving drinks to her husband's killers before he gets home has to be the sort of nonsense you see on the telly or read in a crime novel.'

Gibbie agreed. 'When you spend your days listening to

witnesses and they go too far, something happens. Your brain hints at you. It's like a bargain that's too good to be true. It usually is. Of course, you never heard the best bit. Maybe you read about it. Peters said the Garvie woman got changed into a nightie *after* her man was done in and the body was in the back seat of his car and she and Tevendale disappeared for half an hour. As you know, my job's to stay poker-faced no matter what, but when he came away with that one, I nearly burst out laughing. Even the way he said it, deadpan like. "The next time I saw her she had changed into a short nightdress and the pair of them went away for half an hour." The prosecutor, in that whiny wee voice of his, says, "Tell me, Peters, were you aware what they were doing during the time they were out of your company?" I couldn't look at the jury in case we *all* started laughing! Really, though, where did Peters get that one from? He could not have made *that* up himself! The man doesn't have the wit to dream that up! Drinks before her man gets done in, then houghmagandie after it? What's wrong with the usual routine that's usually followed in cases like this – you make yourselves scarce as quickly as possible after the man's been murdered?'

Geddes went up to the bar to buy a round and to give himself time to think. When he returned, he was still not convinced. 'Ok, Peters is easily led. We know that. But he stuck to what he said even when cross-examined by the other lawyers, did he not?'

'Aye, he did that alright. When juries like somebody, it goes a long way. Anyway, fear made the boy thrawn, fear of Tevendale if he forgot the script, so he couldn't be budged and by the end of the case, the jury had two options – the Alan Peters version or the Sheila Garvie version, as His Lordship put it. Ok, they could have gone their own way and disbelieved both if they wanted, but how many juries are going to do that? Very few, if any at all.'

'So how did the Garvie woman come across? They

clearly didn't believe her.'

Gibbie waved an index finger in the air. 'Some did, some didn't. I'm told it was a close-run thing. Both of them. Both Peters and Garvie were majority verdicts and both close, but if the ball crosses the line, it's a goal. She was on her feet for three days giving her version and Peters's lawyer, *Doctor* Taylor, had a real go at her. In fact, he did her more damage than the prosecutor did. Her own counsel was a good speaker, but didn't do her many favours. Truth be told, the man's knowledge of the theatre and books is second to none, but his human nature know-how – I mean Ebberdeen human nature – needed to be better. He starts with, "In taking the oath here you raised your right hand. Now raise your left hand." She does, and he says, "Has the ring on the third finger of your left hand ever been removed?" and she says, "No". What's the bloody point of that? Was he trying to make out she was a devoted wife? She didn't sound like one, even if her man was, well, a bit strange.'

Geddes wished he had been there. 'Did the evidence come out about the book she was going to write?'

'You mean *A Kinky Husband comes to a Bloody End*? Yes, the prosecutor brought that out. She wrote to Tevendale just after they'd both been arrested without realising the prison staff would look at them! How stupid can the woman be? Or how trusting? Anyways, the judge thinks the letters show how their relationship worked, with her responsible for making sure Tevendale was happy, like he was her child, her wee boy. A dangerous bastard child maybe, but still dependent on her, like trying to please his mammy.'

'Hold on a second there.' Geddes obviously knew about the letters and the title of the story she joked she was going to write, but was puzzling over Lord Thomson's theory. 'Are you saying she invented the idea of her writing a story so as to cheer Tevendale up?'

Gibbie nodded, fortified in the knowledge that the point

had judicial approval. 'Aye, I am. Look at it from her point of view for a second. There's this young, stupit loon who can't believe his luck after the husband chucks his bonny wifie at him and so he's desperate to please her so he can keep her. The husband's hooked on drink and tablets and is getting angry because the wife now sees the lover as protecting her from the husband, who's getting too handy with the rough stuff. So he can impress and please her, he thinks he's doing her a favour ...'

Geddes was going along with the idea for the moment. 'You mean by doing the husband in?'

Gibbie raised a let-me-finish hand and continued. 'That's right. Like a cat plonking a half-dead speuch at its owner's feet thinking it's a wee present they'll appreciate.'

'So, how does that tie in with the bloody end coming to the kinky husband?' Geddes was genuinely confused.

Gibbie was happy to explain. 'She said it herself in evidence. She thought she owed loverboy because he'd got rid of a crazy husband for her without her asking. What was it now? "Morally responsible", that's it, morally responsible for what had happened. In her eyes, she needed to keep shtum about what he'd done, then keep his spirits up by writing cheery notes to him in prison.'

Geddes looked doubtful.

Gibbie continued. 'Alright. There are no easy answers in this case, but tell me this, if the lassie wasn't protecting the lover beforehand why did she wait until she found out he'd tried to pin it on her before she gave the voluntary statement? There's no doubt she was telling at least a big chunk of the truth when she gave it. She even dragged *daft laddie* into it when that did her no favours, whereas lover boy never mentioned him at all when he first spoke to the police.'

Geddes pondered the stages. First, the crime gets investigated and witnesses are tempted to slant things the way they'd prefer them to go. That's the stage in the enquiry that Wilkie calls 'the wringer of truth'. 'Put them through the wringer,' he'd say, 'then we'll see how it looks'. That was what he'd done with Tevendale and it set Wilkie off in the wrong direction like a bewildered Spaniel with aniseed in its nostrils. Room for error straight away. Then there's the differences between the stories each accused comes up with, all vouchsafed as one hundred percent genuine. The whole concoction then goes to the prosecution, who shake it about to see where the bits might fall into place, then there's the free entertainment for the masses who turn up with their flasks and sandwiches and mint sweeties, looking for pantomime baddies and unsung heroes. Finally, reluctant members of the voters' roll get dragged into it and the process starts again until they come up with yet another version of the truth, this time with consequences. Of course, it just might be that the system's never been right and when the jury just want away or it's all been too confusing for them, they do what most people would and settle it by falling back on their prejudices.

Gibbie's voice interrupted his thoughts. 'Another thing. What was thon wee mannie' – Geddes understood that to be a reference to the Solicitor General – 'thinking about when he started going on about Garvie's money? That was a real wrong turning he took there. You know he tried to say she wanted him dead so she could get all the cash when that obviously had nothing to do with it! He went on to say that the wedding presents she gave Peters were her trying to buy his silence. Surely Tevendale turning round and clubbing him to death would likely be a better deterrent to speaking up than a bottle of wine, a chicken and a fiver?'

Without waiting for an answer, Gibbie gestured, 'Same again?', then went to the bar after Geddes nodded without hesitation. Despite getting the inside story – or as much of it as he could – something still bothered Geddes. A missing jigsaw piece was needed for all the rest of the bits to fall into place and for the picture on the front of the box to emerge.

Gibbie returned with the drinks and carried on where he had left off. 'The Garvie woman's counsel, Mr Daiches, spoke last Friday and all the press boys said she would have got off if the trial had stopped there. I'm not so sure, though. By the time they'd all spoken, the Garvie woman was Lady this and Lady that and the jury were bamboozled and fed up! It was like they were being spoken down to, the lawyers saying things like, 'Listen, all this is probably a bit too complicated for you country folk, so if it is and you're all confused just do as I say …'

The idea chimed with what Geddes had been thinking. 'You mean patronising?'

'Yes, patronising, and we know how that would go down in this city.' Gibbie had a further thought. 'I take it you've got no doubts about her being guilty now?'

Geddes hesitated. 'Not doubts as such. It's just that something's not quite right, not fitting into place.'

'You mean, she might have agreed to her man getting beaten up rather than done in?'

'She might have, but that's not it. Something deeper than that.'

'Ok, that she covered up for her lover after he killed her man doesn't prove she was in on it – is that it?' Gibbie was running out of suggestions.

'Not that either. It's to do with Trudy. Nothing fazed her, not even when she gave evidence.'

Gibbie's view was obvious if predictable. 'She's no beauty. Maybe Garvie liked boys. Her with her boy haircut and him wanting to do what he did to her. Is that it? If some of those folk in Union Street the other day had been on the jury, the Garvie woman would have been sitting in West Cairnbeg tonight. The Union Street mob saw through Trudy Birse alright!'

Geddes thought about it. 'No, that's not it either.'

Gibbie glanced at his watch. No time for more chat.

270

'Right, gents, closing time, drink up, please!' the barman shouted as he rang an eardrum splitting handbell. 'Time to face the music at home! She's waiting for you with smoochy music and a face pack on! Drink up!'

'Think I'll just stay here,' said a man they passed as they put their coats on and left to face the freezing cold of a December night in the stony grey city.

Chapter 36:

The Geddes House, Castle Street, Johnshaven, Kincardineshire,

Sunday, 29 December 1968

Even Essie had doubts. After the two life sentences were imposed, he began to puzzle over how the jury came to the verdicts they did, particularly as Peters had walked away a free man.

'Are juries not told to decide cases on evidence, not sympathy?' he said to Geddes as they worked a Sabbath shift together. 'How stupid would they have to be to let that boy off? Tevendale tells him he's needing to sort a bloke out, so one night they get dressed up like Sinatra and the Rat Pack, kidding on they're going to fix some motors. They drive about and go for a couple of beers to waste time, then end up inside West Cairnbeg where Tevendale shoots the man after clubbing his head in with Peters standing there. He helps carry the body out into his car, then bury it, and he gets a Not Proven cause he didn't know what was going on? Utter bollocks! That's what it is, Bob, utter bollocks!'

It was Essie too that told Geddes about the *News of the World's* coverage of the trial. '*Death of a Nudist* – subtle, eh?' he said the Monday after it first appeared in late November, and he started bringing his copies into the office so Geddes could see them too. The front page had separate shots of a smiling Max, hands by his sides, and a happy-looking Sheila. Both pictures had been carefully cropped to stop short of indecency – Heaven forfend! – and the reporting of the trial featured 'Kinky Cottage' and an inaccurately titled 'Mixed Foursomes' with images of a wistful Trudy at the sides.

Geddes stockpiled them as the weeks went by rather than read them individually. Having given evidence and witnessed Trudy's performance in the witness box, he began to feel unsettled about the justice system in general and he tried to distance himself from his misgivings by putting *Her Majesty's Advocate against Peters and others* to the back of his mind. The meetings with Gibbie had reinforced the growing notion that it was more of a bagatelle than a system, one lot of jurors seeing things differently from another and individuals with fixed ideas and views dominating their less confident colleagues, an unimportant game of chance with dire consequences for those on the wrong side of their verdict.

When he finally scooped all the articles out of his desk drawer and took them home, his wife Irene knew his interest in the case had been reawakened, her only comment being that owning a newsagent's shop in the Mearns was never going to pay the bills as only one copy of every publication was sold and then passed around the neighbourhood to save *bawbees*.

Setting out to show the flaw in Irene's theory, Geddes went out that final Sunday of the year and bought his very own copy of the *News of the World* for 29 December 1968 before settling down in the *sittootery* – as house extensions are often known as in the area – with that day's edition, all the back copies Essie had given him and a fresh cup of tea.

As Essie had said, *Death of a Nudist* was sensationalist and inaccurate, but that was only to be expected. After the trial had finished, though, the series had continued with the subtitle *The secret diaries of Trudy Birse,* which ran every Sunday from the 8th of the month until that date. Geddes recalled her referring to her diary in court when certain dates were being questioned. At the time, it had seemed to him that she had volunteered that she kept a diary a little too quickly when Daiches had asked her about certain dates, but it now became obvious why she did so – she had already sold her story to the paper and her diary – or a 'secret' one – had to get into the shorthand writer's notes, probably for contractual reasons. It also explained why she had typed out her 'statement' at the request of a firm of solicitors before she gave evidence – so she could be held to account if the deal fell through and in case she reneged from its terms in the course of her evidence. In case she reneged *and told the truth* would be taking it too far, but the existence of the deal she had with the Sunday tabloid did at least explain why she was at pains to dramatise and embellish her testimony.

Geddes felt annoyed that she could have got away with it so easily.

Not only was no-one aware of her pre-trial agreement, but she was clearly getting paid to give her evidence in a certain way; at least that might explain the cringeworthy declarations of undying love for the dead man – it was all an act. Might her tabloid story have repercussions for the case or was it too late to do something about it? Had Daiches known about her sordid little deal with the *News of the World,* it would have undoubtedly changed how he questioned her, Geddes reckoned. Might it also have changed the guilty verdict brought against Sheila? It certainly would not have helped the Crown case if the jury knew Trudy had probably been paid to 'liven up' what she had to say to the court. The unexpected additions to her evidence – that Sheila admitted to her that she let them into the house when there was no need to, that she had led them to a spare bedroom whilst waiting for Max to come home and that she told them when he was asleep – were possibly because of the pre-trial deal that was now out in the open. It even made Peters's testimony suspect when he magically added details such as Sheila and Brian going somewhere more private, presumably for no doubt deeply satisfying post-murder intercourse. And how far back did this go? Had the Tevendales got to Peters before the police did? Had Brian or Trudy told him what to say should the police begin to sniff about, under pain of execution and entombment on the grounds of Lauriston Castle?

With a feeling of trepidation, Geddes picked up the edition of 8 December 1968. At first, he really didn't want to read what Trudy had told the press in the misguided notion that she would achieve temporary, shoddy 'stardom' at the cost of God knows what. On the front page under 'exclusive' there was a picture of Trudy beside '*Death of a Nudist*' and '*The secret diaries of Trudy Birse.*' She was pictured sitting side-on to the photographer straining her neck to the distant horizon beyond his left shoulder. Her face looked incongruously solemn and her dress was pulled up to well beyond her knees; her right hand was resting on the side of her thigh and her left hand was across her body, resting on her right so as to show her wedding ring, still extant and in place despite all her brazen exploits. Geddes could almost hear the likely cockney voice of the photographer as he snapped away and gave instructions to her – 'That's it, love … head a bit more to the right … now show me more of those lovely long legs, that's it … a bit further, love … yes … much better … a bit more now … perfect! … now left hand across … that's it … on top of the right … good … so all the readers can see you're still married … aren't you?'

Geddes stared at the picture as he imagined it being posed for and taken. What the hell had she been thinking about? Was she willing to destroy everything? Had she ever cared?

The article told of the abuse Trudy had received during and after the trial, which had apparently 'shocked the world'. As 'an unwitting chief Crown witness', she was being criticised for sending her brother and his mistress to jail for life for killing her husband – 'my lover'.

Geddes mulled her words over, if indeed they were hers. He was pretty sure the angry mob outside the court in Union Street was definitely chasing her, her mother and Fred because of what she had done in her personal life rather than because she had 'sent the lovers to jail'. Perhaps they even instinctively understood she was inexplicably perjuring herself for improper reasons. He read on, engrossed with the patently fabricated narrative.

In the torture of my six hours in the witness box, I had to reveal secrets of a life I'd accepted, because, for the first time, I'd known what it was to be a woman willing, desperate even, to submit to her lover's whims. Now my lover is dead. I've been forced to listen to how he was found with a sheet from his wife's bed as his shroud in a sewer on the grounds of an eighteenth-century castle.

Geddes took a draught of his tea. So, she was a woman *desperate* to submit to her lover's whims, was she? And who was it that made her attend every day of the trial and forced her to hear how Max was found? *They should be ashamed of themselves,* he mused, *making her do such things when she was so obviously head over heels in love with poor Max!*

He was beginning to enjoy the sheer cant of the tale and was now looking forward to reading the rest of the gibberish. *'I must live with this sickening memory, this horrifying contrast to the gaiety and abandon of the hectic four months I knew Maxwell Garvie.'*

Geddes turned to pages four and five as instructed, eager to be further amazed at how misguided Trudy actually was and how she had so misjudged the nous of her fellow citizens. Inside, however, instead of further 'revelations' from her 'secret diary', was a catalogue of her life, where she grew up, how she met and married Fred, including a tale of her and Max making love on a thick rug in candlelight in front of a fire at West Cairnbeg and later in his car one night after he had left her house before her kids got home. The headline read, '*It was almost as if he had hypnotised me ...*'

Geddes chuckled at the idea. She was so obviously helpless and vulnerable! Turning eagerly to the edition for the following week, his eye fell upon Trudy's inexplicably harsh demeanour in a pose of her wearing a bra beside the line, '*Love was sky high with Max ... while the plane was controlled by automatic pilot.*'

Surely not? Surely she was not pretending she and Max had sex whilst airborne? It was a two-seater Bolkow Junior with two deep-set side-by-side seats and sex would have been physically impossible unless she turned round and leaned over the edge of the fuselage at the obvious risk of both of them jointly ending their lives in a mid-coital plunge from 15,000 feet!

Sure enough, there it was on page six – '*They made love in the cramped two-seat cockpit with the plane on automatic pilot,* and *above the fleecy white clouds in the clear blue sky* she *lost all sense of time and reality.*' The question, Geddes thought, was whether her loss of reality was permanent. Those seeking more details about the encounter in the clouds would have been disappointed. That was all it said. No more than that. It gave new meaning to the phrase 'unsafe sex', Geddes chortled inwardly.

Turning to the 22 December, he read on. She gushed:

For the three most horrifying months of my life, I lived with the knowledge that my lover had been murdered. For three months of nightmare, I lived in terror of the repercussions which would follow when the crime was discovered. The torment of emotions, divided loyalties and despair came close to crushing me. Our frenzied foursome, which had been formed with such excited rapture nine months earlier, had brought only disaster. The morning I heard of the death of Max Garvie, the rampaging, rumbustious gentleman farmer with an unparalleled zest for living, and that my brother Brian Tevendale and Max's beautiful wife Sheila were somehow involved, my mind fell into a state of numbness which is with me even today.

She went on:

Fred had gone off fishing when Sheila turned up that morning (15 May). She was ashen-faced and trembling. We stood and looked at each other without saying anything. Then it came out. "It had to be done, Trudy. I couldn't take any more. There was no other way out." That was it. Without a detail being given, I knew that Max, the man I thought of in my secret heart as "My Max", had been murdered.

Hang on, Geddes thought. *Did she not say in court that <u>Brian</u> first told her Max had been murdered and did Sheila not say that she never went to Aberdeen on 15 May?* Why let the facts – even those apparently given on oath – spoil a good story? He read on, this time about her and Max on their own and loose in Edinburgh. It was all good fun and fiction:

We wandered hand in hand around the city the next day, even dancing in Princes Street Gardens to music that no one but ourselves could hear, and, after again saying she had been blamed for helping send the lovers to prison, added, *I'm blamed, too, for admitting that, as a woman hungering for fulfilment, I allowed Max Garvie to love me in ways that are branded as unspeakable – and dared to admit it to the world from the witness box.*

Finally: '*And I don't want to change the hairstyle and colouring which Max insisted on and which are now part of me.*'

Mrs Geddes appeared at the door, having heard her husband chuckling and laughing. 'So, what's so funny?'

'Trudy,' he answered simply. 'She protesteth too much and is convincing nobody!'

She turned to go, then stopped. 'She should have known better than to get involved with newspapers like that one. Anyway, Trudy Birse deserves to be pitied, not pilloried. Let's hope that's going to be the final word on a very sad episode for the Mearns ...'

Irene Geddes was almost right about that.

Her husband, though, would have wished she was completely wrong. He was beginning to have new, grave doubts about the evidence he and his colleagues had carefully collated. Just how much sway did the *News of the World* have over what had been said and how it was presented in court? When Wilkie found out about the pre-trial approach one of the journalists had made to Tevendale about him selling Sheila's letters so they could be published, he rightly contacted the hack at his London office and warned him that any such *sub-judice* activity would not be viewed lightly. Mere mention of attempts to derail the course of justice was apparently enough to halt the proposed deal, or so it was said, until the trial was over. Trudy's involvement with the tabloid had clearly predated the start of the trial, had continued during it and must have had *some* impact on the evidence she gave. *Bloody annoying! All that work goes into a case, then some flash tabloid joker appears and starts dishing out cash! Some folk will do anything for money, good money, even lie under oath by saying what the hacks want to hear.*

Geddes began to think about how widespread the blatant chequebook journalism had been. More worrying was the gnawing realisation that Alan Peters had probably been got at; Tevendale had been approached, clearly through Trudy's links with the paper, so what was to stop them contacting Peters? It was evident that he was terrified of Tevendale and would have done anything to placate him after he was arrested and told Wilkie and him that Tevendale had pulled the trigger. Geddes could envisage Tevendale's reaction to the news: 'Fair enough! Peters had to crack at some stage,' he could hear him say in that slow, sinister drawl of his. 'I'll just get Trudy to say that Peters killed Garvie with an iron bar and he was dead before I shot him. Mind you, Peters is going to have to even things up a bit now he's squealed on me. What did Trudy say the journos liked to hear about? That's it. Drink and sex. I'll get Peters to add a few bits that'll please them …'

Chapter 37:

Ramsay Street, Edzell, Angus,

Saturday, 25 January 1969

The trial over and the unwelcome spotlight of publicity gone, Mrs Geddes's wish for no more mention of the Garvie case looked as if it might be granted. More than a month had passed since Trudy's rocket to stardom had lit up the skies over prurient breakfast tables all over Britain, then fizzled out and landed limply to earth, its burned out carcase landing somewhere between West Cairnbeg and Aberdeen. Trudy continued to be reviled wherever she went, whilst the recently unemployed Fred was universally mocked for being so publicly humiliated. Unlike his wayward wife, though, Fred kept a dignified front, in public at least. The offers of magazine interviews and Hollywood stardom Trudy seemed to have expected unsurprisingly failed to materialise and Fred's public forbearance was beginning to fray. His long-held private disapproval of his overbearing wife's behaviour was tested to near breaking point.

Encouraged by his wife, Geddes was reluctantly and finally beginning to let go of his misgivings about the outcome of the trial of Max Garvie's killers. He went back to believing that crime was just part of life and it sometimes cropped up and appeared as surely as people lived and died. He had long held the cynical belief that it happened when people imagined they could get away with something without fear of detection, a truly sad reflection on human nature. Geddes and Essie had come to an unspoken understanding about the fate of Sheila Garvie, who was now serving life in the spartan women's prison called Gateside in Greenock, in the west of Scotland. Not quite agreeing to disagree, Geddes and Essie instead chose a non-confrontational silence about the outcome of the trial, Geddes becoming monosyllabic when it was mentioned and Essie strangely diffident, compared to his previously strongly held views on the motives behind, and the culprits involved in, Max Garvie's slaying.

Anyway, with over twenty years' service, it was time for Geddes to make sure he steadied rather than rocked the boat so that it coasted nicely into port without mishap, him collecting a decent pension and his wife diverting him towards the cultivation of home-grown tomatoes and hothouse plants.

That Saturday, being one of his days off, she persuaded him to go for a drive to the nearby market town of Edzell, a pleasant trip to a pleasant town with its wide main street to accommodate farm vehicles, its solid Victorian buildings and the ornate Dalhousie Arch dominating the southern exit. Mrs Geddes always felt safe in this town. It harked back to a time of shared values, a time of social certainty where everyone knew where they stood, the uncomplaining poor providing farm labour or manpower for colonial adventure and conquest, and those that the arch commemorated naturally assuming their elevated status in life.

It was one of those glorious, icy days that crops up between bouts of constant rain and grey January skies now turned cloudless and azure blue. Geddes parked in Ramsay Street and they walked along the main road, stopping at certain shops to buy onions, carrots and neeps for soup and finely ground oats for porridge. Laden with their purchases, Irene suggested they stop at a tea shop for tea and scones before heading home. They spent an enjoyable half-hour chatting to locals, catching up with small town issues – who was ill, who had passed away, who was selling up – until an elderly woman mentioned the Garvies. 'My niece was in West Cairnbeg, you know. She was the one the Garvie man forced to come back with them when her shift in the hotel was finished. When she heard what was said at the trial, she nearly fainted! Go to bed with Fred Birse? Is that what she was meant to be doing? She had no idea! She's a good lass, but my sister and her man shelter her too much! Ignorance is bliss right enough!'

The mere mention of the trial frustrated Irene Geddes. She had hoped the excitement of the case might have died down a bit by now. Before Geddes could be drawn into the conversation, she finished her tea and indicated it was time to go. He drained the teapot, drank up, then picked up the vegetable basket and left in her wake, paying the bill on the way out.

She explained her reasoning once they were outside in the crisp, cold air. 'You – *we* – need a break from that awful case. Let's try to have a Garvie free day if we can and just enjoy our time together. You can help me make the soup before we visit my sister.'

Geddes had no desire to disagree. It probably was the right thing to do. The case was over and both Sheila and Brian's solicitors had publicly stated there would be no appeals against their clients' convictions. The soup-making and in-law visiting might not be weighty distractions, but they would serve their purpose. He unlocked their small white Hillman Imp, pressed the handle on the front passenger seat and moved it forward before putting the basket in the back seat, making a mental note that any emergency braking would scatter vegetables under the front seats. Having surveyed the ingrained mud splashes around the doors and wheel arches, Mrs Geddes was ready to add car washing to the scheduled day's activities when an old, black, sit-up-and-beg Ford Prefect reversed into the spaces in front of them and Jenny Thom sprang out of the passenger side.

'Hello, Irene, doing some light shopping?'

Mrs Geddes walked back towards the minister's wife. 'Yes. The vegetables are always fresh here and, anyway, we're fond of the town.'

'So are we,' the Rev Thom said as he closed the driver's door before joining the others on the pavement. 'I still have cousins here. Good farming people, like my own dear father was.'

Geddes was about to mention the minister's role in the trial, but a premonitory glance from Irene stifled the notion, and so the four of them stood talking about jumble sales, coffee mornings and church fundraisers. The thought occurred to him that the Thoms too had an understanding about not mentioning the trial. Arrangements having been made for the Geddeses to attend the Spring Ceilidh in the church hall, it looked like they were about to separate when the minister looked at his watch and turned to lock the car, his taller wife finishing a tale about ice on the inside of the Manse windows that morning, when he stopped and spoke quietly to Geddes.

'What an awful business that was. We were both witnesses, of course, and the outcome was a terrible disappointment – for me, anyway, having to see those poor children lose both parents and Edith being too ill to look after them ...'

Geddes also kept his voice low. 'Yes, I wondered what was going to happen at West Cairnbeg. If Edith can't look after them, I suppose they will have to be fostered out if relatives can't step in.'

Rev Thom agreed. 'I suppose so. I have tried my best. Short of us taking them – which we decided was impossible – that looks like the only option. Perhaps I shouldn't ask this, but what did you make of the verdicts? I take it we're allowed to talk freely about it now?'

The two women had stopped talking and were now

listening, Jenny more intently than Irene.

Geddes spoke louder and in his official police voice. 'The verdicts did surprise me – a bit – but I'm afraid that's how the system works. Whatever the jury decide we have to accept whether we agree or not.'

'I fully understand that,' the minister replied, 'and that's the end of it. Both Jenny and I tried our very best to keep the Garvies together for the sake of the children. We visited them, encouraged them to take a holiday together and offered to take the children to school. After Maxwell apparently disappeared, we helped Sheila and Edith as much as we could, right up to when the poor woman could take no more and went to the police. In my view, the key to the case was Sheila's infatuation with Brian Tevendale. She was overly loyal to him and that caused her mother to bring the whole sorry situation to a close. We still find it hard to believe that Sheila had anything to do with planning Maxwell's murder, she's such a genuine woman.'

Glancing at Irene, Geddes was given a green light to answer. 'We've talked about that too and, for what it's worth, that's my own private view as well.'

Irene cut him short. 'Right, we have lots to do. Let's get back home.'

The minister had one more thing to say.

'Jenny loves books. Don't you, dear?'

Jenny looked on, wondering what information her husband was about to impart after such a mysterious opening.

He continued. 'Whilst her main love is medieval poets, she has been known to read less esoteric publications ... like Agatha Christie!'

Jenny looked more disappointed than annoyed, as if her supposedly declining literary standards were now public knowledge. She spoke up in her own defence.

'No shame in that! I like nothing better than a good murder mystery where all the clues are there for the astute investigator to piece together. "*The truth, however ugly in itself, is always curious and beautiful to the seeker after it*", as a famous Christie detective once said, and what is curious and beautiful to me in the clues around Maxwell's murder is very likely to be ugly for most other people.'

Rev Thom explained further. 'What my wife is saying is that she has studied the evidence in the case and has her own view on what happened. Perhaps you might come round to the Manse one night so you can tell us how the professionals do it.'

'Yes, us amateur sleuths must be so annoying to you when you know much more about the facts,' Jenny said without irony.

As Geddes drove slowly north along the icy roads, Irene agreed it might be harmless fun if, in a few weeks' time, when the sensitive wounds of the Garvie case had healed slightly, they spent an hour or so listening to the eccentric theories of the redoubtable lady of the Manse.

Chapter 38:

Fordoun Manse, Kincardineshire,

Friday, 21 March 1969

Life, as someone once said, is what happens when you are busy making plans. Both couples went about their business and made their plans without any thoughts of fixing Mrs Thom's crime fiction night for any specific date. A chance meeting between Geddes and Rev Thom in Stonehaven changed that as much as it made the event more likely, the actual date being left to the higher authority of the respective wives.

Before the Geddeses arrived at the chilly manse that Friday night, Irene had taken the precaution of dressing warmly, wearing long thermal underwear beneath stout twill trousers and an old-fashioned bodice under a warm blouse and heavy Aran sweater. On arrival, the minister offered his guests tea or coffee and a selection of plain, unappetising biscuits, which the Geddeses accepted out of politeness rather than craving.

'The lecture will commence in the study in ten minutes,' he announced in a formal voice. Geddes was looking forward to experiencing an unusual evening with the unconventional pair who presently occupied the manse at Fordoun. It was as if they had all stepped back in time and they were making their own entertainment, Victorian-style, with no sign of ownership of a television, so no prospect of the likes of *The*

Avengers or *Perry Mason* spoiling the evening's events. Precisely ten minutes after his pronouncement, Rev Thom led the Geddeses through to the study, with its walls covered with ceiling-high mahogany bookcases, where Jenny stood, her hair curled in old maid earphones and a pair of small round glasses perched on the end of her wayward nose. The Geddeses looked at each other, then laughed. After the events at nearby West Cairnbeg, an Agatha Christie themed evening in the manse was, by comparison, light and wholesome.

Jenny was standing to the side of a teacher's blackboard. A wooden backed duster was perched on a narrow shelf at the base along with several lengths of white chalk. Already scrawled on the board were headings sectioned off in long, straggly lines: 'Motive?' 'Means?' 'Opportunity?' 'Suspects?' 'Evidence?' Geddes was intrigued to see 'Truth?' With the words 'not applicable' scrawled beside them.

A well-stacked coal fire blazed at the other side of the room. Geddes noticed Irene already beginning to look flushed and uncomfortably warm as Jenny opened proceedings.

'Alright, we are gathered here today,' she began, sounding like her husband in the course of his day job, 'to examine an unfortunate case of murder of a man known locally as hard-working, very able, yet become inexplicably dissatisfied with what to others seemed like a well-earned position of respect in our community and what should have been a contented home life. I shall be asking those present this evening for their views should they wish to express them.' She paused for effect. 'Should anyone feel the need to incriminate themselves, as can happen, then I shall call upon the others as onlookers and witnesses to agree they are conscience-bound to testify to that fact in due course.'

The introduction was meant to be tongue-in-cheek, but, of the audience, only Rev Thom raised a slight chortle, the other two not quite tuned in to the ironic tone of the evening yet.

'We shall begin with "Motive". What could Mrs Garvie's motive have been? This is open to the floor.'

Geddes felt obliged to be first to respond. 'Money. The prosecution said it could have been to get enough money for her and her lover to live a life of wealth and luxury.'

Before Jenny could respond, Irene unexpectedly spoke up. 'I don't think so. I didn't know her as well as the rest of you, but I don't think that's what drove her to kill. If she did. I think it was love. Love of Tevendale.'

Jenny seemed gratified that the guests were entering into the spirit of the proceedings. 'I agree because, if she was involved, it was a *crime passional*, although it would have added spice if she had been able to use her husband's wealth to set up home with her lover. Gives the killer extra satisfaction, maybe.'

Rev Thom stood up from the sofa he was on by himself and turned to face the Geddeses, somehow imagining he was in church, addressing a flock of two. 'That's all very well, but if it was a crime of passion, why should Sheila resort to actually arranging for Maxwell to be murdered? It strikes me she could have left Maxwell without having to kill him!'

Jenny held up her hand in schoolmistress fashion, as if ready to add a further pearl of wisdom to an eager pupil's growing stock of knowledge. The Geddeses were getting the inside on how the Thoms operated behind the scenes – constant debate. 'Arthur, you are forgetting that the two lovers *did* run off together and it was a disaster. She came back when she heard her son crying for her on the telephone.'

Rev Thom nodded sagely. 'Yes, I am aware of that. My point is that, for her, the children were the reason she came back from Bradford. Does that not tell us that they meant more to her than Tevendale?'

Jenny disagreed. 'I think you will find it was the other way round, once Maxwell was disposed of. She got her poor mother to look after them whilst she went to spend regular time with Tevendale.'

Fearing that the evening might degenerate into a domestic squabble, Geddes intervened. 'Surely Tevendale had the greatest motive? He hated Max and he stood to profit from his death as the new laird of West Cairnbeg once the dust had settled.'

Jenny began awarding points to each of the accused's names, with Tevendale now well in the lead, ahead of Sheila, while Peters was yet to get off the mark.

Geddes anticipated the next issues, as outlined on the blackboard. 'So, what about the other two of the three? We've had "Motive", so what about "Means" and "Opportunity"? How do the accused fair on them?'

Jenny returned to the blackboard now brandishing a metre stick, pointing at headings as she spoke. '"Means". That was obvious. Maxwell had firearms for killing rabbits and the like, so that was maybe too obvious. It would have been so much neater if they had only tampered with the plane or one of his cars. Peters and Tevendale both knew about engines and poor old Maxwell really would have made it so easy for them, always pie-eyed when driving *and* flying.'

Geddes found himself agreeing. 'He never did adapt to the latest thinking on road safety. That's why the Jag was away getting bodywork repairs after Max did some off-roading into a field not far from here in late April of last year. Drunk as a skunk, I'm told, he walked home and called it in the next morning. Said it was a deer on the road that made him swerve.'

Jenny totted the points up without comment. 'Ok, what about the third leg? The problem I have with "Opportunity" is that Sheila would have been mad to have chosen the evening of 14 into the night of 15 May of last year as the opportunity to get rid of her unwanted husband.' Geddes and Arthur Thom exchanged glances, Jenny's clinical sounding phrase 'her unwanted husband' possibly adding a personal note to her discourse. She continued. 'To start with – and this was said in court by her counsel – the children were asleep in the room next door. Why not do it – or have it done – when Maxwell was drunk, as he often was, and *ergo* more vulnerable?'

Irene was beginning to enjoy the exercise in criminal logic. 'I tend to agree. If Max was habitually drunk, there must have been plenty of times he could have been clunked on the head and dropped into the harbour at Stonehaven. There's no reason in waiting for him to fall asleep beside you if you've planned the whole thing properly. Instinct alone would tell you not to do it at West Cairnbeg, especially in your own bedroom. That, on the other hand, was where Brian Tevendale knew he could find him that night. Other things occurred to me. There were two parts of Alan Peters's evidence that were strange. Firstly, he said they got to the house at about 10.30, before Max got home, so why wait for him to go inside to bed before killing him? Why not get it done as he came out the car, outside in the driveway?'

Jenny beamed in approval at one member of her *whodunnit* class showing such promise. 'And the second?' she asked encouragingly.

Irene effortlessly carried on with her surprising observations. 'Yes, I wondered where Tevendale got the .22 bullets that Peters said he produced from his pocket. If that bit's true, he most likely stole them when he was out shooting with Max when they were the supposed best of friends. It looks to me that Brian Gordon Tevendale had been planning Garvie's murder for quite a long time.'

Geddes sat back open-mouthed as his wife spoke. For years he had assumed she had no interest in criminal matters, and so kept as much of his job as he could to himself. *Perhaps Agatha Christie proved one thing beyond a reasonable doubt – women are sometimes much better at hiding their secret, inner thoughts than their male counterparts.* He felt he had to butt in. 'If either of you wanted rid of your husbands, would you have us shot in the marital bed?'

For a few tense moments, both men awaited answers. Jenny spoke first. 'Of course not! If I wanted rid of Arthur, I would be far more subtle than that! I would poison him! Who would suspect me of it – me the faithful lady of the manse? Arthur would be dead and buried, his death recorded as cardiac arrest and me free to do as I please. What about you, Irene?'

Arthur had assumed an uneasy, slightly troubled look as his wife outlined possibilities that sounded uncomfortably advanced in their thinking.

Irene answered Jenny's query too easily for Geddes's liking. 'As Bob thinks he's a do-it-yourself expert, I would arrange for an unsteady ladder from the loft or dead wires which became unexpectedly live. Something like that …'

Rev Thom saw an urgent need to restore focus. 'Going back to "Means" for a moment, what does everyone think about Tevendale using Alan Peters? My view is that his inclusion tends to show who organised it all.'

Jenny came in. 'Yes, it does, and it wasn't Sheila Garvie.'

Geddes agreed. 'That did not fit in at all. Here's a desperate wife at her wits' end, planning her husband's shooting and, presumably, the disposal of his body and she doesn't even know who the necessary third conspirator is?'

Irene added, 'Nor where the body was to be disposed of. Surely that tells its own tale?'

'Perhaps she just didn't want to know,' Rev Thom said, relieved that they were back on a less personal course. 'She could have stipulated he bring in a third party to help move the body on the basis that she had never met him before and she was never to know where Maxwell actually was.'

'Unlikely,' said Geddes. 'How could she have peace of mind not knowing if she could trust the third man and not knowing where the body was and if it was likely to be found? She seemed to think it was in the sea somewhere. For all she knew, the body might have been buried somewhere on the grounds of the farm.'

Jenny was pleased with the audience participation so far. She decided to drop another couple of her thought-provoking observations directly into the debate. 'What do you make of the idea that Sheila had to let the other two into the house? My recollection of the evidence is that all of the outside doors were left unlocked. Don't you think the entire trial was somewhat side-tracked by Alan Peters's story about Sheila letting him and Tevendale into the house when in truth the Garvies, like everyone else around here, never locked their doors of an evening? Why would Tevendale need to be let into the house, then directed upstairs? He knew the place well, having spent a lot of time there.' Geddes assured the others that he and his CID colleagues had thought long and hard about much of what Jenny was now saying.

Jenny spoke again. 'Another thing – and you might have a view on this, Bob – can anyone tell me what the chances were of Sheila coming up with a word like "squealing" when she gave evidence about confronting Tevendale with how he and Peters thought they were ever going to get away with what they'd done? You'll remember the bit when she said Tevendale told her that if she squealed he would make sure she was implicated and that she would get twenty-five years in prison.'

Geddes again felt obliged to be the first to respond. 'Yes, we did give that some thought, but, as you know, once a case gets reported to the Procurator Fiscal, it's really out of our hands, particularly if there's a sufficiency of evidence. The prosecutor's view is often that a trial is the best way to test all those bumps and bends on the road and see what happens at the end. Jenny, we are but humble investigators without the final say in evaluating matters such as that. Personally, having spoken to the woman, I have to admit that she's probably not the type to use words like "squeal" or "grass", for that matter, mostly because she's probably not seen any of the Ealing comedies that sort of language is used in.'

A high-pitched ring from the hall stopped the discussion. The Thoms looked at each other and then went into a clearly well-rehearsed plan of action as Jenny went into the chill of the hall to answer the stylish old telephone. Geddes recognised the routine; Jenny filtered the calls so that her husband would not be dealing with continual parish trivia at all times. She returned quickly, looking defeated. 'That was Mr Wallace. Christine's not got long to go and could you go round as soon as you can.' She turned to address her house guests. 'Sorry, it looks like one of our amateur detectives has to leave us.'

After Rev Thom made a hurried departure, the conversation inevitably turned to the pressures of the ministry and the number of calls the manse received at all hours of the day and night. The first part of the evening had been worthwhile and, for the husbands anyway, unsettlingly revealing. Irene too had enjoyed the debate, but was now looking as if she had been freshly retrieved from the oven of the old Raeburn in the kitchenette. Her cheeks had gone from blossom pink to cherry red and were about to progress to a damask purple as the three of them made their way to the sturdy oak double doors of the old house. 'It's a pity Arthur had to go. I was enjoying our little get together, and we never even got to the evidence,' Jenny mused.

'Or how it affected the suspects,' Irene added.

'I was wondering about that,' Geddes said. 'By the time the evidence was over, it only showed two things for certain and that was that Brian Tevendale killed Max Garvie and that he and Alan Peters hid the body on the grounds of Lauriston Castle. It needed Alan Peters's involvement for Sheila Garvie to be seriously dragged into it. And Trudy, of course.'

Jenny sounded regretful. 'That's what I was building up to. This is between the three of us. I think the evidence shows there should have been a fourth name on the indictment.' Jenny's manner had suddenly become guarded.

'Did someone else bear a deadly grudge against Max? A girlfriend we don't know about? A business rival?' Irene was guessing by now.

'No, neither of those.' Jenny was enjoying the tension her theory was creating, particularly as half of her audience was one of the officers who had investigated the case. They were standing at the door, and the evening had turned chilly, even more chilly than in some of the rooms in the manse. 'Come back inside for a moment,' she said. 'I wonder if you think I'm being too speculative, too *conspiratorial* when I say this.'

They were now back in the hall, beside the quaint old telephone and the vintage telephone table, Jenny's voice reduced to a loud whisper in case a hardy outsider was risking hypothermia by hiding amongst the rhododendron bushes at the door, listening out for incriminating, defamatory plots being discussed inside the manse. Geddes went back to close the door over as she spoke, instinctively co-operating with her secretive tone.

'You'll recall what Peters said in his statement to you ...'
Geddes nodded. 'Of course.'

'He started off saying he picked Tevendale up at Trudy's that night. She didn't appear to notice they weren't wearing overalls as they usually did, but put that to one side for the moment. What he said after that was, well, revealing. He said they went from Aberdeen to Stonehaven. Do you remember that?'

Geddes nodded in agreement.

'It's what he said just after that that made me think. Having said they went to Stonehaven, he quickly changed that to "No, we didn't, we went straight through Stonehaven onto the coast road".'

Geddes listened intently as Jenny pieced her theory together. 'Apart from the *News of the World* type additions, you know – Sheila getting them a drink and she and Tevendale going away for half an hour, a non-existent white car being in the garage, that sort of thing – Peters almost gave the game away right at the beginning when he said, "No, we didn't, we went straight through Stonehaven onto the coast road".'

'Alright, Miss Marple, I give in,' Geddes said. 'So what?'

Jenny ignored the jibe and resumed explaining her hypothesis. 'The truth is not important. In court, all that matters is the truth of the allegation, not the underlying facts. Juries convict when the Crown manages to bolster one piece of evidence with another and so the charge is deemed to be proved. Justice is often symbolic rather than perfect.'

Geddes automatically felt the need to respond to such an obvious attack on the justice system; a moment later he abandoned the idea, having realised the truth of the words just spoken.

Irene was feeling more comfortable in the cool of the hallway and she too had been drawn into Jenny's thinking. 'Alright, are you saying justice has not been done?'

'Not that it's not been done. It's not been done fully. Alan Peters and Brian Tevendale weren't just driving about with no purpose that night. They were out to get Maxwell and began by checking the places he would be drinking in that night. You have to remember that Tevendale had not been in touch with Sheila for a few weeks and he and Peters were probably looking for the distinctive Mark ten Jaguar and were going to run him off the road.'

Geddes considered what she said. 'You think they were looking for him before he got home that night? That could explain them driving about, waiting to see if they could intercept him on one of the country roads.'

Jenny nodded. 'It might. Now let's turn to something Sheila Garvie said in her statement. Up until Tevendale blamed her for killing Maxwell, she had stuck faithfully to saying nothing and incriminating nobody.'

'True,' Geddes commented, now interested as to where this was going.

Jenny carried on.

'Well, firstly, why would she mention Alan Peters being there when Tevendale failed to? It's not as if Tevendale was loyal at any time to either of his co-accused, was it?'

Geddes agreed. 'No, he wasn't, but we did discuss that in the office. Maybe Sheila hoped that she would deflect the blame by bringing Peters into it?'

'I don't think so. Anyway, she didn't tell the truth. She pretended she didn't know Peters's name and she had been at his wedding a few weeks before! No, our Sheila is more wily than she looks!'

Geddes cast his mind back to Sheila's statement, his impression being that she meant she didn't know Peters *at the time of the murder*. In the spirit of the evening, he chose to put his doubts to one side and go along with Jenny's enthusiastic speculation. 'So why mention him at all?'

Jenny smiled confidently. 'I may just be an amateur crime buff, but I'm pretty sure she was basically telling the truth. Why do I say that? She blunders into things that go against her interests. What about the mattress? Why was Trudy so keen to "help" her by giving her a replacement and taking the old one away? She even charged Sheila £18! The nerve of her! It only cost her £15, 19 shillings and sixpence! She must have charged Sheila for the cost of her petrol!'

Irene was puzzled. 'Why shouldn't she? She and Brian had done her a favour. Had they not?'

Before replying, Jenny briefly waved a hand up and down in a calming motion. 'No, she most definitely did not, neither in nor out of court! In fact, it was Sheila who did Trudy the favour.'

Geddes was being drawn in. 'And how do you come to that conclusion?'

Jenny smiled an argument-clinching smile. 'The key for me was something Sheila said in all apparent innocence when she gave the voluntary statement. You will remember the extreme shock that poor, broken-hearted Trudy experienced when she testified that her brother told her about her lover – who had dumped her like an old shoe – being murdered? That was at about eight o'clock on the morning of 15 May?'

The other two nodded.

'That was another one of her lies. Just as Sheila said in her evidence, Tevendale called her from a telephone box about six o'clock that morning on the way back to Trudy's house to say that they had left Maxwell's clothes in the garage and, after she became upset, he said to take them to Trudy and she would get rid of them. So, if that was true, Trudy was in on it two hours *before* Tevendale got back to Aberdeen! And why must that be true? Two reasons. One, because how would Sheila know what Trudy was going to claim in court months later regarding the exact moment she found out about the murder? And two, because that's exactly what happened! Trudy *did* get rid of the clothes by getting poor old Fred to burn them. As with the mattress, Trudy organised things down to the tiniest detail. She knew everything that was going on because she and her brother wanted revenge for what Maxwell had done, and I mean to both of them. She never questioned her brother and Peters going out dressed as they were that night *and* she washed their clothes the next morning. Then she organised getting rid of the mattress and Maxwell's clothes – because *she* planned the whole thing from the start! And who hosted the Peterses' wedding bash? Not Sheila but Trudy! She's the brains of the outfit! So devious she even managed to make sure that "her beautiful

298

friend Sheila" took the blame! There's the fourth name on the indictment!'

'Or the third. In place of Sheila Garvie!' Irene added. Irene was now doing something Geddes had never seen before – she was actually *thinking* about one of his cases rather than fobbing him off with '*Yes, dear*' platitudes whilst planning the next day's dinner. And she wasn't finished. 'Hang on a second, though. That still doesn't explain why Tevendale's counsel made it worse for Sheila in court. The papers said Tevendale and Sheila were planning on getting married in prison. How does that square with him wanting to get her convicted for murder?'

Jenny had a ready answer. 'Bradford!'

'Bradford?' Geddes heard himself say. 'How does that come into it?'

'With all due respect, as they say in court as if they mean it, it all falls into place because of Bradford,' Jenny explained. 'Trudy was livid about getting the heave-ho from Max, so she spent her time plotting revenge against him, getting in touch with her friend south of the border and even driving the pair of them down there. She was equally annoyed when Sheila upped and left her brother there to go back to Maxwell. After all, the poor boy had no job to go back to whilst all Sheila was losing was her lifestyle, her house and her children. You'll notice I never included her husband there.'

Irene nodded in agreement.

Jenny continued. 'So, Tevendale comes back here and Trudy knows Sheila's still in love with him and can be easily manipulated, but her brother's her brother, so she's able to convince him that a great wrong's been done to the family honour now that they've both been dumped!'

'And so, turns Tevendale against her! I see what you mean,' Irene concluded on Jenny's behalf.

In her enthusiasm, Jenny hadn't noticed that her bespoke

hairstyle for the evening's amusement had begun to unravel at one side and strands of greying dark hair were now straddling her left shoulder whilst the other side held in place, giving her a lopsided, slightly eccentric appearance. 'That's the real reason Brian couldn't go into the witness box. A proper exploration of any evidence he might give could surely lead to suspicion about his sister's role in the whole, sorry mess! The press hammered on about Sheila keeping her husband's murder a secret, but Brian had an even greater one!'

Geddes went to the door. He turned back, the keys of the Hillman Imp in his hand. 'You may have a point, Jenny, you may have a point. Of course, she can't be charged now she's been used as a Crown witness. I suppose she hoodwinked everyone, even the *News of the World* – as if they'll be bothered! They've sold all the copies they're likely to on the back of the Garvies' misfortune.'

Bob and Irene bid Jenny goodnight and went into their little car.

Once inspired Irene was unrelenting. 'I wasn't really looking forward to tonight, but I've got to say I enjoyed it.' *It's amazing how someone, anyone except me, can unlock Irene's mind; maybe we've been together for too long,* Geddes thought as he drove along the manse's bumpy track.

Irene wasn't finished either. 'You know what I think?' Geddes knew a comment either way was pointless, so kept quiet. 'I think Jenny's right and it was Trudy who planned the murder. Why would Sheila leave herself without any transport to take the children to school the next morning if she had played any part in organising it? And if Tevendale and Peters had managed to get Max before he got home, there would be no real case against her either!'

Geddes drove on in silence, unwilling to remind his wife that he and his colleagues had already considered all the pre-trial inconsistencies before the case went to Crown Office. *Maybe Irene's practical, female view of things – that murdering Max that night would leave Sheila without transport for the next day – might just have something to it.*

'You know something else? I think Jenny's a better detective than you and Wilkie are!'

Geddes kept a dignified silence without revealing he was now puzzling over whether Irene was suffering the symptoms of hyperthermia or whether she was just talking sense.

Chapter 39:

Gateside Prison, Greenock,

Tuesday, 27 May 1969

When Dowdall returned from court on the Monday, he had the usual bundle of urgent messages to deal with. Knowing his routine well, his secretary, Evelyn, waited ten minutes after he went into his office before updating him on the day's events.

A respectable-looking businessman sat nervously awaiting legal advice about a potentially embarrassing drink-driving charge; a married man with a young family, he had stupidly gone drinking with a much younger woman he worked beside and the police had found them in a back seat clinch in a country lay by. Hastily adjusting his clothing, he had then failed a roadside breath test and his life was destined to alter dramatically. Before Dowdall saw the client, Evelyn nipped into his office without knocking, clutching a sheaf of 'while you were out' messages. Seated in a maroon-coloured Admiral's chair behind an imposing walnut desk with dark brown coloured leather panels, Dowdall was finishing a phone call. He gestured for her to sit in the client's chair on the other side of the desk whilst he finalised a guilty plea with the local fiscal.

After replacing the receiver, he removed his glasses and rubbed his eyes as Evelyn filled in the details of the day's events. 'Before you see Mr Green, who is in the waiting room, there are some messages you need to attend to.' She knew the best way to deal with Dowdall was to press on and never allow him time to think or protest on the grounds of a mounting workload.

'Mr Green? What's that about?' he said as he blinked, then cleaned his large, black-rimmed glasses with a velvet spectacle cloth.

'Failed roadside test, girl and him in back of car ...'

Dowdall shook his head as Evelyn continued with the clues.

'Lay by near Strathblane ...'

Nothing.

'Captain of the local golf club there ...'

'*That* Mr Green! Yes, show him in as you leave.'

With no need for social niceties between them, Evelyn turned to the messages. 'Your trial in Stornoway Sheriff Court – the illegal drinking den charge – is definitely starting on Wednesday next week and Mr Bovey called back about the drugs case you were talking to him about.'

One of the features of a successful legal practice was a lack of false pride and never being afraid of seeking the opinions of others with more expertise in certain areas. 'Remind me to call him first thing tomorrow.'

Evelyn noted the instruction and moved briskly on. 'Oh, and Sheila Garvie called asking if you would come and see her.'

'She did?' he said. 'And did she say what it was that was bothering her?'

Evelyn shook her head. 'No, she didn't, but she did sound upset.'

After the trial, Dowdall and Daiches had consulted with Sheila to advise her that there were no grounds in law for an appeal against conviction. She had taken the news impassively as Dowdall had expected, but as her case was different in so many ways, he had done his best to help her as much as he could after that, including several visits to Gateside Women's Prison in Greenock, where she was now detained, theoretically for life.

'Right, how's my diary looking tomorrow mid-morning?'

'It's clear right now.'

'Ok, arrange a visit for me at midday, then. And show Mr Green in, please.'

As Dowdall drove through the Clyde Tunnel towards Greenock the following day, he began to realise how much Sheila Garvie's conviction still rankled with him. Despite her previous lifestyle and even the way she spoke, the addicts and prostitutes she now lived amongst were protective towards her as she slowly adapted to 'slopping out' and strip searches. With the worldwide publicity the case had attracted, many of the inmates at Gateside had become armchair experts on the facts of the case in preference to succumbing to the deadly routine of prison existence. Some of the more inventive inmates had even devised a scheme to entice Trudy to the prison so they could throw her off the landing at B Hall, but Sheila had politely declined the offer.

As he sat waiting to see her in the confined, musty-smelling interview room, Dowdall wondered what it was she wanted to see him about. If it was anything to do with the arrangements for the children, he could take the details and pass it on one of his assistants to deal with it. Anyway, he inferred during the trial that Sheila's mother Edith had taken over their welfare ever since they had lost their father and Sheila was remanded. His impression of Edith had been that she would do a good job, despite the circumstances. After the trial, though, he had concentrated on the slew of new criminal cases that came his way and inevitably blanked out less urgent, non-criminal matters.

If it was about the tenancy of West Cairnbeg – which the Garvie family understandably wanted to transfer back to their ownership – then again, he would take the details and pass them on to someone who specialised in commercial leases and who could act for them.

Whatever it was, Dowdall knew that neither he nor his staff would see a penny for their efforts. Once a criminal case is finished, a solicitor's involvement with an accused is usually happily terminated by both sides. Not so in Sheila's case.

And, because of that, he was about to hear the reason she asked him to attend.

The key clunked into place on the other side of the door, which then swung open, and Sheila appeared. She barely resembled the stylish but distraught client he had first met nine months before. Her hair had reverted to its natural light brown colour and was tied back in severe fashion with a frayed elastic band. She wore a shapeless smock that tightened as she sat down and clung to the bony outlines of her shoulders. She wore no makeup. Her skin was grey-white and paper-thin, and it looked like she had been crying just before she came into the room. The days of foreign holidays, ponies for the children and expensive clothes and hairstyling were long gone.

After conviction, the plan had been for her to see the children every few months, but that had never happened, although she still usually asked Dowdall if he had heard any news of them, which made him uncomfortable. As it was well beyond his remit, he had arranged for Evelyn to make the occasional call to social services, but they were never too forthcoming about future plans and it eventually became pointless. Even so, he had told Evelyn to try again, and what she told him as he rushed out the office that morning was that Edith may not be looking after the children anymore, which surprised him, although he could not think why she should have given up on their welfare. He decided he would explain that to Sheila if he had to, and get Evelyn to further investigate what had happened, but what Sheila was about to tell him amply cleared the matter up.

Sheila had also previously asked about Brian, but had stopped doing that ever since Dowdall told her about him trying to sell her letters to the *News of the World*.

They had also sometimes discussed Trudy's evidence and the deadly and unexpected additions to it that had sealed Sheila's conviction, Dowdall all the time hoping she might realise how guileless she had been in expecting Mrs Birse to stick to the truth. He decided not to tell her that Fred and Trudy had reportedly split up – Fred getting custody of the kids – just in case she became side-tracked from the real reason she had asked him to visit.

Her voice quivered as she struggled to speak. 'Mr Dowdall, this time last year, I never knew you. Now you're my link to the outside world and my sanity. I always knew I could trust you, even within minutes of our first meeting.'

Dowdall felt embarrassed and interrupted her. 'Now, now, my dear, you seem to overlook one thing – despite all our efforts you were convicted!'

He smiled as he spoke, but she carried on in the same soft but determined voice.

'I *deserved* to be convicted for being too loyal and too trusting even though I had nothing to do with Maxie's murder. The reason I needed to see you was because my mam, Edith, has gone, and I needed to tell someone and, like it or not, you're the only one I can turn to now. I knew she was ill, but it never occurred to me she would go as soon as this. They won't even let me go to her funeral. She arranged for this letter to be passed to me the other day.'

Sheila pushed an envelope across the table between them and Dowdall picked it up. On the outside it said, *'Mrs Sheila Garvie'* and *'Only to be opened by Sheila if anything should happen to me. From Mum.'*

Sheila's hand had remained halfway across the table

where it had been when she had let the letter go. As Dowdall began to read, he stretched his left hand across to meet hers, then placed it gently on top of her fingers. He blinked rapidly beneath his trademark spectacles as he read what Edith had written:

My Dearest Sheila,

If you ever receive this, I will be with my Mum and Dad. Don't ever grieve for me, except that if you are still in Gateside I will not be with the bairns and that thought is terrible to me, however, you cannot bargain with God, if I could I would gladly give up my life to be able to let you go free. Don't ever give up, keep your head high, you were never bad, never, so always remember that. If I can, I will be looking after you from somewhere, so think of me standing beside you always. It was, if we had known, the saddest part of your life when you married into the Garvies, no wonder I cried all the time you were being married. You have always been greatly loved by me and the love I have for you has never changed, although perhaps at one time you thought so. I cannot write more, my heart is too full at having to leave you and the bairns, so please let God bless you and may you be happy yet, as I think you will. All my love forever until we meet again.

Your most loving Mother

Sheila,

I think I was only given about this time by the doctors in Aberdeen, so all the recent happenings had actually nothing to do with my illness.

Dowdall later wrote:

The striking features of a remarkable case which linger

307

in my mind are Sheila Garvie's hopeless infatuation with Tevendale, her prejudicial and unrepentant association with him after the murder, the betrayal by her distraught mother, the egregious Trudy Birse, the anomaly of the three diametrically opposed and totally irreconcilable voluntary statements, the probing cross-examination of Ewan Stewart, the speech by Lionel Daiches, the remarkable forensic triumph of Dr Taylor and last, but above all, the yellowed skull of Maxwell Garvie gazing out over the courtroom.

And:

To my mind the story told to the police by Peters that Mrs Garvie let them in – thus implying they could not gain entry without her – was completely refuted by the evidence of her mother and the joiner about the fitting of the Yale lock. In examination in chief, Peters did not say that Mrs Garvie let them in, but said that she met them at the end of the corridor ... I still wonder where the truth lies.

He ended: *'Was Sheila Garvie guilty? I for one did not doubt her story, nor apparently did a minority of the jury.'*

Who was the real mastermind behind the murder of Maxwell. Robert Garvie? If it was not the woman who was convicted of murdering her strange, impulsive, troubled husband, was it the woman who had become his mistress?

Postscript

Changed Days?

Society has changed since the time of Sheila Garvie's trial now that chauvinistic attitudes towards women have begun to be seriously questioned. The *zeitgeist* of the time allowed Sheila to be portrayed as amoral and depraved. She was the one who needed psychiatric help, not Max.

With the connivance of the press, Trudy exploited the then-prevailing view of women as being lesser creatures, prone to impulsive bouts of unrequited love and defenceless as to its consequences. Within the mores of the time, she – rather than Sheila – was unconvincingly depicted as being the victim of Max's whimsical ways.

Although the role women play in society began truly changing during the Great War, perceptions have lingered far behind reality.

That necessary shift in society's outlook was clearly in its very early stages in 1960s Britain. It still has a long way to go.

The Howe of the Mearns and Grassic Gibbon

Max and Sheila Garvie's story is firmly set in the Mearns of Lewis Grassic Gibbon. Writing in the *Scottish Daily Express*, the journalist Jack Webster noted two curious features of life imitating art. Firstly, he commented on how very close the locus of the murder was to the setting of Gibbon's acclaimed *Sunset Song* and, secondly, the unusual surname of the troubled Ewan in the story bearing a strong resemblance to that of Max's killer. He wrote: *'The crime was committed within shooting distance of Blawearie Braes, where Ewan Tavendale worked.'*

It's said that Gibbon used the 'Tavendale' surname having noticed it on a gravestone in Arbuthnott churchyard, a mere eight miles or so from the now modernised farmhouse at West Cairnbeg. 'Tavendale' and 'Tevendale' surely have to be linked, but neither name is said to be that common in the area.

Sunset Song, of course, was a record of a world which died with the Great War, but the sensational details of the Garvie case outdid anything Gibbon might ever have imagined in the community whilst confirming just how strange, shallow and selfish people can sometimes be. What would Gibbon have made of Maxwell Robert Garvie, Gertrude Tevendale or Birse or any of the three accused?

Whatever it might have been, it would certainly have been memorable.

An Observer's View

Author, journalist and publisher Paul Harris, who attended the trial, had some noteworthy comments about it:

Anyone with any mental perception at all who attended the Garvie trial could not fail to come away with the conviction that the affair was a circus rather than a trial in a court of law. The evidence could hardly be heard at times for the crackling of toffee papers, the gasps of affected horror, the tut-tutting of outraged morality and the chatter of gloating. Yet basically those ten days were about tragedy ... but this seemed lost too often on those both within and without that courtroom.

And: *'No-one should be convicted on impressions and*

it is quite possible that she knew nothing beforehand of the murder and only went along with it after the event. If so, she certainly paid the penalty for her silence.'

Lastly: *'We will never know what really happened that fateful night at West Cairnbeg. The point is, the nine men and five women on the jury didn't either.'*

The Press

Newspaper sales rocketed during the trial, locally and across the country. South of the border, the *Daily Mirror* and *The Times* carried daily reports and headlines of the case. The *News of the World*, of course, was deeply and ominously involved in the case from an early stage. When announcing Trudy's 'secret diaries', it ran a front page with the following memorably hollow explanation:

Today, Trudy Birse, whose life has become a nightmare of catcalls and abusive letters since she gave evidence of her torrid love affair with the murdered man, asks for understanding of the dark and violent passions to which she fell prey. Using her secret diaries, she has recalled days and scenes she would rather not remember. Her story makes shocking – and often moving – reading and is a grim indictment of the "dolce vita" into which she was plunged.

As the proverb says, *'If silence be good for the wise, how much better for fools?'* Or did the journalistic invention of 'secret diaries' conveniently fit in with her plan for revenge, further deflecting blame by portraying her as an innocent, lovestruck adolescent trapped like a butterfly in a wicked, grown-up net of intrigue, passion and lies?

Whatever the truth, after one hundred and sixty-eight years, the *News of the World* finally fell foul of its underhand methods and stopped production in 2011. The reason? When it emerged that the newspaper had employed someone who had become *too* involved in the criminal enquiry into the disappearance of missing teenager Milly Dowler – he had intercepted the voicemail from her phone – there was a public backlash against it. Overdue comeuppance, some thought, just as they thought about Sheila Garvie. What goes round …

The Law in Context – Secret Recordings of Communings Between Suspects

There are two issues here today; the first relates to fairness. Now that the prosecution is obliged to disclose everything that might aid an accused's defence, the existence of the secret tapes – and whether their contents assisted those investigating the case – would certainly lead to a preliminary objection about the clandestine nature of the recordings being prejudicial to the interests of the accused. The accused, or Sheila, at least, appear to have had no inkling at any point in the case of what had occurred when she spoke to Brian Tevendale at that early stage of the enquiry. Taylor's questioning of Sheila during the trial closely verged on him casting doubt on certain things she had said in her evidence in chief when compared to what she said during her two 'discussions' with Brian when they imagined they were able to converse freely; or was Brian in on it – if that doesn't stretch the idea too much – and he was hoping to persuade her to go along with the exculpatory fiction that *she* shot Max? At that juncture, of course, it appeared that some of the enquiry police actually believed she had shot her husband.

The other aspect of the secret recordings is that the lawyers knew or learned of their existence during the trial, but, publicly at least, did nothing about it. In modern times, their inactivity in that regard would have run the real risk of a retrial being ordered by the appeal court and being civilly sued by the accused for defective representation.

Alternatively, the cynical view is that, in 1968, even murder trials were gentlemanly exercises during which it was simply not 'the done thing' to rock the boat lest any of the occupants fell overboard into a sea of professional disfavour and isolation.

The Law in Context – Notice of Intention to Attack Character and Homosexuality

Brian alleged that Max made homosexual advances towards him on two occasions; whether true or not, what is beyond doubt is that Sheila's notice reflected the law just as attitudes were changing. Here is a reminder of what it said:

Dowdall for the Second-named Pannel, Sheila Watson or Garvie, hereby gives notice that it is intended on behalf of the said Second-named Pannel to attack the character of the deceased Maxwell Robert Garvie in respect of his unnatural and perverted sexual practices.

'Pannel' is one of those archaic Scottish legal terms only now used by certain thrawn practitioners, simply meaning 'accused'.

The practices referred to – Max's fondness for anal sex – were still very much taboo in 1968 and were seen as highly suggestive of homosexual behaviour, which was still a criminal offence in Scotland. There had been signs of a changing approach to the prosecution of homosexual activity when the Lord Advocate gave an undertaking only the year before that private acts between consenting adults would not be subject to criminal sanction, but it was still too soon for society to regard Max's penchant as anything other than 'unnatural and perverted sexual practices'. What is perhaps even more telling is that very little seems to have been made of whether Sheila genuinely *consented* or not, the special defence being silent in that regard and failing to finish with the words 'and carried out on the said Second-named Pannel against her will and without her consent.'

Today, Max could run the risk of being charged with rape in that he did not have her genuine consent when forcing her to participate in his then 'unnatural' practice or coerced her to do other things she was unwilling to do.

The Law, Murder and Sheila Garvie; Case One – Her Majesty's Advocate against Jessie McIntosh or McLachlan

At first reading, there does not seem to be much in common between the murder of Max Garvie in West Cairnbeg in 1968 and the murder of Jessie McPherson at 17 Sandyford Place in Glasgow on a warm July weekend in 1862. She was a domestic servant there, employed by an accountant called John Fleming. Fleming had left Glasgow on Friday, 4 July to travel to the other house he owned near Dunoon, as he often did at weekends in the summer months. That left Jessie McPherson in the house along with Fleming's eighty-seven-year-old father, James. Jessie had confided in friends that 'Old Fleming' made her uncomfortable and was an old 'devil' towards her. The old man had a tendency to drink when his respectable son was away at weekends, which was also when he made his unwanted moves on Jessie McPherson. It also emerged that the old man had impregnated a domestic servant ten years previously when he was an obviously sprightly seventy-seven-year-old.

That night, however, Jessie McPherson received a visit from Jessie McLachlan, who had previously been employed in the Fleming household. The women were unable to shake off Old Fleming's company and he joined them to drink some spirits. In the hierarchical society of the time, he was in a position to tell Jessie McLachlan to go out to buy some more drink and she duly obliged, leaving the old man and the murder victim alone together. The door was locked when she came back and Old Fleming took his time to open it. According to at least one version of what Jessie McLachlan later told the authorities, Jessie McPherson was badly injured with deep cuts to her head when she finally got into the house. She busied herself tending to her friend by bathing her wounds and trying to keep her warm, all the while asking Old Fleming to fetch a doctor, which he simply refused to do. A woman's bare footprints – too large to be Jessie McPherson's – were outlined in blood on a floorboard which was later seized as evidence. Some time later that night, she claimed the old man had attacked Jessie McPherson again with a meat cleaver, saying she wasn't going to survive anyway and finishing her off this time.

The problem for Jessie McLachlan was that she gave several versions of events after the body was found on the Monday following, and by that time, she had disposed of some silver plate from the house as well as some clothes that belonged to the murdered woman. Indeed, the first public airing of the details of her incrimination of Old Fleming as the perpetrator was after she had been unanimously convicted of murder when her counsel was allowed to read out a statement she had given her legal advisers well before any evidence had been led in her trial. In light of that evidence, she had some explaining to do, but, at that time, an accused was not allowed to give evidence on his or her own behalf. Her predicament was further compounded by her counsel electing to make the Crown prove that she was even *in* 17 Sandyford Place that night. That, of course, they did by tying her in with the items stolen from the house and recovered in a pawn shop.

Should there be any truth in Jessie McLachlan's post-conviction pronouncement, it has to be wondered why someone who had nothing to do with the murder should allow themselves to be dragged into its aftermath. Given the hold Old Fleming had over her in terms of their respective social positions, he had a natural advantage over her. In her court statement, she also alleged that he had made her swear on the Bible that she would never reveal the truth of what had really happened and that he convinced her that neither of them could be implicated if she just did as he said about disposing of the incriminating items from the house, which the evidence showed she clearly did. He also falsely promised that he would set her up financially and make her 'comfortable'. Jessie McLachlan's lies and post-incident actions nearly got her hanged, but she avoided the rope due to a public outcry and petition, which led to an enquiry and commutation of the death sentence the judge had imposed. Contemporary accounts show her spirit belatedly emerging when sentence was pronounced by the judge. In traditional fashion, he donned a black cap and ordered she be returned to prison and kept on a diet of bread and water until hanged on 11 October 1862. Adding, 'And may God Almighty have mercy on your soul,' she shouted back from the dock, 'Mercy? Aye, he'll have mercy for I'm innocent!' The consensus today is that the wrong person was convicted and Old Fleming was the real perpetrator.

Sheila Garvie was to maintain that, by becoming Tevendale's lover, then falling in love with him, she had allowed a situation to develop that she felt responsible for. The way she too acted after the murder was to lead directly to her conviction.

Juries can be a cynical lot. Why do all these things unless you're guilty? And why not speak up and tell the truth if you are not guilty? And what if the guilty party has a major hold over you?

At least Sheila Garvie was allowed to speak *before* she was convicted!

The Law, Murder and Sheila Garvie; Case Two – Her Majesty's Advocate against Alexander Dingwall

One hundred and one years before Sheila Garvie received a life sentence for murder, another case from Stonehaven was heard in the North Circuit in Aberdeen. It, too, was a charge of murder, and it explored whether an accused person's state of mind at the time of the crime should determine whether the correct verdict ought to be murder or the lesser charge of culpable homicide.

Alexander Dingwall left the Indian Army in the 1840s and lived off an income from property until 1855, when his addiction to alcohol led him into debt. A trust deed was drawn up, which fixed where he should live and limited his allowance, and which was disbursed through his wife, Grace, and others. His lawyer acknowledged his client's fondness for whisky and allowed him to buy a fixed amount – a relatively generous five bottles – each month, but it was never enough for the old soldier and he often took to selling or pawning household items to buy more drink.

He did the rounds of friends and neighbours on New Year's Eve and had several glasses of whisky, but matters came to a head early on New Year's Day 1867 when he suspected Grace of withholding cash and, probably far worse, more of his favourite tipple. So, in a rage, he stabbed her on her side. She lingered on in life for a fortnight before dying and was able to confirm what he had done to her. She claimed that, when not in drink, her husband was 'a kind man'. She also mentioned that, after she was injured, she could not find the bell-pull to summon assistance from their landlord. It was later discovered to have been thrown up on top of the frame of the bed, so it seemed that Sandy Dingwall had planned, or at least thought about, hindering any assistance that might arrive to help his wife, injured at his own hand.

The landlord and his wife confirmed Dingwall himself

had described his actions as 'murder' and he also went on to say he was sorry 'he had missed his mark'. He seemed quite calm when they spoke to him.

At his trial, a defence of insanity was lodged on his behalf and reference was made to him suffering sunstroke in India and bouts of *delirium tremens*.

Defining culpable homicide as 'murder with extenuating circumstances', the judge left the matter to the jury and, within half an hour, they returned with a verdict of culpable homicide rather than murder. Dingwall was given ten years of penal servitude.

The case broke new ground. On one view, here was a man who stabbed his wife in a fit of pique, even regretting he had 'missed his mark', yet the jury came to the conclusion there were 'extenuating circumstances' because his state of mind was disturbed. However the jury came to their verdict, the judge had opened the door to the idea that weakness of mind could reduce murder to culpable homicide. It seems Grace had done Dingwall a parting favour by describing him as 'kind' when not drunk, but the suspicion remains that he stabbed her simply because he thought she had denied him more drink, rather than it being due to any mental disorder.

Needless to say, Sheila Garvie's psychiatric records were there for all to see, yet her state of mind was hardly mentioned. Nowadays, her treatment at sentencing would be entirely different and she would be regarded as an abused spouse as per Kim Galbraith, below.

The Law, Murder and Sheila Garvie; Case Three – Her Majesty's Advocate against Kim Galbraith

Thirty-one years after Sheila Garvie's conviction for murder, a woman called Kim Galbraith killed her allegedly abusive policeman husband in their home in Furnace, Argyll. She waited until he was asleep, then shot him in the head using his own rifle. At her first trial, she was convicted of murder, but on appeal it was decided that the judge had misdirected the jury and a second trial was ordered. When that happened, she tendered a plea of guilty to culpable homicide on the basis of diminished responsibility, the plea was accepted and she was given an eight-year sentence.

The similarities between the Garvie and Galbraith cases at first seem obvious, but in the relatively short space of thirty-one years, the way the individual cases were dealt with could not have been more different.

Kim Galbraith's alleged abuse had one source – herself – whereas Sheila's abuse was well documented and, of course, Kim acted on her own, firing the fatal shot by her own hand, while Sheila was not even in the same room when the deed was done. Sheila's actions after the murder were seen as damning evidence whereas Kim's – she told police that two men had broken in, killed her husband, then raped her before they set fire to the cottage – were not. Kim had also tampered with the brakes of her husband's car a few weeks before she shot him. Even so, her plea to the lesser charge was accepted on the grounds of diminished responsibility based on her impaired ability to control her actions.

The psychological effects of domestic abuse on victims are now more widely acknowledged. These include anxiety, low self-esteem, depression and even post-traumatic stress disorder. Any combination of these symptoms would be put forward today as explaining much of Sheila's apparently erratic post-incident behaviour, including her instant cover-up and her protracted deception about Max simply disappearing, both crucial factors in her conviction. Whether that conviction should have been for murder or culpable homicide was not the subject of a submission at the trial, nor was the question of an appeal against the conviction contemplated, so, to that extent, it was an 'all or nothing' defence that was ultimately unsuccessful.

Her self-blame continued even after her release, when she wrote, *'I had no hand in my husband's murder, but I deserved my sentence because I failed to halt the tide of events which led inexorably to his death.'*

On the evidence led at her trial, would Sheila Garvie be convicted today and, if so, what of?

The Law, Murder and Sheila Garvie; Soneryls in Hindsight.

Not much appears to have been made by Sheila's counsel about the effect taking two Soneryls might have had on top of taking alcohol; in a modern murder trial it might be expected that an expert witness be called to give an opinion about the likely consequences of the tablets on a person's behaviour.

Soneryls are no longer available in the United Kingdom, nor are they marketed under their more recent name Butobarbitol, which was used to treat insomnia. It was discovered that they have a high dependency factor and should not be taken by patients with addiction issues. People like Max. Perhaps his habit of washing them down after taking vast quantities of alcohol goes some way to explaining *his* erratic behaviour or even his failure to react to two strangers making an unexpected appearance in his bedroom early on that May morning. Moreover, it was also found to be dangerous to *stop* taking the tablets unless under medical supervision, as that could lead to withdrawal symptoms such as anxiety, outbursts of bad temper, tremors and even convulsions.

If Sheila was telling the truth about taking two of them as well as a probably generous measure of gin poured by Max, it might go a long way to explaining the dreamy, confused mental state she was in when, she says, Brian came into the bedroom. There seems to have been no dispute that the tablets were in the house and that Max called them his 'anti-sex pills'. Perhaps, like a boastful teenager, he never really progressed beyond trying to impress Sheila with his sexual prowess, and their use of Soneryls only contributed to their problems.

The Main Players; What Fate had in Store

It's probably fair to say that Alan Peters's marriage to Helen was not blessed with good fortune from the start. They divorced after two children and five years together. He died of cancer in Kintore near Inverurie in his beloved Aberdeenshire in 2007.

Like Sheila, Brian was released after serving ten years of a life sentence. Also like her – and Alan Peters – all three accused steadfastly stuck to their own version of what happened on the night of 14 May 1968. Although unable to say it when it mattered in court, Brian maintained that Sheila was indeed complicit in the plot to murder Max. He claimed to be 'under her spell'. Had he given evidence, though, he could have been quizzed about being under another woman's spell – his sister's – had that occurred to anyone at the time, before the *News of the World* articles appeared and helped explain many of the alterations in her evidence.

In April 1979 Brian met a twenty-one-year-old mother of two whom he married in 1981. He became the landlord of a pub in Perthshire and died of a heart attack aged fifty-eight in Scone, Perthshire in December 2003 whilst making plans to start a new life in Gambia.

Sheila herself served ten years in prison, latterly in Cornton Vale near Stirling. Like all long-term prisoners, a survival strategy to fend off reality proved important, and she spent much of her time reading, sewing and cooking.

Whilst she was serving her sentence, Laurence Dowdall was approached by a film producer who wanted to make a film about the case with the actress Maggie Smith playing Sheila. Dowdall reflected how far off the mark the Crown were in alleging Sheila was motivated by money as, despite a healthy sum being mentioned had she consented, she was not interested. Alternatively, it's probably accurate to add that her lack of interest in the project was down to a deep-seated apathy about life, together with a touch of cynicism about the outcome of her case.

Trudy, on the other hand, would undoubtedly have been keen to take up such an offer. After the trial, she finally split from Fred in 1971, with him getting custody of their three children. He remarried in 1984, but died of cancer in 1985. Trudy moved away from Aberdeen and died in Dunkeld in 1988 aged fifty-one.

Sheila was to marry twice more. In her book she explained she was attracted to a 'certain type of man' and, although free, she was also alone.

That 'certain type of man' was former Rhodesian soldier David McLellan, whom she met when he was a guest at the boarding house she ran and, although he was thirteen years younger than her, – she was then forty-four – they married in a civil ceremony in Aberdeen. A mere nine months later she applied for an interdict to stop her new husband from approaching her, as she claimed she needed protection from his unwelcome attentions.

Despite two marital failures, seven months after divorcing McLellan she married a Charlie Mitchell from Aberdeenshire on Christmas Eve 1981, the marriage seemingly successful until she was widowed in 1992.

She died in a care home in Stonehaven in 2014 suffering from Alzheimer's Disease.

Bibliography

Garvie, S. *Marriage To Murder: My Story.* W & R Chambers Ltd, Edinburgh, 1980.

Harris, P. *The Garvie Trial: The Crime that Shocked Scotland.* Impulse Books, Aberdeen, 1969.

Newspaper References (for 1968)
   News of the World
   Scottish Daily Express

Acknowledgments

I am very grateful to Lord Matthews for his excellent Foreword and to Raquel Aleman Cruz of Ringwood Publishing for her outstanding editing.

About the Author

Allan MacKenzie Nicol was born in Buckie, but grew up in Drumchapel and Scotstoun in Glasgow. After qualifying as a Solicitor, he joined Crown Office and became a Procurator Fiscal Depute for 12 years. He qualified as an Advocate in 1993 and then defended clients charged with more serious offences until 2011, when he re-joined Crown Office and became an Advocate Depute, prosecuting in High Courts throughout Scotland.

His previous books, *Manuel: Scotland's First Serial Killer* and *The Monster Butler: Inside the Mind of a Serial Killer* were published by Black & White Publishing.

He wrote *Manuel: Scotland's First Serial Killer* in 2008; the second edition appearing in 2016 and coinciding with the television series *In Plain Sight*, for which he was script adviser.

His first novel, *Liberation,* based on a real Glasgow case of a murder by a serving police officer, was published by Ringwood Publishing in 2021.

'Perhaps it's the combination of law and history that attracts me to trials from the past,' he writes, 'at best, they are reconstructions of events that reveal a small percentage of the story.'

Other Titles from Ringwood

All titles are available from the Ringwood website in both print and ebook format, as well as from usual outlets.

www.ringwoodpublishing.com
mail@ringwoodpublishing.com

Midnight in Glasgow, 28th of July 1950: a stolen car drives backwards and forwards, backwards and forwards over a prone, broken body. A mother of two is brutally murdered. Away from her body, on the edge of the pavement, two faux-leather shoes sit innocuously, the first clue for police that this is not just a simple traffic accident.

A family man; a religious devotee, honoured member of the mysterious Plymouth Brethren: more than this, P.C. James Robertson was a man of the law. How can he be connected to a case of this nature?

The involvement of a respectable bobby in an unmarried mother's murder made for one of the most scandalous High Court trials in Glasgow's history. The brutal murder and unlikely suspect are only the first striking details of this case, however. Robertson's performance in the witness box and his total disregard for his eventual fate at the gallows baffled his legal advisers and continues to mystify students of the case even today. A.M. Nicol's incisive novel stays true to the known facts of the case whilst examining how the blind faith of a devout can co-exist with the cold-blooded indifference of a murderer.

'Allan Nicol is not only an excellent storyteller, he takes you right into the world in which these real events occurred.'

– Donald Findlay.

ISBN: 978-1-901514-56-8 £9.99

Ruxton - The First Modern Murder

Tom Wood

It is 1935 and the deaths of Isabella Ruxton and Mary Rogerson would result in one of the most complex investigations the world had ever seen. The gruesome murders captured worldwide attention with newspapers keeping the public enthralled with all the gory details.

But behind the headlines was a different, more important story: the ground-breaking work of Scottish forensic scientists who developed new techniques to solve the case and shape the future of scientific criminal investigation.

ISBN: 978-1-901514-84-1
£9.99

ISBN: 978-1-901514-43-8
£9.99

The Ten Percent

Simon McLean

An often hilarious, sometimes scary, always fascinating journey through the ranks of the Scottish police from his spell as a rookie constable in the hills and lochs of Argyll, through his career in Rothesay and to his ultimate goal: The Serious Crime Squad in Glasgow.

We get a unique glimpse of the turmoil caused when the rules are stretched to the limit, when the gloves come off and when some of their number decide that enough is enough. A very rare insight into the world of our plain clothes officers who infiltrate and suppress the very worst among us.

Cuddies Strip

Rob McInroy

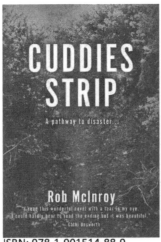

Cuddies Strip is based on a true crime and faithfully follows the investigation and subsequent trial but it also examines the mores of the times and the insensitive treatment of women in a male-dominated society.

It is a highly absorbing period piece from 1930s Scotland, with strong contemporary resonances: both about the nature and responsiveness of police services and the ingrained misogyny of the whole criminal justice system.

ISBN: 978-1-901514-88-9
£9.99

Barossa Street
Rob McInroy

Set in Perth, Barossa Street offers, not only a look at the mishandling of justice in the face of 1930's prejudice, but also serves as a commentary of the British public's response to the government's shortcomings. Set on the backdrop of King Edward VIII's abdication and the threat of war Barossa Street is as much a critique of the times as it is a thrilling murder mystery.

With twists and turns down every street, follow Bob Kelty in this suspenseful thriller to see whether he can solve the latest who-done-it and find that much needed relief from the trials of life.

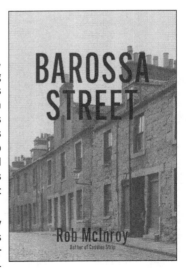

ISBN: 978-1-901514-41-4
£9.99

Not the Life Imagined
Anne Pettigrew

A darkly humorous, thought-provoking story of Scottish medical students in the sixties, a time of changing social and sexual mores. None of the teenagers starting at Glasgow University in 1967 live the life they imagine.

In *Not the Life Imagined*, retired medic Anne Pettigrew tells a tale of ambition and prejudice that provides a humorous and compelling insight into the complex dynamics of the NHS fifty years ago.

ISBN: 978-1-901514-70-4
£9.99

Not the Deaths Imagined
Anne Pettigrew

In a leafy Glasgow suburb, Dr Beth Semple is busy juggling motherhood and full-time GP work in the 90s NHS. But her life becomes even more problematic when she notices some odd deaths in her neighbourhood. Though Beth believes the stories don't add up, the authorities remain stubbornly unconvinced.

Is a charming local GP actually a serial killer? Can Beth piece together the jigsaw of perplexing fatalities and perhaps save lives? And as events accelerate towards a dramatic conclusion, will the police intervene in time?

ISBN: 978-1-901514-80-3
£9.99

Murder at the Mela

Leela Soma

DI Alok Patel takes the helm of an investigation into the brutal murder of an Asian woman in this eagerly-awaited thriller. As Glasgow's first Asian DI, Patel faces prejudice from his colleagues and suspicion from the Asian community as he struggles with the pressure of his rank, relationships, and racism.

This murder-mystery explores not just the hate that lurks in the darkest corners of Glasgow, but the hate which exists in the very streets we walk.

ISBN: 978-1-901514-90-2
£9.99

Clutching at Straws
Charles P. Sharkey

Clutching At Straws is a gritty and realistic dive into Glasgow's criminal underworld. The novel follows Inspector Frank Dorsey and his partner DC George Mitchell as they investigate a dead body they believe to be linked to the Moffats, one of the most notorious crime families in Glasgow. However, as they begin to delve further into the case, it becomes apparent that they have a complex web of connected mysteries and murders to make sense of.

ISBN: 978-1-901514-72-8
£9.99